Stochastic Processes

**A series of advanced mathematics texts
under the editorship of
Carl B. Allendoerfer**

Stochastic Processes

Basic Theory
and Its Applications

N. U. Prabhu

Reader in Mathematical Statistics
The University of Western Australia

The Macmillan Company, New York
Collier-Macmillan Limited, London

Library of Congress catalog card number: 65–15174

The Macmillan Company, New York

Collier-Macmillan Canada, Ltd., Toronto, Ontario

Printed in the United States of America

To my Teacher
C. RACINE, S.J.

Preface

The literature in stochastic processes is now very extensive, but is widely scattered in periodicals and monographs. The purpose of this book is to give a formal treatment of some of the important classes of stochastic processes, emphasizing concepts and results. In an introductory chapter the notion of a stochastic process is explained, and its essential characteristics are described; a brief summary of some of the basic concepts of probability theory is also given.

Continuity, differentiability, and integrability properties of regular (or second-order) stochastic processes are developed in Chapter 1. Chapter 2 treats Markov chains (both the denumerable and the general case); in particular, the recurrence properties of sums of independent random variables and the first passage problem of sequential analysis are discussed.

Markov processes are considered in Chapters 3 (diffusion processes) and 4 (discontinuous processes). The treatment is analytical and is based on the Feller-Kolmogorov equations; such a treatment has been found to be very useful in several applications and is relatively easier than the more modern one based on properties of sample functions.

The two remaining chapters are concerned with renewal theory. The classical part of the theory, dealing with nonnegative random variables, is developed in Chapter 5, the theory of recurrent events being presented as a special case. The results are then extended to the general case in Chapter 6, and some aspects of the fluctuation theory of sums of random variables are also discussed.

In each chapter the main results are presented in the form of theorems, and illustrative examples as well as applications are then considered.

Among the applications considered are random walks, branching processes, queuing theory, brownian motion, population growth, and counter models. However, no attempt has been made to treat the applications exhaustively, since there exist several books dealing with the diverse applications of stochastic processes. At the end of each chapter there is a collection of complementary details and further problems, which, it is hoped, will be useful to students. A list of references is given at the end of each chapter.

This book developed out of a one-year course of lectures given by the author at the University of Western Australia over the last few years to students and research workers in applied probability. Readers are assumed to have a knowledge of advanced calculus and modern probability theory at an introductory level.

The author is grateful to Professor Frank Spitzer of Cornell University for his criticism of the manuscript and for his encouragement. Thanks are also due to Miss Christine Bourke for her efficient typing of the manuscript, to the University of Western Australia for a research grant towards the preparation of the manuscript, and to Dr. C. C. Heyde for comments on the manuscript and help in proofreading.

N. U. Prabhu

Contents

ix

2

Markov Chains   42

3

Diffusion Processes   87

4

Discontinuous Markov Processes

5

Renewal Theory

CONTENTS

6

Further Results from Renewal Theory 202

Stochastic Processes

Introduction

1. THE CONCEPT OF A STOCHASTIC PROCESS

Stochastic process is a description of random phenomena changing with time. Such phenomena occur in physics, biology, economics, engineering, sociology, and several other fields and have attracted increasing attention in recent years. The earliest investigations date back to the end of the nineteenth century, and although sometimes of a heuristic nature, they have laid the foundations of the modern theory of stochastic processes. It is the aim of this book to develop the basic features of this theory and illustrate them with examples from some of the applied fields mentioned above.

A stochastic process (random process, or random function) may be thought of as a family of random variables $X(t)$ depending on a parameter $t \in T$. Here the parameter set T may, in general, be an abstract set, but we shall take it to be the real line $(-\infty < t < \infty)$; we shall interpret t as the "time." For each t the random variable $X(t)$ is defined on a sample space Ω, where we are given a Borel field $\mathscr{B}$ of subsets of Ω, and a probability measure P on $\mathscr{B}$. The basic concepts of probability spaces $(\Omega, \mathscr{B}, P)$ and random variables defined on such a space are summarized in Section 5 of this chapter. To emphasize its dependence on t and ω, we shall denote the stochastic process as $X(t, \omega)$, $t \in T$, $\omega \in \Omega$. For each $\omega \in \Omega$, $X(t, \omega)$ is a function of $t \in T$; this is called a *realization* of $X(t, \omega)$.

To fix the ideas, let us consider a sequence of N tosses of an unbiased coin. The sample space corresponding to this sequence is the N-dimensional space Ω_N consisting of the 2^N points $(0, 0, \ldots, 0)$, $(1, 0, 0, \ldots, 0)$, $(0, 1, 0, \ldots, 0)$, $\ldots$, $(1, 1, \ldots, 1)$, where 1 and 0 correspond to occurrence of heads and tails respectively, and each of these points ω has a probability 2^{-N} attached to it. Let $X(n, \omega)$ be the number of heads in the first n tosses; clearly $X(n, \omega)$ is a random variable defined on the given probability space. For each n, we have

$$X(n, \omega) = r \tag{1.1}$$

if exactly r among the first n coordinates of ω are equal to unity, and the

1

range of values of $X(n, \omega)$ is $R_n = (0, 1, \ldots, n)$; this leads to the so-called binomial distribution. On the other hand, let us consider the sample point $\omega = (1, 1, 0, 1, 0, \ldots, 0)$; at this point we have

$$X(n, \omega) = \begin{cases} 1 & \text{if } n = 1 \\ 2 & \text{if } n = 2 \\ 2 & \text{if } n = 3 \\ 3 & \text{if } n \geqslant 4. \end{cases} \tag{1.2}$$

The realization of $X(n, \omega)$ given by (1.2) may be called a sample sequence; its probability is 2^{-N}. In general, to every sample point $\omega \in \Omega_N$ there corresponds the sample sequence

$$\{x(1, \omega), x(2, \omega), \ldots, x(N, \omega)\} \tag{1.3}$$

and the space of such sequences is the product space

$$R = \prod_{1}^{N} R_n. \tag{1.4}$$

Actually, the situation here is very simple because $X(n, \omega)$ can be expressed, with probability one, in the form

$$X(n, \omega) = Y_1(\omega') + Y_2(\omega') + \cdots + Y_n(\omega') \qquad \omega' \in \Omega_1, \tag{1.5}$$

where each of $Y_1, Y_2, \ldots, Y_n$ is the number of heads in a single toss of the coin; to speak of $X(n, \omega)$ as a stochastic process may therefore be considered an unnecessary sophistication if one is concerned with a finite number N of tosses. However, many problems in elementary probability theory (for instance, the problem of waiting time for a head to turn up for the first time) are formulated, at least implicitly, in terms of an unlimited sequence of tosses, and this introduces the concept of a stochastic process. In such a situation we have to work with a sample space Ω_∞ of a denumerable number of dimensions, and have to define a measure on every set $A \in \mathscr{B}$.

The above example indicates how the definition of a stochastic process can be formulated in the case where the parameter set T is denumerable. The stochastic process here is in fact a sequence $\{X_n(\omega), n = 0, 1, 2, \ldots\}$, and the *sample sequences* are of the form

$$(x_0(\omega), x_1(\omega), x_2(\omega), \ldots); \tag{1.6}$$

we have then to consider the family of sets of these sample sequences. In the more general case where T contains a continuous infinity of points t, a similar definition of a stochastic process $X(t, \omega)$ in terms of its realizations, or *sample functions*, can be given, but needs some rather difficult concepts, and will therefore not be attempted here [see Loève (1963), pp. 497–504]. We shall, however, consider two simpler definitions, which are commonly used.

2. DEFINITION OF A STOCHASTIC PROCESS

Analytic Definition: Let $X(t) = \phi(t; A_1, A_2, \ldots, A_k)$ where ϕ is an ordinary function of t, and of a set of random variables $A_1, A_2, \ldots, A_k$ ($k \geqslant 1$) defined on a probability space independent of t, and ϕ is measurable on this space. The following are examples of such a definition.

(i) $X(t) = At + B$. Here the sample functions are of the form $at + b$, where (a, b) is a sample pair of values of (A, B). For each t we have

$$\Pr\{X(t) \leqslant x\} = \int\limits_{at+b \leqslant x} \int \Pr\{a < A < a + da, b < B < b + db\}. \quad (2.1)$$

(ii) $X(t) = A \cos \theta t + B \sin \theta t$, where θ is a constant. The sample functions here are the trigonometric functions $a \cos \theta t + b \sin \theta t$. The probability distribution of any such sample function can be obtained as in the last example. In particular, if A and B are uncorrelated, and each has mean 0 and variance σ^2, then

$$E\{X(t)\} = 0, \qquad \text{Var}\{X(t)\} = \sigma^2(\cos^2 \theta t + \sin^2 \theta t) = \sigma^2. \quad (2.2)$$

Definition in Terms of Probability Distributions: We define $X(t)$ by specifying the joint distribution function (d.f.)

$$F(x_1, x_2, \ldots, x_n; t_1, t_2, \ldots, t_n)$$
$$= \Pr\{X(t_1) \leqslant x_1, X(t_2) \leqslant x_2, \ldots, X(t_n) \leqslant x_n\} \quad (2.3)$$

for $t_1, t_2, \ldots, t_n \in T$, and $n = 1, 2, \ldots$. This d.f. is subject to the following two conditions.

(a) Symmetry Condition: For every permutation $(j_1, j_2, \ldots, j_n)$ of $(1, 2, \ldots, n)$ we must have

$$F(x_{j_1}, x_{j_2}, \ldots, x_{j_n}; t_{j_1}, t_{j_2}, \ldots, t_{j_n})$$
$$= F(x_1, x_2, \ldots, x_n; t_1, t_2, \ldots, t_n). \quad (2.4)$$

(b) Compatibility Condition: For $m < n$ we must have

$$F(x_1, x_2, \ldots, x_m, \infty, \infty, \ldots, \infty; t_1, t_2, \ldots, t_m, t_{m+1}, \ldots, t_n)$$
$$= F(x_1, x_2, \ldots, x_m; t_1, t_2, \ldots, t_m). \quad (2.5)$$

Kolmogorov (1931) proved that given any system of distribution functions satisfying the consistency conditions (a) and (b), there exists a probability space $(\Omega, \mathscr{B}, P)$ and a stochastic process $X(t, \omega)$ such that

$$F(x_1, x_2, \ldots, x_n; t_1, t_2, \ldots, t_n)$$

gives the joint probability distribution of

$$X(t_1, \omega), X(t_2, \omega), \ldots, X(t_n, \omega).$$

As an example of the above definition we consider the following.

(iii) *The Gaussian Process*: This is a process $X(t)$ such that for $n \geqslant 1$, $t_1, t_2, \ldots, t_n \in T$, the random variables $X(t_1)$, $X(t_2)$, ..., $X(t_n)$ have an n-variate Gaussian distribution with

$$E\{X(t_p)\} = m(t_p)$$

$$\text{Var}\{X(t_p)\} = \Gamma(t_p, t_p) \tag{2.6}$$

$$\text{Covar}\{X(t_p), X(t_q)\} = \Gamma(t_p, t_q) \qquad (p \neq q) \qquad (p, q = 1, 2, \ldots, n).$$

Let us denote the variance-covariance matrix as $\Gamma = (\Gamma_{pq})$, where $\Gamma_{pq} = \Gamma(t_p, t_q)$; it is assumed that Γ is nonsingular. Let $\Gamma^{-1} = \Lambda = (\Lambda_{pq})$ be the inverse matrix; then the joint frequency function of

$$X(t_1), X(t_2), \ldots, X(t_n)$$

$$f(x_1, x_2, \ldots, x_n; t_1, t_2, \ldots, t_n)$$

$$= \frac{|\Lambda|^{\frac{1}{2}}}{(2\pi)^{n/2}} \exp\left\{-\frac{1}{2}\sum_{p,q=1}^{n} \Lambda_{pq}[x_p - m(t_p)][x_q - m(t_q)]\right\}. \tag{2.7}$$

It is more convenient to work with the characteristic function defined by

$$\phi(\theta_1, \theta_2, \ldots, \theta_n; t_1, t_2, \ldots, t_n)$$

$$= \int_{R_n} \exp\left(i\sum_{1}^{n} \theta_p x_p\right) f(x_1, x_2, \ldots, x_n; t_1, t_2, \ldots, t_n)\, dx_1, dx_2, \ldots, dx_n \tag{2.8}$$

where $i = \sqrt{-1}$, and R_n is the region $(-\infty < x_1, x_2, \ldots, x_n < \infty)$. It is known that

$$\phi(\theta_1, \theta_2, \ldots, \theta_n; t_1, t_2, \ldots, t_n)$$

$$= \exp\left(i\sum_{1}^{n} \theta_p m(t_p) - \frac{1}{2}\sum_{p,q=1}^{n} \Gamma_{pq}\theta_p\theta_q\right). \tag{2.9}$$

Clearly, for any permutation $(j_1, j_2, \ldots, j_n)$ of $(1, 2, \ldots, n)$ we have

$$\phi(\theta_{j_1}, \theta_{j_2}, \ldots, \theta_{j_n}; t_{j_1}, t_{j_2}, \ldots, t_{j_n}) = \phi(\theta_1, \theta_2, \ldots, \theta_n; t_1, t_2, \ldots, t_n). \tag{2.10}$$

Further, if $m < n$,

$$\phi(\theta_1, \theta_2, \ldots, \theta_m; 0, 0, \ldots, 0; t_1, t_2, \ldots, t_m, t_{m+1}, \ldots, t_n)$$

$$= \exp\left[i\sum_{1}^{m} \theta_p m(t_p) - \frac{1}{2}\sum_{p,q=1}^{m} \Gamma_{pq}\theta_p\theta_q\right]$$

$$= \phi(\theta_1, \theta_2, \ldots, \theta_m; t_1, t_2, \ldots, t_m). \tag{2.11}$$

Since the properties (2.10) and (2.11) imply (2.4) and (2.5) for the joint d.f. $F(x_1, x_2, \ldots, x_n; t_1, t_2, \ldots, t_n)$ [or the corresponding frequency function defined by (2.7)], it follows that the set of frequency functions (2.7) determines the Gaussian process.

If in the above definition (2.3) the parameter set T has only a finite number, p, of points, then the theory of such distributions belongs to the branch of Mathematical Statistics known as Multivariate Analysis. The really interesting case is therefore the one in which T is an infinite set. We shall deal with the two cases where (a) T is the set of nonnegative integers, and (b) $T = [0, \infty)$.

We also remark that $X(t)$ is, in general, a k-dimensional stochastic process, so that for each t the random variable $X(t)$ is a vector of the form $\{X_1(t), X_2(t), \ldots, X_k(t)\}$. We shall, however, be mostly concerned with univariate stochastic processes. Further, we have assumed that $X(t)$ is a real stochastic process. If $X(t)$ and $Y(t)$ are two real stochastic processes, then

$$Z(t) = X(t) + iY(t) \qquad \left(i = \sqrt{-1}\right) \tag{2.12}$$

defines a complex stochastic process; each process on the right-hand side of (2.12) has to be specified either analytically or in terms of distribution functions. As an example of a complex process, consider the following:

(iv) $Z(t) = \sum_1^N A_p e^{i\theta_p t}$, where $\theta_1, \theta_2, \ldots, \theta_N$ are real constants, $A_1, A_2, \ldots, A_N$

are real random variables. This can be written as

$$Z(t) = \sum_1^N A_p \cos \theta_p t + i \sum_1^N A_p \sin \theta_p t. \tag{2.13}$$

The above definition of a stochastic process in terms of a family of distribution functions is found to be satisfactory in the discrete parameter case. In the continuous parameter case, however, there are a number of important questions that cannot be answered on the basis of such a definition. For example, the above definition does not tell us whether we can associate a probability measure with the set

$$A(t) = \{\omega \,|\, b < X(\tau, \omega) < a \qquad \text{for } 0 \leqslant \tau \leqslant t\}, \tag{2.14}$$

where a and b are two constants. To see the relevance of such a set, consider the variable defined by the relation

$$T = \inf \{t \,|\, X(t, \omega) \leqslant b \qquad \text{or } X(t, \omega) \geqslant a\}, \tag{2.15}$$

where $b < X(0, \omega) < a$. If T were to be a random variable, then

$$\Pr \{T > t\} = \Pr \{A(t)\} ; \tag{2.16}$$

however, since the right-hand side of (2.16) has not been defined, we cannot speak of T as a random variable on the basic space of $X(t, \omega)$. One way to deal with such a situation is to introduce the notion of *separability* of a process [see Doob (1953)].

In this book we shall work with the analytic definition and (more often) with the definition in terms of distribution functions. We shall have occasion to discuss variables of the type (2.15), but it will be assumed that the process is such that they are random variables.

3. CHARACTERISTICS OF A STOCHASTIC PROCESS

Let $X(t)$ be a stochastic process defined in terms of its distribution functions as in (2.3). We define the characteristic function

$$\phi(\theta_1, \theta_2, \ldots, \theta_n; t_1, t_2, \ldots, t_n) = E\left\{\exp\left[i \sum_1^n \theta_p X(t_p)\right]\right\}$$

$$= \int_{R_n} \exp\left(i \sum_1^n \theta_p x_p\right) dF(x_1, x_2, \ldots, x_n; t_1, t_2, \ldots, t_n) \tag{3.1}$$

for $n \geq 1$, $t_1, t_2, \ldots, t_n \in T$. This exists for all real $\theta_1, \theta_2, \ldots, \theta_n$.

We next define the moment

$$\mu_{r_1 r_2 \ldots r_n}(t_1, t_2, \ldots, t_n)$$

$$= E\{[X(t_1)]^{r_1}[X(t_2)]^{r_2} \ldots [X(t_n)]^{r_n}\}$$

$$= \int_{R_n} x_1^{r_1} x_2^{r_2} \ldots x_n^{r_n} dF(x_1, x_2, \ldots, x_n; t_1, t_2, \ldots, t_n) \tag{3.2}$$

if it exists. In particular, let

$$m(t) = \mu_1(t) = E\{X(t)\} \tag{3.3}$$

$$\mu_2(t) = E\{X(t)\}^2, \mu_{11}(s, t) = E\{X(s) X(t)\}. \tag{3.4}$$

Then $m(t)$ is the mean of $X(t)$,

$$\sigma^2(t) = E[X(t) - m(t)]^2 = \mu_2(t) - [m(t)]^2 \tag{3.5}$$

is its variance, and

$$\Gamma(s, t) = E[X(s) - m(s)][X(t) - m(t)]$$

$$= \mu_{11}(s, t) - m(s)m(t), \tag{3.6}$$

is the covariance function. Further,

$$\rho(s, t) = \frac{\Gamma(s, t)}{\sigma(s)\sigma(t)} \tag{3.7}$$

gives the correlation function of the process.

For a complex process $Z(t) = X(t) + iY(t)$, we define

$$E\{Z(t)\} = E\{X(t)\} + iE\{Y(t)\}, \tag{3.8}$$

$$\mu_2(t) = E|Z(t)|^2, \qquad \mu_{11}(s, t) = E\{Z(s)\bar{Z}(t)\}, \tag{3.9}$$

where $\bar{Z}(t) = X(t) - iY(t)$.

A stochastic process $X(t)$ is said to be *stationary in the strict sense* if

$$F(x_1, x_2, \ldots, x_n; t_1 + \tau, t_2 + \tau, \ldots, t_n + \tau)$$

$$= F(x_1, x_2, \ldots, x_n; t_1, t_2, \ldots, t_n) \tag{3.10}$$

for $n \geqslant 1$, $t_1, t_2, \ldots, t_n, \tau \in T$. If (3.10) is satisfied, then the distribution of $X(t)$ is independent of t, since

$$\Pr\{X(\tau) \leqslant x\} = F(x; \tau) = F(x; 0) = F(x) \text{ (say).} \tag{3.11}$$

Therefore,

$$E\{X(t)\} = m, \qquad \text{Var}\{X(t)\} = \sigma^2, \tag{3.12}$$

where m and σ^2 are constants. In this case we can take $m = 0$, $\sigma^2 = 1$ without loss of generality. Then the covariance function is given by

$$\Gamma(s, t) = \int_{R_2} \int xy \, dF(x, y; s, t)$$

$$= \int_{R_2} \int xy \, dF(x, y; 0, t - s) \tag{3.13}$$

$$= \Gamma(0, t - s) = R(t - s) \text{ (say);}$$

$R(t)$ is thus the correlation function of the process. Clearly, $R(0) = 1$. If only the properties (3.12) and (3.13) hold, $X(t)$ is said to be *stationary in the wide sense*.

Examples

(i) $X(t) = At + B$, where A and B are uncorrelated random variables with

$$E(A) = \alpha, \quad E(B) = \beta$$

$$\text{Var}(A) = \sigma_1^2, \quad \text{Var}(B) = \sigma_2^2. \tag{3.14}$$

We have

$$m(t) = E\{X(t)\} = t\alpha + \beta \tag{3.15}$$

$$\sigma^2(t) = \text{Var}\{X(t)\} = t\sigma_1^2 + \sigma_2^2. \tag{3.16}$$

Moreover, since

$$\mu_{11}(s, t) = E\{X(s)X(t)\} = E\{(sA + B)(tA + B)\}$$

$$= stE(A^2) + (s + t)\alpha\beta + E(B^2),$$

we obtain

$$\Gamma(s, t) = \text{Covar}\{X(s), X(t)\}$$

$$= \mu_{11}(s, t) - (s\alpha + \beta)(t\alpha + \beta) \tag{3.17}$$

$$= st\sigma_1^2 + \sigma_2^2.$$

(ii) $X(t) = A \cos \theta t + B \sin \theta t$, where A and B are uncorrelated random variables, each having mean 0 and variance σ^2. In Section 2 we have already found that

$$m(t) = 0, \qquad \sigma^2(t) = \sigma^2. \tag{3.18}$$

We have

$$\Gamma(s, t) = E\{X(s)X(t)\}$$

$$= E\{(A \cos \theta s + B \sin \theta s)(A \cos \theta t + B \sin \theta t)\}$$

$$= \sigma^2 (\cos \theta s \cos \theta t + \sin \theta s \sin \theta t) \tag{3.19}$$

$$= \sigma^2 \cos \theta(t - s).$$

From (3.18) and (3.19) we find that the process is stationary in the wide sense. The correlation function is given by

$$R(t) = \cos \theta t. \tag{3.20}$$

(iii) *The Stationary Gaussian Process*: If, in the Gaussian process defined in example (iii) of Section 2, $m(t) = m$ (a constant), and the function $\Gamma(t_p, t_q)$ depends only on the difference $t_p - t_q$, then the process is seen to be stationary in the wide sense. However, since a Gaussian distribution is completely determined by the means $m(t_p)$ and the variance-covariance matrix Γ, it follows that the process is in fact stationary in the strict sense.

(iv) $Z(t) = \sum_1^N A_p e^{i\theta_p t}$, where $\theta_1, \theta_2, \ldots, \theta_N$ are real, $A_1, A_2 \ldots A_p$ are random variables which are uncorrelated, and have mean 0 and $\text{Var}(A_p) = \sigma_p^2$ $(p = 1, 2, \ldots, N)$. We have

$$m(t) = E\{Z(t)\} = 0, \tag{3.21}$$

$$\Gamma(s, t) = E\{Z(s)\bar{Z}(t)\} = E\left(\sum_1^N A_p e^{i\theta_p s}\right)\left(\sum_1^N A_q e^{-i\theta_q t}\right)$$

$$= \sum_{p,q=1}^N E(A_p A_q) e^{i(\theta_p s - \theta_q t)}$$

$$= \sum_{p=1}^N \sigma_p^2 e^{i\theta_p(s-t)}, \tag{3.22}$$

and in particular,

$$\text{Var}\{Z(t)\} = E|Z(t)|^2 = \sum_1^N \sigma_p^2. \qquad (3.23)$$

From (3.21)–(3.23) we see that the process $Z(t)$ is stationary in the wide sense.

(v) $X_n = \sum_{p=0}^N a_p \xi_{n-p}$ $(n = \ldots, -2, -1, 0, 1, 2, \ldots)$, where $\xi_1, \xi_2, \ldots$

are mutually independent and identically distributed real random variables with mean 0 and variance unity, and the a_p are (complex) constants. We have

$$E(X_n) = 0, \qquad (3.24)$$

$$E(X_m \bar{X}_n) = \sum_{p,q=1}^N a_p \bar{a}_q E(\xi_{m-p} \xi_{n-q})$$

$$= \sum_{\substack{0 \le p \le N \\ 0 \le n-m+p \le N}} a_p \bar{a}_{n-m+p}, \qquad (3.25)$$

and, in particular,

$$E|X_m|^2 = \sum_{0 \le p \le N} |a_p|^2. \qquad (3.26)$$

We have here a discrete time process that is stationary in the wide sense.

(vi) Let $\{X_n\}$ be a sequence of uncorrelated random variables with $E(X_n) = 0$, $\text{Var}(X_n) = \sigma^2$. We have then

$$\Gamma_{m,n} = E(X_m \bar{X}_n) = \begin{cases} 0 & \text{if } m \ne n \\ \sigma^2 & \text{if } m = n, \end{cases} \qquad (3.27)$$

which shows that $\{X_n\}$ is stationary in the wide sense. If, in addition, the X_n are identically distributed, $\{X_n\}$ is stationary in the strict sense.

(vii) *Processes with Independent Increments*: These are defined for a continuous parameter t and have the property that for $t_1 < t_2 < \cdots < t_n$, the random variables

$$X(t_2) - X(t_1), X(t_3) - X(t_2), \ldots, X(t_n) - X(t_{n-1}) \qquad (3.28)$$

$(n \ge 3)$ are mutually independent. We can write

$$X(t_n) = X(0) + \sum_1^n [X(t_q) - X(t_{q-1})] \qquad (t_0 = 0). \qquad (3.29)$$

If the increment $X(t_q) - X(t_{q-1})$ has a distribution depending on the difference $t_q - t_{q-1}$, then the process is said to be stationary. In this case let the characteristic function of $X(t) - X(s)$ $(s < t)$ be denoted by

$$\phi(\theta, t - s) = E\{e^{i\theta[X(t) - X(s)]}\}.$$ (3.30)

Let us assume that $X(0) = 0$; then the characteristic function of $X(t_1)$, $X(t_2), \ldots, X(t_n)$ is given by

$$\phi(\theta_1, \theta_2, \ldots, \theta_n; t_1, t_2, \ldots, t_n)$$

$$= E\left\{\exp\left[i\sum_1^n \theta_p X(t_p)\right]\right\}$$

$$= E\left[\exp\left\{i\sum_1^n \theta_p \sum_1^p [X(t_q) - X(t_{q-1})]\right\}\right]$$

$$= E\left[\exp\left\{i\sum_1^n [X(t_q) - X(t_{q-1})]\left(\sum_q^n \theta_p\right)\right\}\right]$$ (3.31)

$$= \prod_{q=1}^n E\left[\exp\left\{i\left(\sum_q^n \theta_p\right)[X(t_q) - X(t_{q-1})]\right\}\right]$$

$$= \phi\left(\sum_1^n \theta_p; t_1\right)\phi\left(\sum_2^n \theta_p; t_2 - t_1\right)\phi\left(\sum_3^n \theta_p; t_3 - t_2\right)$$

$$\ldots \phi(\theta_n; t_n - t_{n-1}).$$

From (3.31) it is easily verified that the consistency conditions are satisfied.

Processes with independent increments (or additive processes) have been studied in great detail by Cramér (1937), Lévy [(1937), (1948)], and others. The following are two important special cases of such a process:

(a) The Wiener–Einstein Process: This is a real process with stationary independent increments such that $X(t) - X(s)$ has a Gaussian distribution with mean 0 and

$$\text{Var}\,[X(t) - X(s)] = \sigma^2|t - s|.$$ (3.32)

The characteristic function (3.31) simplifies in this case to

$$\phi(\theta_1, \theta_2, \ldots, \theta_n; \quad t_1, t_2, \ldots, t_n)$$

$$= \prod_{q=1}^n \exp\left[-\tfrac{1}{2}\sigma^2(t_q - t_{q-1})^2\left(\sum_q^n \theta_p\right)^2\right]$$ (3.33)

$$= \exp\left[-\tfrac{1}{2}\sigma^2\sum_1^n (t_q - t_{q-1})^2\left(\sum_q^n \theta_p\right)^2\right],$$

where we recall that we have assumed that $X(0) = 0$. The covariance function is given by

$$\Gamma(t, t') = EX(t)X(t')$$

$$= EX(t)\{[X(t') - X(t)] + X(t)\}$$

$$= E[X(t)]^2 + EX(t)[X(t') - X(t)]$$

where we have taken $t' > t$; this gives $\Gamma(t, t') = \sigma^2 t$ $(t' > t)$, or, in general,

$$\Gamma(t, t') = \sigma^2 \min(t, t'). \tag{3.34}$$

(b) The Poisson Process: This is a real process with stationary increments, the distribution of the increment $X(t) - X(s)$ $(s < t)$ being given by

$$\Pr\{X(t) - X(s) = j\} = e^{-\lambda(t-s)} \frac{\lambda^j}{j!} (t - s)^j \qquad (j = 0, 1, 2, \dots). \tag{3.35}$$

The characteristic function of $X(t) - X(s)$ is given by

$$\phi(\theta, t - s) = \sum_0^\infty \exp[-\lambda(t - s) + ij\theta] \frac{\lambda^j}{j!} (t - s)^j \tag{3.36}$$

$$= \exp[-\lambda(t - s)(1 - e^{i\theta})].$$

From (3.36) it is found that

$$E[X(t) - X(s)] = \text{Var}[X(t) - X(s)] = \lambda(t - s). \tag{3.37}$$

Proceeding as in (a) we find that the covariance function is

$$\Gamma(t, t') = \lambda \min(t, t'). \tag{3.38}$$

4. LIMITING PROPERTIES

Consider first the case where the parameter set $T = (0, 1, 2, \dots)$, so that we have a random sequence $\{X_n\}$. The notion of a limit for this sequence is an important one, and may be formulated in several ways. Thus we have the following (the main results are stated without proofs; see the references cited in the next section):

(a) Convergence with Probability One: We say that the sequence $\{X_n\}$ converges, with probability one, to a random variable X if, for every $\varepsilon > 0$,

$$\Pr\{\text{at least one of the inequalities } |X_k - X| \geq \varepsilon,$$

$$k = n, n + 1, \dots \text{ holds}\} \to 0 \qquad \text{as } n \to \infty. \tag{4.1}$$

This means that all realizations of the sequence $\{X_n\}$ converge to X with probability one.

(b) Convergence in Probability: The sequence $\{X_n\}$ converges in probability to X if, for every $\varepsilon > 0$

$$\Pr\{|X_n - X| \geqslant \varepsilon\} \to 0 \qquad \text{as } n \to \infty. \tag{4.2}$$

If $X_n \to X$ with probability one, then it is seen that $X_n \to X$ in probability. Conversely, if $X_n \to X$ in probability, then there is a subsequence $\{X_{n_k}, k = 1, 2, \ldots\}$ which converges to X with probability one.

(c) Convergence in the Mean Square: The sequence $\{X_n\}$ converges to X in the mean square (m.s.) if

$$E|X_n - X|^2 \to 0 \qquad \text{as } n \to \infty. \tag{4.3}$$

Convergence in the m.s. implies convergence in probability; for, by Chebyshev's inequality

$$\Pr\{|X_n - X| \geqslant \varepsilon\} \leqslant \frac{1}{\varepsilon^2} E|X_n - X|^2 \to 0 \qquad \text{as } n \to \infty, \tag{4.4}$$

if $X_n \to X$ (m.s.). Conversely, convergence in probability does not always imply convergence (m.s.).

If $X_n \to X$ (m.s.), then since

$$|X_m - X_n|^2 \leqslant 2|X_m - X|^2 + 2|X_n - X|^2,$$

we find that

$$E|X_m - X_n|^2 \leqslant 2E|X_m - X|^2 + 2E|X_n - X|^2 \to 0 \tag{4.5}$$

as $m, n \to \infty$. Conversely, if $E|X_m - X_n|^2 \to 0$ as $m, n \to \infty$, then it can be proved that $X_n \to X$ (m.s.). Thus we have the m.s. criterion of convergence: $X_n \to X$ (m.s.) if, and only if,

$$E|X_m - X_n|^2 \to 0 \qquad \text{as } m, n \to \infty. \tag{4.6}$$

Let $E|X_n|^2 < \infty$ for each n. If $E|X_n - X|^2 \to 0$ as $n \to \infty$, then $E|X_n - X|^2$ remains finite for all $n >$ some N. Since

$$E|X|^2 \leqslant 2E|X_n|^2 + 2E|X_n - X|^2, \tag{4.7}$$

it follows that $E|X|^2 < \infty$. Also, since

$$|E(X_n - X)| \leqslant E|X_n - X| \leqslant \sqrt{E|X_n - X|^2} \to 0$$

as $n \to \infty$, we find that

$$\lim_{n \to \infty} E(X_n) = E \lim_{n \to \infty} X_n \qquad \text{(m.s.).} \tag{4.8}$$

(d) Convergence in Distribution: Let $F_n(x)$ be the distribution function of X_n. If there exists a distribution function $F(x)$ such that as $n \to \infty$ $F_n(x) \to F(x)$ at every continuity point of $F(x)$, then we say that the sequence $\{X_n\}$ converges in distribution.

If $\{X_n\}$ converges in probability, then it converges in distribution; in fact $F_n(x) \to F(x)$, when $F(x)$ is the distribution function of X.

The above definitions of convergence can be extended to the continuous parameter case. In particular, the notion of m.s. convergence of a stochastic process $X(t)$ $(-\infty < t < \infty)$ will be developed in the next chapter. Convergence with probability one introduces difficulties of the type described at the end of Section 2.

In the remainder of this chapter we shall summarize the basic concepts of probability.

5. BASIC CONCEPTS OF PROBABILITY THEORY

5.1. The Probability Space; Random Variables

The elementary theory of probability is based on the idea of an *experiment* (real or conceptual, but capable of being repeated), whose outcomes are called *events*. The collection of all events is called the *sample space*, whose points (the *sample points*) are the irreducible (simple) events. There are relations between the events, which make new events out of those given. With each sample point is associated a real number, called its probability, which is subject to certain consistency conditions. With this intuitive background, the modern theory introduces abstraction, and is developed as a part of the general theory of measure. The following is a brief outline of the basic concepts of the theory.

We are given a space Ω of points ω, and a Borel field $\mathscr{B}$ of subsets of Ω, that is, a class of subsets $A_1, A_2, \ldots$ having the following properties:

(i) $\Omega \in \mathscr{B}$;

(ii) if $A \in \mathscr{B}$, then $\bar{A} \in \mathscr{B}$, where $\bar{A}$ is the complement of A;

(iii) if $A_1, A_2, \ldots \in \mathscr{B}$, then $\bigcup_1^\infty A_n \in \mathscr{B}$.

From (i)–(iii) it is seen that the empty set $0 = \bar{\Omega} \in \mathscr{B}$. Moreover, if A_1, $A_2, \ldots \in \mathscr{B}$, then

$$\bigcap_1^\infty A_n = \overline{\left(\bigcup_1^\infty \bar{A}_n \right)} \in \mathscr{B}. \tag{5.1}$$

Finally, if $A \in \mathscr{B}$ and $B \in \mathscr{B}$, then

$$A - B = A \cap \bar{B} \in \mathscr{B}. \tag{5.2}$$

For sets $A \in \mathscr{B}$ we define a measure $P(A)$ by the following conditions:

(a) $P\{A\} \geqslant 0$;   (b) $P\{\Omega\} = 1$;

(c) for any denumerable collection of sets A_1, A_2, ..., such that $A_n \in \mathcal{B}$, $A_m \cap A_n = 0$,

$$P\left\{\bigcup_1^\infty A_n\right\} = \sum_1^\infty P\{A_n\}.$$

Axioms (a)–(c) then define a completely additive nonnegative set function $P(A)$ defined for sets $A \in \mathcal{B}$. In particular, let $A \in \mathcal{B}$, $B \in \mathcal{B}$, and $A \subset B$, then

$$P(A) \leqslant P(B). \tag{5.3}$$

For, $B = A \cup (\bar{A} \cap B)$, where $A \cap (\bar{A} \cap B) = 0$, so that from (a) and (c) we find that

$$P(B) = P(A) + P(\bar{A} \cap B) \geqslant P(A),$$

which gives (5.3). From (5.3) we deduce that $P(A) \leqslant P(\Omega) = 1$, since $A \subset \Omega$; we thus have

$$0 \leqslant P(A) \leqslant 1. \tag{5.4}$$

We may speak of sets $A \in \mathcal{B}$ as events, and $P(A)$ as the probability measure of the event A. To emphasize the probability aspect of this measure, we shall denote it as $\Pr\{A\}$ in this book. We thus have a probability space $(\Omega, \mathcal{B}, P)$.

A random variable $X(\omega)$ is a single-valued function of $\omega \in \Omega$, whose values belong to the real line $R = (-\infty, \infty)$, such that for any subset A' of the Borel field (say $\mathcal{B}_x$) in R, the set

$$A = \{\omega \,|\, X(\omega) \in A'\} \in \mathcal{B}. \tag{5.5}$$

Let

$$P_X\{A'\} = P\{A\}, \tag{5.6}$$

where the set A is defined by (5.5), $A \in \mathcal{B}$, and the measure on the right-hand side of (5.6) has been defined above. It will be found that the measure defined by (5.6) for $A' \in \mathcal{B}_X$ satisfies the axioms (a)–(c). We thus have a probability space $(R, \mathcal{B}_X, P_X)$, which is said to be induced by the random variable $X(\omega)$. We may then choose to work with this induced space, and keep the basic space $(\Omega, \mathcal{B}, P)$ in the background. For convenience, we denote

$$P_X\{A'\} = P\{X(\omega) \in A'\}. \tag{5.7}$$

The class of random variables is closed under the usual operations of analysis. Thus a linear combination of random variables is a random variable, and the limit (if it exists) of a sequence of random variables is also a random variable.

In the above definition of a random variable, it is sufficient to take intervals as the sets $A' \subset \mathscr{B}_X$. In particular, let us consider the intervals $(-\infty, x]$, and

$$
\begin{aligned}
F(x) = P_X\{(-\infty, x]\} &= P\{X(\omega) \leqslant x\} \\
&= P\{\omega \mid -\infty < X(\omega) \leqslant x\} \quad (-\infty < x < \infty).
\end{aligned} \tag{5.8}
$$

We define $F(x)$ as the distribution function of $X(\omega)$. It is easily seen that $F(x)$ is a monotone nondecreasing function of x, continuous to the right, and is such that

$$
F(-\infty) = 0, \qquad F(+\infty) = 1. \tag{5.9}
$$

If the integral

$$
\int_{-\infty}^{\infty} |x| \, dF(x)
$$

exists, then we put

$$
E(X) = \int_{-\infty}^{\infty} x \, dF(x), \tag{5.10}
$$

and call $E(x)$ the expectation of $X(\omega)$, or its mean.

Let $g(x)$ be a finite Borel function of $x \in R$. Then $g(X(\omega))$ is also a random variable; its distribution is determined by the probability measure P_X of X. We define the expectation of $g(X(\omega))$ as

$$
E[g(X)] = \int_{-\infty}^{\infty} g(x) \, dF(x), \tag{5.11}
$$

provided, of course, the integral in (5.11) converges absolutely. In particular,

$$
\phi(\theta) = E(e^{i\theta X}) = \int_{-\infty}^{\infty} e^{i\theta X} \, dF(x) \tag{5.12}
$$

is called the characteristic function of $X(\omega)$, and

$$
\mu'_r = E(X^r) = \int_{-\infty}^{\infty} x^r \, dF(x) \tag{5.13}
$$

is called its rth moment. For $r = 1$, μ'_1 is the mean defined by (5.10); the variance of $X(\omega)$ is defined by

$$
\text{Var}(X) = \int_{-\infty}^{\infty} (x - \mu'_1)^2 \, dF(x). \tag{5.14}
$$

If the derivative $F'(x) = f(x)$ exists, then $f(x)$ is called the frequency density function of X. The integrals appearing in the above definitions can then be expressed in terms of $f(x)$.

The above discussion can be extended to the case of a set

$$
(X_1(\omega), X_2(\omega), \ldots, X_k(\omega)) \qquad (k \geqslant 1)
$$

of random variables. This set induces a probability space $(R_k, \mathscr{B}_k, P_X)$ where R_k is the k-dimensional Euclidean space, $\mathscr{B}_k$ is a Borel field of subsets of R_k and $P_X \equiv P_{X_1, X_2, \ldots, X_k}$.

5.2. Independence

Let $(\Omega, \mathscr{B}, P)$ be a probability space. Two events A, B (that is, sets $\in \mathscr{B}$) are said to be stochastically independent if

$$P\{A \cap B\} = P\{A\} P\{B\}. \tag{5.15}$$

Two random variables $X_1(\omega)$ and $X_2(\omega)$ defined on $(\Omega, \mathscr{B}, P)$ are said to be independent if, for every pair of sets $A'_1 \in \mathscr{B}_{X_1}$, $A'_2 \in \mathscr{B}_{X_2}$, the sets

$$A_1 = \{\omega \mid X_1(\omega) \in A'_1\}, \; A_2 = \{\omega \mid X_2(\omega) \in A'_2\} \quad (A_1 \in \mathscr{B}, A_2 \in \mathscr{B}) \tag{5.16}$$

are independent. We then have

$$\begin{aligned} P_{X_1 X_2}(A'_1, A'_2) &= P\{\omega \mid X_1(\omega) \in A'_1, X_2(\omega) \in A'_2\} \\ &= P\{A_1 \cap A_2\} = P\{A_1\} P\{A_2\}, \end{aligned} \tag{5.17}$$

or, using (5.7),

$$P\{X_1(\omega) \in A'_1, X_2(\omega) \in A'_2\} = P\{X_1(\omega) \in A'_1\} P\{X_2(\omega) \in A'_2\}. \tag{5.18}$$

The random variables $X_1(\omega)$, $X_2(\omega)$ thus induce a product measure defined by (5.18) for subsets of the product Borel field $\mathscr{B}_X \cdot \mathscr{B}_Y$ in the product space $R_{X_1} \cdot R_{X_2}$.

In terms of the joint distribution function of X_1, X_2 the property (5.18) can be expressed as

$$\begin{aligned} F(x_1, x_2) &= P\{X_1(\omega) \leqslant x_1, X_2(\omega) \leqslant x_2\} \\ &= P\{X_1(\omega) \leqslant x_1\} P\{X_2(\omega) \leqslant x_2\} \quad (x_1 \in R_{X_1}, x_2 \in R_{X_2}). \end{aligned} \tag{5.19}$$

5.3. Conditional Probability and Expectation

Let $A \in \mathscr{B}$ and $P(A) \neq 0$. For $B \in \mathscr{B}$ we define

$$P_A(B) = \frac{P\{A \cap B\}}{P\{A\}}, \tag{5.20}$$

and call it the *conditional probability* of B given A. This probability measure has the following properties:

    (i) $P_A(A) = 1$;
    (ii) $P\{A \cap B\} = P\{A\} P_A\{B\}$;
    (iii) if $A_1, A_2, \ldots, A_n$ are sets of $\mathscr{B}$ such that $P(A_j) \neq 0$, $A_j \cap A_k = 0$,

and $\Omega = \bigcup_1^n A_j$, then for $B \in \mathscr{B}$ we have

$$P(B) = \sum_{j=1}^{n} P(A_j) P_{A_j}(B).$$

Now let us define the random variable $X(\omega)$ on Ω as follows:

$$X(\omega) = \begin{cases} x & \text{if } \omega \in A \\ 0 & \text{if } \omega \in \bar{A}; \end{cases} \tag{5.21}$$

then we define

$$P(B \mid X(\omega) = x) = P_A(B) \tag{5.22}$$

as the conditional probability of B given that $X(\omega) = x$. It is now easy to define the conditional distribution of a random variable $Y(\omega)$ given that $X(\omega) = x$; thus

$$P\{Y(\omega) \in B' \mid X(\omega) = x\} = P_A(B), \tag{5.23}$$

where $B = \{\omega \mid Y(\omega) \in B'\} \in \mathscr{B}$. This leads, in particular, to the conditional distribution function of Y for a given X. The conditional mean of Y for a given X is then merely the expectation of this with respect to this conditional distribution.

The above definitions break down when $P(A) = 0$. In this case the notion of conditional probabilities and expectations is developed in a fairly abstract manner. Consider first the sets $A_1, A_2, \ldots, A_n$ defined in (iii) above. Let us define the random variable $X(\omega)$ on Ω as follows:

$$X(\omega) = x_j \qquad \text{if } \omega \in A_j. \tag{5.24}$$

Let the probability space induced by $X(\omega)$ be $(R_X, \mathscr{B}_X, P_X)$. For $A' \in \mathscr{B}_X$ write

$$A = \{\omega \mid X(\omega) \in A'\} \in \mathscr{B}; \tag{5.25}$$

in particular, if $A' = A'_j = \{x_j\}$, then $A = A_j (j = 1, 2, \ldots, n)$. On the space R_X we define a measure $\mu_B(A')$ as follows:

If $A' \in \mathscr{B}_X$,

$$\mu_B(A') = P(B \cap A), \tag{5.26}$$

$$\mu_\Omega(A') = P(A). \tag{5.27}$$

From (5.26) and (5.27) we then find that

$$\frac{\mu_B(A'_j)}{\mu_\Omega(A'_j)} = P_{A_j}(B) = P(B \mid X(\omega) = x_j)$$

$$= P(B \mid x_j) \text{ (say).} \tag{5.28}$$

We can therefore consider a random variable $P[B \mid X(\omega)]$ with the values

$$P[B \mid X(\omega)] = P(B \mid x_j) \qquad \text{if } \omega \in A_j \qquad (j = 1, 2, \ldots, n). \tag{5.29}$$

We have thus defined a conditional probability as a random variable. Let us note that

$$\int_A P[B \,|\, X(\omega)] \, dP(\omega)$$

$$= \sum \int_{A \cap A_j} P[B \,|\, X(\omega)] \, dP(\omega) = \sum \frac{P(B \cap A \cap A_j)}{P(A \cap A_j)} P(A \cap A_j) \quad (5.30)$$

$$= \sum P(B \cap A \cap A_j) = P(B \cap A)$$

(the summation being taken over those j for which $P(A \cap A_j) \neq 0$).

In the general case let $X(\omega)$ be a random variable defined on $(\Omega, \mathscr{B}, P)$ and let $(R_X, \mathscr{B}_X, P_X)$ be the probability space induced by $X(\omega)$. Let $B \in \mathscr{B}$, fixed. For $A' \in \mathscr{B}_X$, define A as in (5.25); $A \in \mathscr{B}$. Write

$$\mu_B(A') = P(B \cap A); \tag{5.31}$$

$\mu_B(A')$ and $\mu_\Omega(A')$ are measures on $\mathscr{B}_X$ such that $\mu_B(A') \ll \mu_\Omega(A')$. We now use the Radon–Nikodym theorem and find that there exists a random variable $Z_B(\omega')$ on R_X, which is integrable on R_X, and such that

$$\mu_B(A') = \int_{A'} Z_B(\omega') \, d\mu_\Omega(\omega'), \qquad A' \in \mathscr{B}_X. \tag{5.32}$$

We define $Z_B(\omega')$ as the conditional probability of B for a given ω'. In (5.32), $Z_B(\omega')$ is defined uniquely modulo $\mu_\Omega(\omega')$. We have

$$0 \leqslant Z_B(\omega') \leqslant 1 \qquad [\mu_\Omega(\omega')], \tag{5.33}$$

since $\mu_B(A') = P(B \cap A) \leqslant P(B) = \mu_\Omega(A')$. Further, if $\{B_n\}$ is a sequence of sets $\in \mathscr{B}$ such that $B_m \cap B_n = 0$, then for $B = \bigcup_1^\infty B_n$ we have

$$\int_{A'} Z_B(\omega') \, d\mu_\Omega(\omega') = P\left(\bigcup_1^\infty B_n \cap A\right)$$

$$= \sum_1^\infty P(B_n \cap A) = \sum_1^\infty \int_{A'} Z_{B_n}(\omega') \, d\mu_\Omega(\omega')$$

$$= \int_{A'} \sum_1^\infty Z_{B_n}(\omega') \, d\mu_\Omega(\omega'),$$

which gives

$$Z_B(\omega') = \sum_1^\infty Z_{B_n}(\omega'). \tag{5.34}$$

Other "desirable" properties of $Z_B(\omega')$ can also be investigated along these lines; thus $Z_B(\omega')$ behaves like a probability measure.

To define conditional expectation in the general case, let $Y(\omega)$ be a random variable defined on $(\Omega, \mathscr{B}, P)$, which has a finite mean. For $A' \in \mathscr{B}_Y$ we define the measure

$$v(A') = \int_A Y(\omega)\, dP(\omega). \tag{5.35}$$

Proceeding as before we find that there exists a random variable $Z_Y(\omega')$ $(\omega' \in R_Y)$ which is integrable over R_Y and such that

$$v(A') = \int_{A'} Z_Y(\omega')\, d\mu_\Omega(\omega'), \; A' \in \mathscr{B}_Y. \tag{5.36}$$

We define $Z_Y(\omega')$ as the conditional expectation of Y given ω'.

For further details of the measure-theoretic treatment of probability, see Kolmogorov (1931) and Loève (1963); the discussion in this section follows Halmos (1950). For a treatment restricted to discrete sample spaces, see Feller (1957). For a good account of the distribution theory of statistics, see Wilks (1962).

6. REFERENCES

Cramér, H. RANDOM VARIABLES AND PROBABILITY DISTRIBUTIONS. *Cambridge Tracts in Math.*, no. 36, 1937.

Doob, J. L. STOCHASTIC PROCESSES. New York: Wiley, 1953.

Feller, W. AN INTRODUCTION TO PROBABILITY THEORY AND ITS APPLICATIONS. 2nd ed. New York: Wiley, 1957.

Halmos, P. R. MEASURE THEORY. New York: Van Nostrand, 1950.

Kolmogorov, A. N. FOUNDATIONS OF PROBABILITY THEORY. New York: Chelsea, 1931. 2nd English ed., 1956.

Lévy, Paul. THÉORIE DE L'ADDITION DES VARIABLES ALÉATOIRES. Paris: Gauthier-Villars, 1937.

―――――. PROCESSES STOCHASTIQUES ET MOUVEMENT BROWNIEN. Paris: Gauthier-Villars, 1948.

Loève, M. PROBABILITY THEORY. 3rd ed. New York: Van Nostrand, 1963.

Wilks, S. S. MATHEMATICAL STATISTICS. New York: Wiley, 1962.

1

Regular
Stochastic
Processes

1. THE COVARIANCE FUNCTION

Let $X(t)$ $(t \in T)$ be a stochastic process, which we shall assume in general to be complex valued. If

$$E|X(t)|^2 < \infty \qquad \text{for all } t \in T, \tag{1.1}$$

we say that $X(t)$ is regular (or of second order). If this condition is satisfied, then

$$|EX(t)\bar{X}(t')| < \infty \qquad \text{for all } (t, t') \in (T \times T). \tag{1.2}$$

This follows from *Schwarz' inequality:*

$$E|X(t)\bar{X}(t')| \leqslant \sqrt{E|X(t)|^2 E|X(t')|^2} \qquad (t, t') \in (T \times T). \tag{1.3}$$

To prove (1.3), let λ be a real constant, and consider

$$\{\lambda|X(t)| + |\bar{X}(t')|\}^2 \geqslant 0. \tag{1.4}$$

Taking mean value of both sides of (1.4) we obtain

$$\lambda^2 E|X(t)|^2 + 2\lambda E|X(t)\bar{X}(t')| + E|X(t')|^2 \geqslant 0; \tag{1.5}$$

the quadratic expression in λ on the left-hand side of (1.5) thus remains nonnegative for all λ. Therefore,

$$\{E|X(t)\bar{X}(t')|\}^2 \leqslant E|X(t)|^2 E|X(t')|^2,$$

which is the required inequality.

Let us now observe that the mean value in (1.2) can be taken to be the covariance function $\Gamma(t, t')$ of $X(t)$, without loss of generality. This amounts to assuming that $E\{X(t)\} = 0$. For, let η be a random variable independent of $X(t)$, and with mean 0 and variance unity. Then for the process $Y(t) = \eta X(t)$ we have

$$EY(t) = E(\eta)EX(t) = 0$$

since $E(\eta) = 0$, and

$$\text{Covar}\{Y(t), \bar{Y}(t')\} = EY(t)\bar{Y}(t')$$
$$= E|\eta|^2 EX(t)\bar{X}(t')$$
$$= EX(t)\bar{X}(t').$$

Thus $EX(t)\bar{X}(t')$ can be taken to be the covariance function of the process $Y(t)$, which proves our assertion. We thus let

$$\Gamma(t, t') = EX(t)\bar{X}(t'); \tag{1.6}$$

for a regular stochastic process, this is thus always finite. Conversely, if $\Gamma(t, t')$ is finite for all $(t, t') \in (T x T)$, then

$$E|X(t)|^2 = \Gamma(t, t) < \infty \qquad \text{for all } t \in T. \tag{1.7}$$

Regular functions in the stationary case were introduced by Khintchine (1934), and were studied by Slutsky (1937), Wold (1938), Cramér (1940), Kolmogorov (1941), and others. For two recent monographs on the subject, see Grenander and Rosenblatt (1956) and Yaglom (1962). The general case was studied by Loève during 1945–46; the treatment here follows Loève (1963).

In this section we study some properties of the covariance function $\Gamma(t, t')$. It will be seen in the next section that the properties of the process are connected with those of $\Gamma(t, t')$.

THEOREM 1.1.   *The covariance function $\Gamma(t, t')$ of a regular process is Hermitian:*

$$\Gamma(t, t') = \overline{\Gamma(t', t)}, \qquad t, t' \in (T x T). \tag{1.8}$$

If the process is real, $\Gamma(t, t')$ is symmetric.

Proof: We have

$$\overline{\Gamma(t', t)} = \overline{EX(t')\bar{X}(t)}$$
$$= EX(t)\bar{X}(t') = \Gamma(t, t'), \tag{1.9}$$

as required.

THEOREM 1.2.   *The covariance function of a regular process is non-negative definite: for every finite subset* T_n *of* T *and every function* $\theta(t)$ *on* T_n, *we have*

$$\sum\sum_{t,t'\in T_n} \Gamma(t,t')\theta(t)\bar{\theta}(t') \geqslant 0. \tag{1.10}$$

Proof: We have

$$\sum\sum_{t,t'\in T_n} \Gamma(t,t')\theta(t)\bar{\theta}(t')$$

$$= \sum\sum_{t,t'\in T_n} \theta(t)\bar{\theta}(t')EX(t)\bar{X}(t')$$

$$= E\left\{ \sum_{t\in T_n} \theta(t)X(t) \sum_{t'\in T_n} \bar{\theta}(t')\bar{X}(t') \right\} \tag{1.11}$$

$$= E\left| \sum_{t\in T_n} \theta(t)X(t) \right|^2 \geqslant 0.$$

THEOREM 1.3.   *Given a function* $\Gamma(t,t')$ *on* $(T \times T)$ *which is of nonnegative type, we can always find a stochastic process* $X(t)$ *for which* $\Gamma(t,t')$ *is the covariance function. This process is real if* $\Gamma(t,t')$ *is real.*

Proof :   Let T_n consist of the points $t_1, t_2, \ldots, t_n \in T$, and write $\theta(t_p) = \theta_p$, $\Gamma(t_p, t_q) = \Gamma_{pq}$ $(p, q = 1, 2, \ldots, n)$. Then we are given that

$$\sum_{p,q=1}^{n} \Gamma_{pq}\theta_p\bar{\theta}_q \geqslant 0. \tag{1.12}$$

If $\Gamma(t,t')$ is real, we choose $\theta(t)$ to be real, and consider the function

$$\exp\left(-\frac{1}{2} \sum_{p,q=1}^{n} \Gamma_{pq}\theta_p\theta_q \right). \tag{1.13}$$

This is the characteristic function (c.f.) of an n-variate Gaussian distribution with zero means and the variance-covariance matrix $\Gamma = (\Gamma_{pq})$. Since. (1.12) holds for every finite subset T_n of T, (1.13) defines a real Gaussian process $X(t)$ with zero mean and covariance function $\Gamma(t,t')$.

If $\Gamma(t,t')$ is complex, let

$$\theta(t) = \alpha(t) - i\beta(t), \quad \Gamma(t,t') = A(t,t') + iB(t,t'), \tag{1.14}$$

where α, β, A, B are all real functions. Substituting (1.14) in (1.12) and simplifying, we find that

$$Q \equiv \sum_{p,q=1}^{n} A_{pq}(\alpha_p\alpha_q + \beta_p\beta_q) - \sum_{p,q=1}^{n} B_{pq}(\alpha_p\beta_q - \alpha_q\beta_p) \geqslant 0. \tag{1.15}$$

A reasoning similar to the one used for (1.13) shows that the characteristic function $e^{-\frac{1}{2}Q}$ defines a real bivariate Gaussian process $\{X(t), Y(t)\}$ with

$$EX(t) = EY(t) = 0 \tag{1.16}$$

$$EX(t)X(t') = EY(t)Y(t') = \tfrac{1}{2}A(t, t') \tag{1.17}$$

$$EX(t)Y(t') = -\tfrac{1}{2}B(t, t'). \tag{1.18}$$

Now consider the process

$$Z(t) = X(t) + iY(t); \tag{1.19}$$

from (1.16)–(1.18) we find that

$$EZ(t) = 0 \tag{1.20}$$

$$
\begin{aligned}
EZ(t)\bar{Z}(t') &= E\{X(t) + iY(t)\}\{X(t') - iY(t')\} \\
&= EX(t)X(t') + EY(t)Y(t') - iEX(t)Y(t') + iEX(t')Y(t) \\
&= \tfrac{1}{2}A(t, t') + \tfrac{1}{2}A(t, t') + \frac{i}{2}B(t, t') - \frac{i}{2}B(t', t) \\
&= A(t, t') + iB(t, t') = \Gamma(t, t'),
\end{aligned}
\tag{1.21}
$$

where we have used the fact that $B(t, t') = -B(t', t)$ which is a consequence of the Hermitian property. The complex Gaussian process $Z(t)$ therefore has the required property, and the theorem is completely proved.

Convergence in the Mean Square: Let $X(t)$ be a regular process, and let t_0 be a limit point of its parameter set T. We say that $X(t)$ converges to a random variable X in the mean square as $t \to t_0$, and write

$$X(t) \to X(\text{m.s.}) \qquad \text{as } t \to t_0, \tag{1.22}$$

if

$$E|X(t) - X|^2 \to 0 \qquad \text{as } t \to t_0. \tag{1.23}$$

From the general property of m.s. convergence we have that $E|X|^2 < \infty$, and moreover $EX(t) \to E(X)$ as $t \to t_0$, that is

$$\lim_{t \to t_0} EX(t) = E \lim_{t \to t_0} X(t) \qquad (\text{m.s.}), \tag{1.24}$$

which means the operations of m.s. limit and stochastic average commute.

The following theorem states the necessary and sufficient condition for m.s. convergence in terms of the convariance function.

THEOREM 1.4.   *Let $X(t)$ be a regular process. Then $X(t) \to X$ (m.s.) as $t \to t_0$, where X is a random variable if, and only if, the covariance function $\Gamma(t, t')$ converges to a finite limit as $t, t' \to t_0$. Then*

$$\Gamma(t, t') \to E|X|^2. \tag{1.25}$$

Proof: Let $X(t) \to X$ (m.s.) as $t \to t_0$. We have

$$E\{X(t)\bar{X}(t') - X\bar{X}\} = E\{X(t) - X\}\{\bar{X}(t') - \bar{X}\}$$
$$+ E\{X(t) - X\}\bar{X} + E\{\bar{X}(t') - \bar{X}\}X. \tag{1.26}$$

Using Schwarz' inequality, we find that

$$\left| E\{X(t) - X\}\{\bar{X}(t') - \bar{X}\} \right|^2$$
$$\leqslant E|X(t) - X|^2 E|X(t') - X|^2 \to 0 \qquad \text{as } t, t' \to t_0, \tag{1.27}$$

and similarly for the other two terms on the right-hand side of (1.26). Therefore,

$$\Gamma(t, t') = EX(t)\bar{X}(t') \to E|X|^2 \qquad \text{as } t, t' \to t_0. \tag{1.28}$$

Conversely, let $\Gamma(t, t') \to \gamma$ as $t, t' \to t_0$, where $\gamma < \infty$. We have

$$E|X(t) - X(t')|^2 = E\{X(t) - X(t')\}\{\bar{X}(t) - \bar{X}(t')\}$$
$$= E|X(t)|^2 - EX(t)\bar{X}(t')$$
$$- EX(t')\bar{X}(t) + E|X(t')|^2 \tag{1.29}$$
$$= \Gamma(t, t) - \Gamma(t, t') - \Gamma(t', t) + \Gamma(t', t)$$
$$\to \gamma - \gamma - \gamma + \gamma = 0 \qquad \text{as } t, t' \to t_0.$$

From (1.29) it follows (by the m.s. criterion of convergence) that $X(t) \to X$ (m.s.) as $t \to t_0$, where X is a random variable. The proof of Theorem 1.4 is therefore complete.

We shall need the following result, which is a generalization of the "if" part of the last theorem.

Theorem 1.5. *Let $X(t)$ and $X'(t)$ be two stochastic processes $(t \in T)$, which are both regular. Let t_0, t_0' be two limit points of T. Then if $X(t) \to X$ (m.s.) as $t \to t_0$ and $X'(t') \to X'$ (m.s.) as $t' \to t_0'$, then*

$$EX(t)\bar{X}'(t') \to EX\bar{X}' \qquad \text{as } t \to t_0, \ t' \to t_0'. \tag{1.30}$$

Questions regarding continuity and differentiability of $\Gamma(t, t')$ are intimately related to similar questions regarding the process $X(t)$ itself. Thus we have

$$\frac{\Gamma(t + h, t') - \Gamma(t, t')}{h} = E \frac{X(t + h) - X(t)}{h} \bar{X}(t'), \tag{1.31}$$

which shows that the existence of the partial derivative $(\partial/\partial t)\Gamma(t, t')$ depends on that of the derivative of $X(t)$. We shall need the concept of the second generalized derivative of $\Gamma(t, t')$, defined as the limit (if it exists) as $h, h' \to 0$, of the quotient

$$\frac{1}{hh'}\{\Gamma(t + h, t' + h') - \Gamma(t + h, t') - \Gamma(t, t' + h') + \Gamma(t, t')\}. \tag{1.32}$$

2. CONTINUITY AND DIFFERENTIABILITY OF A REGULAR PROCESS

We now investigate the properties of continuity and differentiability of a random function (stochastic process). These concepts are due to Slutsky (1928); for a regular process, we have the following results [due to Loève (1963)].

Continuity in the Mean Square. Let $X(t)$ be a regular process. We say that $X(t)$ is continuous in the mean square at $t \in T$ if

$$X(t + h) \to X(t) \qquad \text{(m.s.) as } h \to 0 \qquad (t, t + h \in T). \qquad (2.1)$$

THEOREM 2.1.   *A regular process $X(t)$ is continuous (m.s.) at $t \in T$, if, and only if, its covariance function $\Gamma(t, t')$ is continuous at (t, t).*

Proof: For fixed $t \in T$, let us write $Y_h = X(t + h)$. Then from Theorem 1.4, we find that $Y_h \to X(t)$ (m.s.) as $h \to 0$ if, and only if

$$EY_h \bar{Y}_{h'} \to EX(t)\bar{X}(t) \qquad \text{as } h, h' \to 0; \qquad (2.2)$$

this gives

$$\Gamma(t + h, t + h') \to \Gamma(t, t) \qquad \text{as } h, h' \to 0, \qquad (2.3)$$

which is the condition that $\Gamma(t, t')$ is continuous at (t, t).

Differentiability in the Mean Square: We say that $X(t)$ has a derivative $X'(t)$ or $(d/dt)X(t)$ in the mean square at $t \in T$ if

$$\frac{X(t + h) - X(t)}{h} \to X'(t) \qquad \text{(m.s.) as } h \to 0, (t \in T). \qquad (2.4)$$

THEOREM 2.2.   *A regular process $X(t)$ has a derivative at $t \in T$ if, and only if, the second generalized derivative of $\Gamma(t, t')$ exists and is finite at (t, t).*

Proof: For fixed $t \in T$, let us put

$$Y_h = \frac{X(t + h) - X(t)}{h}; \qquad (2.5)$$

then $Y_h \to X'(t)$ (m.s.) as $h \to 0$, where $X'(t)$ is a stochastic process if, and only if, $EY_h \bar{Y}_h$ converges to a limit as $h, h' \to 0$ (by Theorem 1.4). But

$$EY_h \bar{Y}_{h'} = \frac{1}{hh'} E\{X(t + h) - X(t)\}\{\bar{X}(t + h') - \bar{X}(t)\}$$

$$= \frac{1}{hh'}\{\Gamma(t + h, t + h') - \Gamma(t + h, t) - \Gamma(t, t + h') + \Gamma t, t)\}; \qquad (2.6)$$

the limit of which (if it exists) as $h, h' \to 0$, is the second generalized derivative of $\Gamma(t, t')$ at (t, t). This proves the theorem.

The last two theorems yield further results concerning the covariance function of the process. These are stated below.

THEOREM 2.3.   *Let $\Gamma(t, t')$ be the covariance function of a regular process which is continuous in the mean square at all $t \in T$. Then $\Gamma(t, t')$ is continuous at all $(t, t') \in (T \times T)$.*

Proof: For fixed $t, t' \in T$, let us put

$$Y_h = X(t + h), \ Y'_h = X(t' + h); \tag{2.7}$$

since $X(t)$ is continuous (m.s.), $Y_h \to X(t)$, $Y'_{h'} \to X(t')$ (m.s.) as $h, h' \to 0$. Therefore, by Theorem 1.5,

$$EY_h \bar{Y}'_{h'} \to EX(t)\bar{X}(t'),$$

or

$$\Gamma(t + h, t' + h') \to \Gamma(t, t') \qquad \text{as } h, h' \to 0, \tag{2.8}$$

as required.

THEOREM 2.4.   *Let $X(t)$ be a regular process, $t \in T$. If $X(t)$ has a derivative at all $t \in T$, then the derivatives*

$$\frac{\partial}{\partial t} \Gamma(t, t'), \qquad \frac{\partial}{\partial t'} \Gamma(t, t'), \qquad \frac{\partial^2}{\partial t \, \partial t'} \Gamma(t, t') \tag{2.9}$$

of its covariance function $\Gamma(t, t')$ exist and are finite on $(T \times T)$.

Proof: If $X(t)$ has the derivative $X'(t)$ at $t \in T$, then

$$\frac{X(t + h) - X(t)}{h} \to X'(t) \qquad \text{(m.s.)} \qquad \text{as } h \to 0. \tag{2.10}$$

Therefore,

$$\lim_{h \to 0} \frac{\Gamma(t + h, t') - \Gamma(t, t')}{h} = \lim_{h \to 0} E \frac{X(t + h) - X(t)}{h} \cdot \bar{X}(t')$$

$$= E \lim_{h \to 0} \frac{X(t + h) - X(t)}{h} \cdot \bar{X}(t') = EX'(t)\bar{X}(t'), \tag{2.11}$$

where we have used the commutative property (1.24). This shows that the derivative $(\partial/\partial t)\Gamma(t, t')$ exists, and

$$\frac{\partial}{\partial t} \Gamma(t, t') = EX'(t)\bar{X}(t'), \tag{2.12}$$

where the last expression is finite. Similarly,

$$\frac{\partial}{\partial t'} \Gamma(t, t') = EX(t)\bar{X}'(t'). \tag{2.13}$$

Finally,

$$\lim_{h' \to 0} \frac{1}{h'} \left\{ \frac{\partial}{\partial t} \Gamma(t, t' + h') - \frac{\partial}{\partial t} \Gamma(t, t') \right\}$$

$$= \lim_{h' \to 0} EX'(t) \frac{\bar{X}(t' + h') - \bar{X}(t')}{h'} \qquad \text{(from 2.12)}$$

$$= EX'(t)\bar{X}'(t'),$$

(2.14)

which shows that

$$\frac{\partial^2}{\partial t \, \partial t'} \Gamma(t, t') = EX'(t)\bar{X}'(t'). \tag{2.15}$$

The Derivative of $X(t)$: Let $X(t)$ be a regular process ($t \in T$) with mean $m(t)$ and covariance function $\Gamma_X(t, t')$. Suppose that $X(t)$ has a derivative $X'(t)$ on T. Then

$$\frac{d}{dt} m(t) = \lim_{h \to 0} \frac{m(t + h) - m(t)}{h}$$

$$= \lim_{h \to 0} E \frac{X(t + h) - X(t)}{h} = E \frac{d}{dt} X(t),$$

(2.16)

which exhibits the commutative property of the operations of differentiation and taking stochastic mean. Further, (2.15) can be written as

$$\frac{\partial^2}{\partial t \, \partial t'} \Gamma_X(t, t') = \Gamma_{X'}(t, t'). \tag{2.17}$$

3. THE STOCHASTIC INTEGRAL

We now consider the concept of integration of a stochastic process. The following discussion is confined to the Riemann integral, but Lebesgue and Stieltjes integrals can be considered along similar lines.

Let $X(t)$ ($-\infty < t < \infty$) be a regular stochastic process, and consider a t-interval $[a, b]$. Let $a = t_0 < t_1 < \cdots < t_n = b$ be a subdivision of $[a, b]$, $t_{p-1} \leqslant \xi_p \leqslant t_p$ ($p = 1, 2, \ldots, n$), and consider the sum

$$Y_n = \sum_{p=1}^{n} (t_p - t_{p-1}) X(\xi_p). \tag{3.1}$$

If, as $n \to \infty$ in such a way that $\max_{1 \leqslant p \leqslant n} |t_p - t_{p-1}| \to 0$, Y_n converges (m.s.) to a limit, we say that this limit is the Riemann integral of $X(t)$ over $[a, b]$, and denote it by

$$I = \int_a^b X(t) \, dt. \tag{3.2}$$

Clearly, I is a random variable. If (3.2) exists, we say that $X(t)$ is Riemann-integrable over $[a, b]$.

THEOREM 3.1. *A regular stochastic process $X(t)$ with the covariance function $\Gamma(t, t')$ is Riemann-integrable over $[a, b]$ if, and only if, the double integral*

$$\int_a^b \int_a^b \Gamma(t, t') \, dt \, dt' \tag{3.3}$$

exists. If this is the case, then

$$E\left\{\int_a^b X(t) \, dt \cdot \int_a^b \bar{X}(t') \, dt'\right\}$$

$$= \int_a^b \int_a^b \Gamma(t, t') \, dt \, dt'. \tag{3.4}$$

Proof: Let Y_n be defined by (3.1). Then $Y_n \to$ a limit I (m.s.) if, and only if,

$$E Y_n \bar{Y}_m \to E I \bar{I}, \tag{3.5}$$

where Y_m corresponds to a second subdivision $a = t'_0 < t'_1 < \cdots < t'_m = b$ of $[a, b]$, and $t'_{q-1} \leqslant \xi'_q \leqslant t'_q \, (q = 1, 2, \ldots, m)$. Now we have

$$E Y_n \bar{Y}_m = \sum_{p=1}^{n} \sum_{q=1}^{m} (t_p - t_{p-1})(t'_q - t'_{q-1}) \Gamma(\xi_p, \xi'_q), \tag{3.6}$$

and if the limit of this double sum exists as

$$n \to \infty, m \to \infty, \max_{1 \leqslant p \leqslant n} |t_p - t_{p-1}| \to 0 \quad \text{and} \quad \max_{1 \leqslant q \leqslant m} |t'_q - t'_{q-1}| \to 0,$$

then it is the double integral (3.3). This proves the first part of the theorem; the second part follows from (3.5).

We also note that if $m(t) = EX(t)$, then

$$E Y_n = \sum_{1}^{n} (t_p - t_{p-1}) m(\xi_p) \to \int_a^b m(t) \, dt;$$

and since

$$\lim E Y_n = E \lim Y_n = E \int_a^b X(t) \, dt,$$

we obtain the identity

$$E \int_a^b X(t) \, dt = \int_a^b E\{X(t)\} \, dt. \tag{3.7}$$

4. THE STATIONARY CASE

A stochastic process $X(t)$ $(t \in T)$ is said to be second order stationary if it is regular, and if its covariance function $\Gamma(t, t')$ depends only on the difference $t - t'$. Let

$$R(t) = E\bar{X}(s)X(s + t); \tag{4.1}$$

we shall call $R(t)$ the correlation function of $X(t)$ [although this term is strictly true only if the variance $R(0) = 1$]. We have

$$R(0) = E|X(t)|^2 > 0 \tag{4.2}$$

if $X(t)$ is not identically zero. From Schwarz' inequality we find that

$$E|\bar{X}(s)X(s + t)| \leqslant \sqrt{E|X(s)|^2 E|X(s + t)|^2},$$

which gives

$$|R(t)| \leqslant R(0) \qquad (t \in T). \tag{4.3}$$

Theorem 1.1 gives

$$R(t) = \bar{R}(-t) \qquad (t \in T). \tag{4.4}$$

It is seen that the second generalized derivative of $\Gamma(t, t')$ (if it exists) reduces to $-R''(t)$, where $R''(t)$ is the second derivative of $R(t)$. From Section 2 we then obtain the following results, which can also be proved directly.

THEOREM 4.1.   *$X(t)$ is continuous (m.s.) at $t \in T$ if, and only if, $R(t)$ is continuous at $t = 0$. If this is the case, then $R(t)$ is continuous at all $t \in T$.*

THEOREM 4.2.   *$X(t)$ has a derivative $X'(t)$ at $t \in T$ if, and only if, $R''(t)$ exists at $t = 0$. If this is the case, then $R''(t)$ exists at all $t \in T$. Moreover, the correlation function of $X'(t)$ is $-R''(t)$.*

Finally we prove the following important theorem:

THEOREM 4.3.   *A function $R(t)$ $(t \in T)$, with $R(0) = 1$, is the correlation function of a regular stochastic process which is stationary and continuous (m.s.) if, and only if, there exists a distribution function $F(\lambda)$ $(-\infty < \lambda < \infty)$ such that*

$$R(t) = \int_{-\infty}^{\infty} e^{it\lambda} \, dF(\lambda) \qquad (t \in T). \tag{4.5}$$

Proof: Suppose that $R(t)$ can be represented as in (4.5). Let $\theta(t)$ be any function on T and let T_n be a finite subset of T. Then

$$\sum_{t,t' \in T_n} \sum R(t - t')\theta(t)\bar{\theta}(t')$$

$$= \sum_{t,t' \in T_n} \sum \theta(t)\bar{\theta}(t') \int_{-\infty}^{\infty} e^{i(t-t')\lambda} \, dF(\lambda)$$

$$= \int_{-\infty}^{\infty} \left\{ \sum_{t \in T_n} \theta(t)e^{it\lambda} \right\} \left\{ \sum_{t \in T_n} \bar{\theta}(t)e^{-it\lambda} \right\} dF(\lambda) \tag{4.6}$$

$$= \int_{-\infty}^{\infty} \left| \sum_{t \in T_n} \theta(t)e^{it\lambda} \right|^2 dF(\lambda) \geqslant 0,$$

which shows that the function $\Gamma(t, t') = R(t - t')$ is nonnegative definite. By Theorem 1.3 there exists a regular stochastic process $X(t)$ $(t \in T)$, with the covariance function $\Gamma(t, t')$. Clearly, $X(t)$ is stationary, and since $R(t)$ defined by (4.5) is continuous on T, it follows that $X(t)$ is continuous (m.s.) by Theorem 4.1.

Conversely, let $R(t)$ be the correlation function of a regular stochastic process $X(t)$ $(t \in T)$, which is stationary, and continuous (m.s.). Then $R(t)$ is continuous on T, and is therefore Riemann-integrable over $[0, \tau]$. By Theorem 3.1, the integral

$$\int_0^\tau e^{-it\lambda} X(t)\, dt \qquad (-\infty < \lambda < \infty) \tag{4.7}$$

exists, and

$$\int_0^\tau \int_0^\tau e^{-i(t-t')\lambda} R(t - t')\, dt\, dt'$$
$$= E\left\{ \int_0^\tau e^{-it\lambda} X(t)\, dt \cdot \int_0^\tau e^{it'\lambda} \bar{X}(t')\, dt' \right\} \tag{4.8}$$
$$= E \left| \int_0^\tau e^{-it\lambda} X(t)\, dt \right|^2 \geqslant 0.$$

Therefore,

$$P_\tau(\lambda) \equiv \frac{1}{\tau} \int_0^\tau \int_0^\tau e^{-i(t-t')\lambda} R(t - t')\, dt\, dt' \geqslant 0. \tag{4.9}$$

In the double integral in (4.9), put $t - t' = s$, $t = t$, and integrate first with respect to t; we obtain

$$P_\tau(\lambda) = \frac{1}{\tau} \int_0^\tau e^{-is\lambda} R(s)\, ds \int_s^\tau dt + \frac{1}{\tau} \int_{-\tau}^0 e^{-is\lambda} R(s)\, ds \int_0^{\tau+s} dt$$
$$= \int_{-\tau}^\tau e^{-is\lambda} \left(1 - \frac{|s|}{\tau} \right) R(s)\, ds \tag{4.10}$$
$$= \int_{-\infty}^\infty e^{-is\lambda} \phi_\tau(s)\, ds,$$

where

$$\phi_\tau(t) = \begin{cases} \left(1 - \dfrac{|t|}{\tau} \right) R(t) & \text{if } |t| \leqslant \tau \\ 0 & \text{if } |t| \geqslant \tau. \end{cases} \tag{4.11}$$

From (4.10) we obtain

$$\frac{1}{2\pi} \int_{-\Lambda}^{+\Lambda} \left(1 - \frac{|\lambda|}{\Lambda} \right) e^{it\lambda} P_\tau(\lambda)\, d\lambda = \frac{1}{2\pi} \int_{-\infty}^\infty \phi_\tau(s)\, ds \int_{-\Lambda}^{+\Lambda} \left(1 - \frac{|\lambda|}{\Lambda} \right) e^{i(t-s)\lambda}\, d\lambda. \tag{4.12}$$

Now,

$$\int_{-\Lambda}^{+\Lambda} \left(1 - \frac{|\lambda|}{\Lambda}\right) e^{i(t-s)\lambda} \, d\lambda$$

$$= \int_0^{\Lambda} \left(1 - \frac{\lambda}{\Lambda}\right) e^{i(t-s)\lambda} \, d\lambda + \int_{-\Lambda}^0 \left(1 + \frac{\lambda}{\Lambda}\right) e^{i(t-s)\lambda} \, d\lambda$$

$$= 2 \int_0^{\Lambda} \left(1 - \frac{\lambda}{\Lambda}\right) \cos (t-s)\lambda \, d\lambda$$

$$= \left[2\left(1 - \frac{\lambda}{\Lambda}\right) \frac{\sin (t-s)\lambda}{t-s}\right]_0^{\Lambda} + \frac{2}{\Lambda(t-s)} \int_0^{\Lambda} \sin (t-s)\lambda \, d\lambda$$

$$= \frac{4 \sin^2 \frac{1}{2}\Lambda(s-t)}{\Lambda(s-t)^2} ;$$

substituting this in (4.12), we find that the right-hand side expression is

$$= \frac{1}{2\pi} \int_{-\infty}^{\infty} \frac{\sin^2 \frac{1}{2}\Lambda(s-t)}{\frac{1}{4}\Lambda(s-t)^2} \phi_\tau(s) \, ds \to \phi_\tau(t) \qquad \text{as } \Lambda \to \infty. \qquad (4.13)$$

The left-hand side expression in (4.12) is a characteristic function, since it is of the form

$$\psi_\Lambda(t) = \int_{-\infty}^{\infty} e^{it\lambda} q(\lambda) \, d\lambda, \qquad (4.14)$$

where $q(\lambda)$ is a nonnegative function. We have thus proved that as $\Lambda \to \infty$, $\psi_\Lambda(t) \to \phi_\tau(t)$; since $\phi_\tau(t)$ is continuous at $t = 0$, it follows that $\phi_\tau(t)$ is a characteristic function. Now,

$$\phi_\tau(t) \to R(t) \qquad \text{as } \tau \to \infty; \qquad (4.15)$$

and since $R(t)$ is continuous at $t = 0$, it follows that $R(t)$ is also a characteristic function, that is, there exists a distribution function $F(\lambda)$ $(-\infty < \lambda < \infty)$ such that (4.5) holds. The theorem is thus completely proved.

In the discrete parameter case the result (4.5) can be simplified. We have, in fact,

$$\int_{-\infty}^{\infty} e^{in\lambda} \, dF(\lambda) = \sum_{k=0}^{\infty} \left\{ \int_{k\pi+0}^{k\pi+\pi} + \int_{-k\pi-\pi+0}^{-k\pi} e^{in\lambda} \, dF(\lambda) \right\}$$

$$= \sum_{k=0}^{\infty} \int_{0+}^{\pi} e^{in(\lambda+k\pi)} \, dF(\lambda + k\pi)$$

$$+ \sum_{k=0}^{\infty} \int_{-\pi+0}^{0} e^{in(\lambda-k\pi)} \, dF(\lambda - k\pi)$$

$$= \sum_{k=0}^{\infty} \int_{0+}^{\pi} e^{in\lambda}(-1)^{nk}\, dF(\lambda + k\pi)$$

$$+ \sum_{k=-\infty}^{0} \int_{-\pi+0}^{0} e^{in\lambda}(-1)^{nk}\, dF(\lambda + k\pi)$$

$$= \int_{-\pi+0}^{\pi} e^{in\lambda}\, dF_1(\lambda),$$

where

$$F_1(\lambda) = \begin{cases} \displaystyle\sum_{k=0}^{\infty} (-1)^{nk} F(\lambda + k\pi) & \text{if } \lambda > 0 \\[2ex] \displaystyle\sum_{k=-\infty}^{0} (-1)^{nk} F(\lambda + k\pi) & \text{if } \lambda \leqslant 0. \end{cases} \tag{4.16}$$

Thus we have

$$R(n) = \int_{-\pi+0}^{\pi} e^{in\lambda}\, dF_1(\lambda) \quad (n = \ldots, -2, -1, 0, 1, \ldots) \tag{4.17}$$

for the correlation function of a discrete parameter process.

If the process is real, then $R(t)$ is real, and

$$R(t) = \int_{-\infty}^{\infty} \cos t\lambda\, dF(\lambda). \tag{4.18}$$

We have

$$\int_{-\infty}^{\infty} \cos t\lambda\, dF(\lambda) = -\int_{-\infty}^{\infty} \cos t\lambda\, dF(-\lambda),$$

so that in this case $dF(\lambda) = -dF(-\lambda)$, that is, the distribution $dF(\lambda)$ is symmetric about the origin.

Theorem 4.3 exhibits $R(t)$ as a characteristic function of the distribution function $F(\lambda)$. For a given $R(t)$ we can obtain $F(\lambda)$ by using the inversion formula for characteristic functions:

$$F(\lambda_1) - F(\lambda_2) = \lim_{T \to \infty} \frac{1}{2\pi} \int_{-T}^{T} \frac{e^{-i\lambda_1 t} - e^{-i\lambda_2 t}}{it}\, R(t)\, dt, \tag{4.19}$$

where λ_1 and λ_2 are continuity points of $F(\lambda)$. Theorem 4.3 is due to Bochner (1932) in the general case and to Herglotz (1911) in the discrete case; the proof given here is due to Loève [see (1963), pp. 207–209]. The function $F(\lambda)$ is called the *spectral distribution function*. For the process $X(t)$ itself we have the *spectral representation*

$$X(t) = \int_{-\infty}^{\infty} e^{it\lambda}\, dZ(\lambda), \tag{4.20}$$

where $Z(\lambda)$ $(-\infty < \lambda < \infty)$ is a stochastic process with orthogonal increments, that is,

$$E\,|Z(\lambda_1) - Z(\lambda_2)|^2 < \infty \qquad (4.21)$$

$$E[Z(\mu_2) - Z(\mu_1)][Z(\lambda_2) - Z(\lambda_1)] = 0 \qquad (\mu_1 < \mu_2 \leqslant \lambda_1 < \lambda_2). \quad (4.22)$$

It should be noted that the integral in (4.20) is a Riemann–Stieltjes integral. If the result (4.20) holds it is easy to see that (4.5) follows from it. Proceeding formally and using (4.22) we find that

$$R(t - t') = EX(t)\bar{X}(t')$$

$$= \int_{-\infty}^{\infty} \int_{-\infty}^{\infty} e^{it\lambda - it'\lambda'} E\,dZ(\lambda)\,d\bar{Z}(\lambda')$$

$$= \int_{-\infty}^{\infty} e^{i(t-t')\lambda} E\,|dZ(\lambda)|^2.$$

Thus

$$R(t) = \int_{-\infty}^{\infty} e^{it\lambda}\,dF(\lambda), \qquad (4.23)$$

where

$$dF(\lambda) = E\,|Z(\lambda + d\lambda) - Z(\lambda)|^2 \geqslant 0. \qquad (4.24)$$

From (4.21) and (4.24) we see that $F(\lambda)$ is a bounded nondecreasing function; (4.24) determines $F(\lambda)$ up to an additive constant. We can choose this constant by the condition $F(-\infty) = 0$. From (4.23) we obtain

$$F(+\infty) - F(-\infty) = \int_{-\infty}^{\infty} dF(\lambda) = R(0) = 1, \qquad (4.25)$$

so that $F(+\infty) = 1$. We thus find that $F(\lambda)$ in (4.23) is indeed the spectral distribution function.

The result (4.20) is due to Cramér (1942), and can be proved by starting from (4.5). However, we shall not give the proof here. Spectral representation is the starting point of what is usually known as stationary time series analysis [see, for instance, Grenander and Rosenblatt (1956), Hannan (1960) and Whittle (1951), (1963)]. We also remark that the results (4.5) and (4.20) can be extended to the general case where the process is not stationary [see Loève (1963)].

5. EXAMPLES

EXAMPLE 5.1. Let $X(t) = At + B$, where A and B are uncorrelated real random variables with means α, β and variances σ_1^2, σ_2^2 respectively [example (i) of Introduction, Section 3]. We have seen that

$$\Gamma(t, t') = tt'\,\sigma_1^2 + \sigma_2^2, \qquad (5.1)$$

so that $|\Gamma(t, t')| < \infty$ for $(t, t') \in (T \times T)$. Clearly, $\Gamma(t, t')$ is symmetric in t, t'; $\Gamma(t, t) = t^2\sigma_1^2 + \sigma_2^2$ is a continuous function on T, and therefore by Theorem 2.1, the process $X(t)$ is continuous (m.s.). Further,

$$\Gamma(t + h, t' + h') - \Gamma(t + h, t') - \Gamma(t, t' + h') + \Gamma(t, t')$$
$$= \sigma_1^2\{(t + h)(t' + h') - (t + h)t' - t(t' + h') + tt'\} \quad (5.2)$$
$$= hh'\sigma_1^2,$$

so that the second generalized derivative of $\Gamma(t, t')$ is σ_1^2 at all points of $(T \times T)$. Therefore by Theorem 2.2, $X(t)$ has a derivative (m.s.) $X'(t)$ on T, where $X'(t) = A$. We have

$$EX'(t) = \alpha, \qquad EX'(t)X'(t') = \sigma_1^2; \quad (5.3)$$

these results also follow from

$$EX'(t) = \frac{d}{dt}(\alpha t + \beta), \qquad \Gamma_{X'}(t, t') = \frac{\partial^2}{\partial t \, \partial t'}(tt'\sigma_1^2 + \sigma_2^2). \quad (5.4)$$

Finally, since

$$\int_0^t \int_0^t \Gamma(s, s') \, ds \, ds' = \int_0^t \int_0^t (\sigma_1^2 s s' + \sigma_2^2) \, ds \, ds'$$
$$= \tfrac{1}{4}t^4\sigma_1^2 + t^2\sigma_2^2 < \infty \quad (t \in T), \quad (5.5)$$

it follows from Theorem 3.1 that the integral

$$Y(t) = \int_0^t X(s) \, ds \quad (5.6)$$

exists (m.s.). We have the results

$$EY(t) = \int_0^t (\alpha s + \beta) \, ds = \tfrac{1}{2}t^2\alpha + \beta t$$
$$EY(t)Y(t') = \int_0^t \int_0^{t'} \Gamma(s, s') \, ds \, ds' = \tfrac{1}{4}(tt')^2\sigma_1^2 + tt'\sigma_2^2 \quad (5.7)$$

which could have been derived directly from

$$Y(t) = \tfrac{1}{2}At^2 + Bt. \quad (5.8)$$

EXAMPLE 5.2. Let $X(t) = A \cos \theta t + B \sin \theta t$ where A and B are uncorrelated real random variables, each having mean 0 and variance unity, and θ is a real constant [example (ii) of Introduction, Section 3]. The covariance function is here given by

$$\Gamma(t, t') = \cos \theta (t - t'); \quad (5.9)$$

the process is therefore stationary, and the correlation function is $R(t) = \cos \theta t$. Clearly, $|R(t)| \leq 1$, $R(t)$ is an even function of t, continuous and differentiable on T. We have $R''(t) = -\theta^2 \cos \theta t$. It follows that the process $X(t)$ is continuous (m.s.) and differentiable (m.s.) on T. We have

$$X'(t) = -A\theta \sin \theta t + B\theta \cos \theta t, \tag{5.10}$$

and

$$R_{X'}(t) = EX(s)X(s + t) = -R''(t) = \theta^2 \cos \theta t. \tag{5.11}$$

Further, $X(t)$ is Riemann-integrable over $[0, t]$ and

$$Y(t) = \int_0^t X(s)\, ds = \frac{A}{\theta} \sin \theta t - \frac{B}{\theta} \cos \theta t + \frac{B}{\theta}, \tag{5.12}$$

$$EY(t)Y(t') = \frac{1}{\theta^2}\{1 - \cos \theta t - \cos \theta t' + \cos \theta(t - t')\}. \tag{5.13}$$

We can put

$$R(t) = \int_{-\infty}^{\infty} \cos t\lambda \, dF(\lambda), \tag{5.14}$$

where

$$F(\lambda) = \begin{cases} 0 & \text{if } \lambda < -\theta \\ \frac{1}{2} & \text{if } -\theta \leqslant \lambda < \theta \\ 1 & \text{if } \lambda \geqslant \theta, \end{cases} \tag{5.15}$$

since the integral in (5.14) then reduces to $\frac{1}{2} \cos (-\theta t) + \frac{1}{2} \cos \theta t = \cos \theta t$, as required. The spectral distribution here consists of two jumps at the points $-\theta$, $+\theta$, each of magnitude $\frac{1}{2}$.

EXAMPLE 5.3.   Let

$$X(t) = \sum_{p=1}^{N} A_p e^{i\theta_p t}, \tag{5.16}$$

where $\theta_1, \theta_2, \ldots, \theta_N$ are real constants, $A_1, A_2, \ldots, A_p$ are real random variables, which are uncorrelated, and have

$$E(A_p) = 0, \qquad \text{Var}(A_p) = \sigma_p^2 \qquad (p = 1, 2, \ldots, N) \tag{5.17}$$

[example (iv) of Introduction, Section 3]. The covariance function was found to be

$$\Gamma(t, t') = \sum_1^N \sigma_p^2 e^{i\theta_p(t-t')}, \tag{5.18}$$

which shows that the process is stationary, and that

$$R(t) = \sum_1^N \sigma_p^2 e^{i\theta_p t} \tag{5.19}$$

is the correlation function. It is readily seen that $X(t)$ is continuous and differentiable on T. Let us assume without loss of generality that $\theta_1, \theta_2, \ldots, \theta_N$ are all distinct and $\theta_1 < \theta_2 < \cdots < \theta_N$; we can then put

$$R(t) = \int_{-\infty}^{\infty} e^{it\lambda} \, dF(\lambda), \tag{5.20}$$

where

$$F(\lambda) = \begin{cases} 0 & \text{if } \lambda < \theta_1 \\ \sigma_1^2 + \sigma_2^2 + \cdots + \sigma_p^2 & \text{if } \theta_p \leqslant \lambda < \theta_{p+1} \quad (p = 1, 2, \ldots, N - 1) \\ \sigma_1^2 + \sigma_2^2 + \cdots + \sigma_N^2 & \text{if } \lambda \geqslant \theta_N; \end{cases} \tag{5.21}$$

the spectral distribution thus consists of jumps of magnitude σ_1^2, $\sigma_2^2, \ldots, \sigma_N^2$ at the points $\theta_1, \theta_2, \ldots, \theta_N$. From (5.16) it is also seen that

$$X(t) = \int_{-\infty}^{\infty} e^{it\lambda} \, dZ(\lambda), \tag{5.22}$$

where the process $Z(\lambda)$ is defined as follows:

$$Z(\lambda) = \begin{cases} 0 & \text{if } \lambda < \theta_1 \\ A_1 + A_2 + \cdots + A_p & \text{if } \theta_p \leqslant \lambda < \theta_{p+1}(p = 1, 2, \ldots, N - 1) \\ A_1 + A_2 + \cdots + A_N & \text{if } \lambda \geqslant \theta_N. \end{cases} \tag{5.23}$$

It can be verified that $Z(\lambda)$ defined by (5.23) is a process with orthogonal increments.

EXAMPLE 5.4.   *The Wiener–Einstein Process*. This Gaussian process was defined in example (vii) of Introduction, Section 3. We have

$$\Gamma(t, t') = EX(t)X(t') = \sigma^2 \min(t, t') \qquad (t, t' \geqslant 0). \tag{5.24}$$

Since $\Gamma(t, t) = \sigma^2 t$ is continuous for $t \geqslant 0$, we conclude that the process is continuous (m.s.). Actually Wiener (1923) showed that it is continuous with probability one. We have

$$\Gamma(t + h, t' + h') - \Gamma(t + h, t') - \Gamma(t, t' + h') + \Gamma(t, t') \tag{5.25}$$

$$= \min(t + h, t' + h') - \min(t + h, t') - \min(t, t' + h') + \min(t, t'),$$

which shows that the second generalized derivative does not exist, and $X(t)$ does not have a derivative (m.s.).

Finally consider the integral

$$Y(t) = \int_0^t X(s) \, ds. \tag{5.26}$$

We have

$$\int_0^t \int_0^{t'} \Gamma(s, s') \, ds \, ds' = \sigma^2 \int_0^t \int_0^{t'} \min(s, s') \, ds \, ds'$$

$$= \sigma^2 \int_0^{t'} ds' \left\{ \int_0^{s'} s \, ds + \int_{s'}^t s' \, ds \right\}$$

$$= \sigma^2 \int_0^t \left(s't - \frac{1}{2} s'^2 \right) ds'$$

$$= \frac{\sigma^2}{2} t'^2 \left(t - \frac{1}{3} t' \right). \tag{5.27}$$

This shows that the integral (5.27) exists, and

$$EY(t) = \int_0^t EX(s) \, ds = 0$$

$$EY(t)Y(t') = \frac{\sigma^2}{2} t'^2 \left(t - \frac{1}{3} t' \right) \qquad t \neq t' \tag{5.28}$$

$$E[Y(t)]^2 = \frac{\sigma^2}{3} t^3.$$

EXAMPLE 5.5. *The Poisson Process.* This process was defined in example (vii) of Introduction, Section 3. We have

$$\Gamma(t, t') = \lambda \min(t, t') \qquad (t, t' \geq 0). \tag{5.29}$$

Clearly, the process is continuous (m.s.); however, for $s < t$ we have

$$\Pr\{X(t) - X(s) \neq 0\} = 1 - e^{-\lambda(t-s)} > 0, \tag{5.30}$$

so that in every interval $(s, t]$, the process is likely to be discontinuous. This illustrates the fact that the m.s. continuity of a process does not in general imply its continuity with probability one.

EXAMPLE 5.6. Let $\{X_n, n = \ldots, -2, -1, 0, 1, \ldots\}$ be a sequence of uncorrelated random variables, which are identically distributed with mean 0 and variance unity. The covariance function of this sequence is then given by

$$\Gamma_{m,n} = EX_m \bar{X}_n = \begin{cases} 1 & \text{if } m = n \\ 0 & \text{if } m \neq n. \end{cases} \tag{5.31}$$

We have therefore a stationary random sequence. Let $R_n = E\bar{X}_m X_{m+n}$ be the correlation function; then

$$R_0 = 1, \, R_n = 0 \qquad (n \neq 0). \tag{5.32}$$

We have

$$R_n = \int_{-\pi}^{\pi} e^{in\lambda} \frac{d\lambda}{2\pi}, \tag{5.33}$$

so that the spectral distribution has a frequency function

$$f(\lambda) = \frac{1}{2\pi} \qquad (-\pi < \lambda < \pi), \tag{5.34}$$

which is uniform over the interval $(-\pi, \pi)$. This is the spectral density function.

EXAMPLE 5.7.   Let

$$X_n = \sum_{p=0}^{\infty} a^p \xi_{n-p}, \tag{5.35}$$

where a is a real constant, $|a| < 1$, and $\{\xi_n\}$ is a sequence of real uncorrelated random variables with mean 0 and variance σ^2. We find that

$$\Gamma_{m,n} = EX_m \bar{X}_n = \sum_{p,q=0}^{\infty} a^{p+q} E\xi_{m-p} \xi_{n-q}$$

$$= \begin{cases} \sigma^2 \displaystyle\sum_{p=0}^{\infty} a^{2p+n-m} & \text{if } m-n \leqslant 0 \\[4mm] \sigma^2 \displaystyle\sum_{p=m-n}^{\infty} a^{2p+n-m} & \text{if } m-n > 0 \end{cases} \tag{5.36}$$

$$= \frac{\sigma^2}{1-a^2} a^{|m-n|},$$

which shows that the process is stationary, the correlation function being

$$R_n = \frac{\sigma^2}{1-a^2} a^{|n|}. \tag{5.37}$$

Inversion of (5.37) then gives the spectral distribution. Since the sum

$$\sum_{-\infty}^{\infty} |R_n| = \frac{\sigma^2}{1-a^2} \left\{ \sum_{0}^{\infty} a^n + \sum_{1}^{\infty} a^n \right\} < \infty, \tag{5.38}$$

it follows that the spectral density function $f(\lambda)$ exists. We have

$$\frac{1-a^2}{\sigma^2} f(\lambda) = \frac{1}{2\pi} \sum_{-\infty}^{\infty} e^{-in\lambda} R_n \frac{1-a^2}{\sigma^2}$$

$$= \frac{1}{2\pi} \left\{ \sum_{0}^{\infty} e^{-in\lambda} a^n + \sum_{-\infty}^{-1} e^{-in\lambda} a^{-n} \right\}$$

$$= \frac{1}{2\pi} \left\{ \frac{1}{1 - ae^{-i\lambda}} + \frac{ae^{i\lambda}}{1 - ae^{i\lambda}} \right\}$$

$$= \frac{1}{2\pi} \frac{1 - a^2}{(1 - ae^{-i\lambda})(1 - ae^{i\lambda})}$$

$$= \frac{1}{2\pi} \frac{1 - a^2}{1 - 2a \cos \lambda + \lambda^2},$$

so that

$$f(\lambda) = \frac{\sigma^2}{2\pi} \cdot \frac{1}{1 - 2a \cos \lambda + \lambda^2} \qquad (-\pi < \lambda < \pi). \qquad (5.39)$$

6. COMPLEMENTS AND PROBLEMS

Sections 1–4

1. If $\Gamma(t, t')$ is a covariance, then so is its real part; but its imaginary part is a covariance only in the trivial case when it vanishes.

2. The class of covariances is closed under addition, multiplication, and passages to the limit [Loève (1963)].

3. Show that the expansion

$$X(t) = \sum_{n=0}^{\infty} \frac{t^n}{n!} X^{(n)}(0), \qquad (6.1)$$

where $X^{(n)}(t)$ is the nth derivative of $X(t)$, is valid if, and only if, $\Gamma(t, t')$ is analytic at every diagonal point (t, t) of $(T \times T)$. We then say that $X(t)$ is analytic (m.s.) [Loève (1963)].

4. Show that processes obtained by differentiating and integrating Gaussian processes are also Gaussian.

Section 5

5. Let

$$X(t) = \sum_{1}^{N} (A_p \cos \theta_p t + B_p \sin \theta_p t), \qquad (6.2)$$

where $\theta_p > 0$, $A_1, A_2, \ldots, A_N$, $B_1, B_2, \ldots, B_N$ are uncorrelated real random variables with mean 0 and

$$\text{Var}(A_p) = \text{Var}(B_p) = \sigma_p^2 \qquad (p = 1, 2, \ldots, N). \qquad (6.3)$$

Show that the correlation function is given by

$$R(t) = \sum_{1}^{N} \sigma_p^2 \cos \theta_p t, \qquad (6.4)$$

and that the spectral distribution consists of jumps of magnitude $\frac{1}{2}\sigma_p^2$ at the points $\pm\theta_p \, (p = 1, 2, \ldots, N)$.

6. *The Ornstein–Uhlenbeck Process.* This is a Gaussian process $X(t)$ with

$$EX(t) = 0, \qquad EX(t)X(t') = \sigma_0^2 e^{-\beta|t-t'|}, \tag{6.5}$$

where $\beta > 0$. Show that $X(t)$ is continuous, but not differentiable in the mean square. Also, the spectral density function is given by

$$f(\lambda) = \frac{\sigma_0^2}{\pi} \frac{\beta}{\beta^2 + \lambda^2} \qquad (-\infty < \lambda < \infty). \tag{6.6}$$

7. Let $X(t) = ae^{it\xi}$, where a is a constant, and ξ is a real random variable with the characteristic function $\phi(t)$. Show that the correlation function of $X(t)$ is given by

$$R(t) = |a|^2 \phi(t). \tag{6.7}$$

8. Let

$$X_n = \frac{\xi_n + \xi_{n+1} + \cdots + \xi_{n-m+1}}{\sqrt{m}} \qquad (n = \ldots, -2, -1, 0, 1, \ldots), \tag{6.8}$$

where $\{\xi_n\}$ is a stationary sequence of uncorrelated random variables. Show that $\{X_n\}$ is also such a sequence whose correlation function is

$$R_n = \begin{cases} 1 - \dfrac{|n|}{m} & \text{if } |n| \leqslant m \\[2mm] 0 & \text{if } |n| > m. \end{cases} \tag{6.9}$$

7. REFERENCES

Bochner, S. FOURIERSCHE INTEGRALE. Leipzig, 1932.

Cramér, H. ON THE THEORY OF STATIONARY RANDOM PROCESSES. *Ann. Math.*, **41** (1940), pp. 215–230.

———. ON HARMONIC ANALYSIS IN CERTAIN FUNCTIONAL SPACES. *Ark. Mat. Astr. Fys.*, **28**, B, (1942), 17 pp.

Grenander, Ulf, and Rosenblatt, Murray. STATISTICAL ANALYSIS OF STATIONARY TIME SERIES. Stockholm: Almquist and Wiksell, 1956.

Hannan, E. J. TIME SERIES ANALYSIS. London: Methuen, 1960.

Herglotz, G. ÜBER POTENZREIHEN MIT POSITIVEM REELEM TEIL IM EINHEITSKREIS. *Ber. Verh. Kgl. Sachs. Ges. Wiss. Leipzig Math.-Phys.*, **63** (1911), pp. 501–511.

Khintchine, A. KORRELATIONSTHEORIE DER STATIONÄREN STOCHASTISCHEN PROZESSE. *Math. Ann.*, **109** (1934), pp. 604–615.

Kolmogorov, A. STATIONARY SEQUENCES IN HILBERT SPACE (RUSSIAN). *Bull. Math. Univ. Moscow*, **2**, no. 6, (1941), 40 pp.

Loève, M. PROBABILITY THEORY. 3rd ed. New York: Van Nostrand, 1963.

Slutsky, E. SUR LES FONCTIONS ÉVENTUELLES CONTINUES, INTÉGRABLES ET DÉRIVABLES DANS LE SENS STOCHASTIQUE. *C. R. Acad. Sci. Paris,* **187** (1928), pp. 878–880.

————. ALCUNI PROPOSIZIONI SULLA THEORIA DEGLI FUNZIONI ALEATORIE. *Giorn. Ist. Ital. Attuari.,* **8** (1937), pp. 183–199.

Whittle, P. HYPOTHESIS TESTING IN TIME SERIES ANALYSIS. Stockholm: Uppsala, 1951.

————. PREDICTION AND REGULATION BY LINEAR LEAST-SQUARE METHODS. London: The English Universities Press, 1963.

Wiener, N. DIFFERENTIAL SPACE. *J. Math. Phys. Math. Inst. Tech.,* **2** (1923), pp.131–174.

Wold, H. A STUDY IN THE ANALYSIS OF STATIONARY TIME SERIES. Stockholm: Uppsala, 1938.

Yaglom, A. M. AN INTRODUCTION TO THE THEORY OF STATIONARY RANDOM FUNCTIONS. Englewood, N. J.: Prentice-Hall, 1962.

2

Markov
Chains

1. DENUMERABLE MARKOV CHAINS

A sequence of random variables $\{X_n, n = 0, 1, 2, \ldots\}$ is called a Markov chain if, for every finite collection of integers $n_1 < n_2 < \cdots < n_r < n$, we have

$$\Pr\{X_n | X_{n_1}, X_{n_2}, \ldots, X_{n_r}\} = \Pr\{X_n | X_{n_r}\}. \tag{1.1}$$

If the possible values of X_n are $\ldots, -1, 0, 1, 2, \ldots$, the chain is called denumerable. In this case let

$$\Pr\{X_{m+1} = j | X_m = i\} = P_{ij}(m) \qquad (i, j = \ldots, -1, 0, 1, 2, \ldots). \tag{1.2}$$

If $P_{ij}(m)$ is independent of m for all i, j, we say that the chain is (temporally) homogeneous. For a homogeneous Markov chain let us denote

$$\Pr\{X_{m+1} = j | X_m = i\} = P_{ij}, \tag{1.3}$$

and, quite generally,

$$\Pr\{X_{m+n} = j | X_m = i\} = P_{ij}^{(n)} \qquad (n = 1, 2, \ldots). \tag{1.4}$$

We also define $P_{ij}^{(0)} = \delta_{ij}$, where δ_{ij} is Kronecker's delta. The probabilities (1.4) can be expressed in terms of (1.3), as follows:

$$P_{ij}^{(n)} = \sum \Pr\{X_{m+1} = i_1 | X_m = i\} \Pr\{X_{m+2} = i_2 | X_{m+1} = i_1\}$$
$$\times \cdots \Pr\{X_{m+n} = j | X_{m+n-1} = i_{n-1}\} \tag{1.5}$$

$$= \sum_{(i_1, i_2, \ldots, i_{n-1})} P_{ii_1} P_{i_1 i_2}, \ldots, P_{i_{n-1} j}.$$

We have

$$P_{ij}^{(n)} \geqslant 0, \sum_j P_{ij}^{(n)} = 1 \qquad (n = 0, 1, 2, \ldots) \qquad (1.6)$$

The initial probabilities of the chain are defined by

$$a_i^{(0)} = \Pr\{X_0 = i\}. \qquad (1.7)$$

It is seen that the probabilities $a_i^{(0)}$ and $P_{ij}^{(n)}$ specify the chain completely. For the absolute (unconditional) probabilities of X_n are given by

$$a_i^{(n)} = \Pr\{X_n = i\} = \sum_i a_i^{(0)} P_{ij}^{(n)}, \qquad (1.8)$$

while the joint probabilities of any subsequence $(X_{n_1}, X_{n_2}, \ldots, X_{n_r})$, where $n_1 < n_2 < \cdots < n_r$ are given by

$$\Pr\{X_{n_1} = i_1, X_{n_2} = i_2, \ldots, X_{n_r} = i_r\} = a_{i_1}^{(n_1)} P_{i_1 i_2}^{(n_2 - n_1)} \cdots P_{i_{r-1} i_r}^{(n_r - n_{r-1})}. \qquad (1.9)$$

Physical Interpretation. Consider a particle or a physical system in motion. Let the various positions (states) of the system be denoted by $\ldots, -1, 0, 1, 2, \ldots$, and let $P_{ij}^{(n)}$ be the probability of transition of the system from the state i at time m to the state j at time $m + n$ (for any m); this is called an n-step transition probability. The matrix $P = (P_{ij})$ is called a stochastic matrix; from (1.5) we see that $(P_{ij}^{(n)}) = P^n$. Further, the matrix identity $P^{m+n} = P^m \cdot P^n$ yields the relations

$$P_{ij}^{(m+n)} = \sum_k P_{ik}^{(m)} P_{kj}^{(n)} \qquad (m, n \geqslant 0), \qquad (1.10)$$

which are called the Chapman–Kolmogorov equations. (It must be noted, however, that the P^n are, in general, infinite matrices.)

The basic concepts of Markov chains were introduced by A. A. Markov in 1907, who considered only finite chains. These were studied in detail by Hostinsky (1931), Fréchet (1938), Romanovsky (1949), and others by algebraic methods; for a more recent book on finite chains, see Kemeny and Snell (1960). Chains with a denumerable number of states were first considered by Kolmogorov (1936), and further work was done by Doeblin (1939). In 1949 Feller applied his theory of recurrent events to Markov chains, and developed a simpler and more elegant theory, which made no distinction between finite and infinite chains. Further work was done by Chung (see his 1960 monograph).

In Sections 2–6 of this chapter we give an account of denumerable Markov chains, following Feller's treatment of the subject. The basic result is lemma 3.1, which is here stated simply as a property of sequences; this is the ergodic theorem of recurrent events theory, which will be developed in Chapter 5. However, the relevant results are proved directly, and the discussion here can therefore be considered (except for the lemma) as self-contained. For further details see Feller (1957) and Chung (1960).

2. CLASSIFICATION OF STATES

2.1. First Entrance Times

We say that the state j can be reached from the state i, and write $i \rightarrow j$, if $P_{ij}^{(n)} > 0$ for some $n \geqslant 1$. If $i \rightarrow j$ and $j \rightarrow i$, we write $i \leftrightarrow j$.

For each pair i, j of states let us define the random variable

$$T_{ij} = \min \{n \,|\, X_n = j \,|\, X_0 = i\}. \tag{2.1}$$

We have

$$
\begin{aligned}
f_{ij}^{(n)} &= \Pr\{T_{ij} = n\} \\
&= \Pr\{X_n = j, X_m \neq j \ (m = 1, 2, \ldots, n-1) \,|\, X_0 = i\} \tag{2.2} \\
&= \sum_{(i_1, i_2, \ldots, i_{n-1} \neq j)} P_{i i_1} P_{i_1 i_2} \cdots P_{i_{n-1} j} \qquad (n \geqslant 1),
\end{aligned}
$$

and

$$f_{ij} = \Pr\{T_{ij} < \infty\} = \sum_{n=1}^{\infty} f_{ij}^{(n)}. \tag{2.3}$$

Clearly, T_{ij} is the waiting time (in terms of the number of steps required) for the first entrance to the state j from the initial state i, and f_{ij} is therefore the probability that the system, starting from i, eventually reaches j in a finite number of steps; $0 \leqslant f_{ij} \leqslant 1$. Obviously, $f_{ij} > 0$ if, and only if, $i \rightarrow j$. In particular, T_{ii} is the return time to the state i (recurrence time of i) and f_{ii} is the probability that the return to i takes place in a finite number of steps. The state i is called persistent or transient according as $f_{ii} = 1$ or < 1. Since $\Pr\{T_{ii} = \infty\} = 1 - f_{ii}$, it follows that there is a positive probability that the system does not return to a transient i in a finite number of steps. A further property is described in Theorem 2.1.

Let i be a persistent state; then

$$\mu_i = \sum_{1}^{\infty} n f_{ii}^{(n)} \tag{2.4}$$

is its mean return (recurrence) time. If $\mu_i = \infty$, i is called a null state, and if $\mu_i < \infty$, i is called a nonnull state.

The state i is called periodic with period t if $P_{ii}^{(n)} = 0$, except when $n = t, 2t, 3t, \ldots$ and $t > 1$ is the greatest integer with this property.

An aperiodic (not periodic) persistent nonnull state is called ergodic.

Theorem 2.2 provides a criterion to distinguish between persistent and transient states.

Theorem 2.1. *With probability one, the system returns to a persistent state infinitely often, while it returns to a transient state only a finite number of times.*

Proof: Let $g_{ij}(m)$ be the probability that the system enters the state j at least m times from the initial state; then, writing "i.o." for "infinitely often," we have[1]

$$g_{ij} = \lim_{m \to \infty} g_{ij}(m)$$
$$= \Pr\{\text{the system enters } j \text{ i.o. from } i\}.$$

(2.5)

Now the relations

$$g_{ij}(1) = f_{ij}, \; g_{ij}(m+1) = \sum_{n=1}^{\infty} f_{ij}^{(n)} g_{jj}(m) = f_{ij} g_{jj}(m)$$

(2.6)

give, by induction, $g_{ij}(m) = f_{ij}(f_{jj})^{m-1}$ $(m \geq 1)$ and, in particular, $g_{jj}(m) = (f_{jj})^m$. Hence, letting $m \to \infty$, we obtain

$$g_{jj} = \Pr\{\text{the system returns to } j \text{ i.o.}\}$$
$$= \begin{cases} 1 \text{ if } j \text{ is persistent.} \\ 0 \text{ if } j \text{ is transient.} \end{cases}$$

(2.7)

Theorem 2.2 *The state i is persistent or transient according as the series $\sum_0^\infty P_{ii}^{(n)} = \infty$ or $< \infty$.*

Proof: We have the relation

$$P_{ij}^{(n)} = \sum_{m=1}^{n} f_{ij}^{(m)} P_{jj}^{(n-m)},$$

(2.8)

whence

$$\sum_{n=1}^{N} P_{ij}^{(n)} = \sum_{n=1}^{N} \sum_{m=1}^{n} f_{ij}^{(m)} P_{jj}^{(n-m)} = \sum_{m=1}^{N} f_{ij}^{(m)} \sum_{n=0}^{N-m} P_{jj}^{(n)}$$
$$\leq \sum_{m=1}^{N} f_{ij}^{(m)} \sum_{n=0}^{N} P_{jj}^{(n)}.$$

Also, if $N > N'$, we have

$$\sum_{n=1}^{N} P_{ij}^{(n)} \geq \sum_{m=1}^{N'} f_{ij}^{(m)} \sum_{n=0}^{N-N'} P_{jj}^{(n)}.$$

Hence

$$\sum_{m=1}^{N'} f_{ij}^{(m)} \sum_{n=0}^{N-N'} P_{jj}^{(n)} \leq \sum_{n=1}^{N} P_{ij}^{(n)} \leq \sum_{m=1}^{N} f_{ij}^{(m)} \sum_{n=0}^{N} P_{jj}^{(n)}.$$

---

[1] This is not the definition of "i.o." itself, but is equivalent to it.

In this, let first $N \to \infty$, and then $N' \to \infty$; we then obtain

$$f_{ij} = \lim_{N \to \infty} \frac{\sum\limits_{1}^{N} P_{ij}^{(n)}}{1 + \sum\limits_{1}^{N} P_{ii}^{(n)}}. \tag{2.9}$$

In particular, when $i = j$, (2.9) gives

$$1 - f_{ii} = \lim_{N \to \infty} \frac{1}{1 + \sum\limits_{1}^{N} P_{ii}^{(n)}}, \tag{2.10}$$

which proves the theorem.

COROLLARY 2.1. *If j is transient,*

$$\sum_{0}^{\infty} P_{jj}^{(n)} = (1 - f_{jj})^{-1}, \text{ and } \sum_{1}^{\infty} P_{ij}^{(n)} = f_{ij}(1 - f_{jj})^{-1} < \infty.$$

The following theorem states a result which will be used in the sequel.

THEOREM 2.3. *If i is a persistent state and $i \to j$, then $f_{ji} = 1$.*

Proof: If $f_{ji} < 1$, then there is a path from j to i in an infinite number of steps with a probability $1 - f_{ji} > 0$. Since $i \to j$, this implies that with a positive probability the system returns to i in an infinite number of steps, which is absurd because i is a persistent state.

2.2. Transitions Avoiding a Given State
Let

$${}^{k}P_{ij}^{(n)} = \Pr\{X_n = j, X_m \neq k \; (m = 1, 2, \ldots, n - 1) | X_0 = i\}; \tag{2.11}$$

this is clearly the probability that at time n the system enters the state j from the initial state i, avoiding the state k *en route*. In particular, ${}^{j}P_{ij}^{(n)} = f_{ij}^{(n)}$. We have the following:

THEOREM 2.4. *If $f_{jk} > 0$, then the series*

$${}^{k}P_{ij}^{*} = \sum_{n=0}^{\infty} {}^{k}P_{ij}^{(n)} < \infty. \tag{2.12}$$

Proof: If $j = k$, ${}^{k}P_{ij}^{*} = f_{ij} \leqslant 1$. Let $j \neq k$; then since $f_{jk} > 0$, we have $f_{jk}^{(m)} > 0$ for some $m \geqslant 1$. We have

$$f_{ik}^{(m+n)} = \sum_{v \neq k} {}^{k}P_{iv}^{(n)} f_{vk}^{(m)} \geqslant {}^{k}P_{ij}^{(n)} f_{jk}^{(m)},$$

so that

$$^k P_{ij}^* = \sum_0^\infty {}^k P_{ij}^{(n)} \leqslant [f_{jk}^{(m)}]^{-1} \sum_{n=1}^\infty f_{ik}^{(m+n)} \leqslant [f_{jk}^{(m)}]^{-1} < \infty.$$

We may also consider transitions of the system avoiding a given set of states [see Chung (1960)].

3. ASYMPTOTIC BEHAVIOR OF $P_{ij}^{(n)}$

We first quote the following:

LEMMA 3.1.   *Given a sequence $\{f_n\}$ such that $f_0 = 0$, $f_n \geqslant 0$, $\Sigma f_n = 1$, and the greatest common divisor of those n for which $f_n > 0$ is $t \; (\geqslant 1)$. A second sequence $\{u_n\}$ is defined as follows:*

$$u_0 = 1, \; u_n = \sum_{m=1}^n f_m u_{n-m} \qquad (n \geqslant 1). \tag{3.1}$$

Then

$$\lim_{n \to \infty} u_{nt} = \begin{cases} t\mu^{-1} & \text{if } \mu = \sum_1^\infty n f_n < \infty \\ 0 & \text{if } \mu = \infty. \end{cases} \tag{3.2}$$

For proof see Chapter 5, Theorem 3.3.

Although the transition probabilities $P_{ij}^{(n)}$ are bounded functions of n, it is not obvious that for any fixed i, j they converge to any limit as $n \to \infty$ [they might, for instance, oscillate between the limits $(0, 1)$]. The following theorems describe the behavior of $P_{ij}^{(n)}$ as $n \to \infty$.

THEOREM 3.1.   *If the state j is either transient or persistent null, then*

$$P_{jj}^{(n)} \to 0 \qquad \text{as } n \to \infty. \tag{3.3}$$

If j is aperiodic persistent nonnull, then

$$P_{jj}^{(n)} \to \frac{1}{\mu_j} \qquad \text{as } n \to \infty. \tag{3.4}$$

If j is persistent and has period t, then

$$P_{jj}^{(nt)} \to \frac{t}{\mu_j} \qquad \text{as } n \to \infty. \tag{3.5}$$

Proof: If j is transient, then the series $\Sigma P_{jj}^{(n)}$ converges, so that $P_{jj}^{(n)} \to 0$. Let j be persistent, and put

$$P_{jj}^{(n)} = u_n, \; f_{jj}^{(n)} = f_n \qquad (f_0 = 0, u_0 = 1). \tag{3.6}$$

Then the relation

$$P_{jj}^{(n)} = f_{jj}^{(n)} + \sum_{m=1}^{n-1} f_{jj}^{(m)} P_{jj}^{(n-m)} \tag{3.7}$$

can be written as

$$u_n = \sum_{m=0}^{n} f_m u_{n-m}. \tag{3.8}$$

Application of the lemma then gives $P_{jj}^{(nt)} \to t\mu_j^{-1}$, where $\mu_j = \Sigma n f_{jj}^{(n)}$ is the mean recurrence time. If j is persistent null, $\mu_j = \infty$, and hence $P_{jj}^{(n)} \to 0$. If $t = 1$, we have the aperiodic case. Thus the theorem is completely proved.

THEOREM 3.2. *If the state j is either transient or persistent null, then for all i*

$$P_{ij}^{(n)} \to 0 \qquad \text{as } n \to \infty; \tag{3.9}$$

and if j is aperiodic persistent nonnull, then for all i

$$P_{ij}^{(n)} \to \frac{1}{\mu_j} f_{ij} \quad \text{as } n \to \infty. \tag{3.10}$$

Proof: We have the relation

$$P_{ij}^{(n)} = \sum_{m=1}^{n} f_{ij}^{(m)} P_{jj}^{(n-m)}. \tag{3.11}$$

Taking $n > n'$ we can write

$$\begin{aligned}
P_{ij}^{(n)} &= \sum_{m=1}^{n'} f_{ij}^{(m)} P_{jj}^{(n-m)} + \sum_{m=n'+1}^{n} f_{ij}^{(m)} P_{jj}^{(n-m)} \\
&\leqslant \sum_{m=1}^{n'} f_{ij}^{(m)} P_{jj}^{(n-m)} + \sum_{n'+1}^{n} f_{ij}^{(m)}.
\end{aligned} \tag{3.12}$$

Now, if j is either transient or persistent null, $P_{jj}^{(n-m)} \to 0$ as $n \to \infty$. Also, since

$$\sum_{1}^{\infty} f_{ij}^{(m)} < \infty, \quad \sum_{n'+1}^{n} f_{ij}^{(m)} \to 0 \qquad \text{as } n, n' \to \infty.$$

Thus $P_{ij}^{(n)} \to 0$ in these two cases.

On the other hand, let j be aperiodic persistent nonnull; then $P_{jj}^{(n)} \to \mu_j^{-1}$. Writing (3.12) as

$$P_{ij}^{(n)} - \sum_{m=1}^{n'} f_{ij}^{(m)} P_{jj}^{(n-m)} \leqslant \sum_{n'+1}^{n} f_{ij}^{(m)},$$

and letting first $n \to \infty$ and then $n' \to \infty$ we see that

$$P_{ij}^{(n)} \to \frac{1}{\mu_j} \sum_1^\infty f_{ij}^{(m)} = \frac{1}{\mu_j} f_{ij}.$$

The theorem is thus completely proved.

For a discussion of the asymptotic behavior in the periodic case, see Feller (1957).

4. CLOSED SETS; IRREDUCIBLE CHAINS

A set C of states is said to be closed if $P_{ij} = 0$ whenever $i \in C$ and $j \notin C$. In this case we have

$$P_{ij}^{(2)} = \sum_k P_{ik} P_{kj} = \sum_{k \in C} P_{ik} P_{kj} + \sum_{k \notin C} P_{ik} P_{kj} = 0$$

and quite generally $P_{ij}^{(n)} = 0$ for all $n \geqslant 1, i \in C, j \notin C$; thus no state outside C can be reached from any state inside C. Hence

$$\sum_{j \in C} P_{ij}^{(n)} = 1 \text{ for } i \in C,$$

which shows that the set C constitutes a Markov chain which can be studied independently of all other states. In particular, if C contains only a single state i, then we must have $P_{ii}^{(n)} = 1$ for all $n \geqslant 1$; in this case i is said to be an absorbing state. Trivially, the set of all states is closed.

If a Markov chain does not contain any closed set other than the set of all states, it is said to be irreducible.

THEOREM 4.1. *In an irreducible Markov chain every state can be reached from every other state. All states are of the same class: they are all transient, all persistent null, or persistent nonnull states. In every case they have the same period.*

Proof: Since all states which can be reached from a given state form a closed set, it follows that in an irreducible chain every state can be reached from every other state. To prove that all states belong to the same class, let i, j be a pair of states. Since $i \leftrightarrow j$, we have $P_{ij}^{(N)} = \alpha > 0$ and $P_{ji}^{(M)} = \beta > 0$ for some $N \geqslant 1, M \geqslant 1$. Now for any n we have

$$P_{ii}^{(n+N+M)} \geqslant P_{ij}^{(N)} P_{jj}^{(n)} P_{ji}^{(M)} = \alpha\beta P_{jj}^{(n)} \tag{4.1}$$

$$P_{jj}^{(n+N+M)} \geqslant P_{ji}^{(M)} P_{ii}^{(n)} P_{ij}^{(N)} = \alpha\beta P_{ii}^{(n)}. \tag{4.2}$$

From (4.1) and (4.2) we see that the two series $\Sigma P_{ii}^{(n)}$ and $\Sigma P_{jj}^{(n)}$ converge or diverge together, so that i and j are either both persistent or both transient. If i is persistent null, $P_{ii}^{(n)} \to 0$, and from (4.1) $P_{jj}^{(n)} \to 0$, so that j also is persistent null. Finally, if i has period t, then since

$$P_{ii}^{(N+M)} \geqslant P_{ij}^{(N)} P_{ji}^{(M)} = \alpha\beta > 0,$$

$N + M$ must be a multiple of t, and from (4.1) and (4.2) it follows that j also has period t.

The general situation is described by the following theorem:

THEOREM 4.2.   *In a Markov chain the persistent states can, in a unique manner, be divided into closed sets $C_1, C_2, \ldots$, such that from any state of a given set C_k all states of that set and no other can be reached. All states belonging to the same closed set C_k are necessarily of the same class. In addition to the closed sets C_k the chain will in general contain transient states from which states of the closed sets C_k can be reached, but not vice versa.*

Proof: Let i_1 be a persistent state, and $C_1 = C(i_1)$ be the set of all states j such that $i_1 \leftrightarrow j$. If i_2 is a persistent state such that $i_2 \notin C_1$, then let $C_2 = C(i_2)$ be the set of all states j such that $i_2 \leftrightarrow j$. Proceeding in this manner until all persistent states are exhausted, we obtain sets $C_1, C_2, \ldots$, such that (i) no two of the sets have any common states, and (ii) each set is irreducible, and therefore by Theorem 4.1, has states of the same class. The remaining states, if any, are all transient.

The following theorem gives a criterion to distinguish between persistent and null states of an irreducible chain. Other criteria have been given by Foster (1953).

THEOREM 4.3.   *A necessary and sufficient condition for the states $0, 1, 2, \ldots$ of an irreducible chain to be transient is that the system of equations*

$$y_i = \sum_{j=1}^{\infty} P_{ij} y_j \qquad (i = 1, 2, \ldots) \tag{4.3}$$

admits of a nonzero bounded solution.

Proof: Let $y_i^{(n)} = \Pr\{T_{i0} > n\}$ $(n = 1, 2, \ldots)$. We have

$$y_i^{(1)} = \sum_{j=1}^{\infty} P_{ij}, \quad y_i^{(n+1)} = \sum_{j=1}^{\infty} P_{ij} y_j^{(n)} \qquad (n \geq 1). \tag{4.4}$$

From (4.4) it follows that the limiting probabilities

$$y_i = \lim_{n \to \infty} y_i^{(n)} = \Pr\{T_{i0} = \infty\} = 1 - f_{i0} \qquad (i \geq 1) \tag{4.5}$$

exist and satisfy the equations (4.3). We shall prove that $\{y_i = 1 - f_{i0}\}$ is the maximal bounded solution of (4.4). Let $\{y_i\}$ be an arbitrary bounded solution of (4.3), that is, $|y_i| \leq M$ $(i \geq 1)$; without loss of generality we can take $M = 1$. We have then

$$|y_i| \leq \sum_{1}^{\infty} P_{ij} |y_j| \leq \sum_{1}^{\infty} P_{ij} = y_i^{(1)},$$

$$|y_i| \leq \sum_{1}^{\infty} P_{ij} y_j^{(1)} = y_i^{(2)},$$

and, in general, $|y_i| \leqslant y_i^{(n)}$, which gives in the limit as $n \to \infty$, $|y_i| \leqslant 1 - f_{i0}$. However, by Theorem 2.3 we have that if all states are persistent, $f_{i0} = 1$ $(i \geqslant 1)$, while if all are transient, $f_{i0} < 1$ for at least one i. The theorem now follows immediately.

5. STATIONARY DISTRIBUTION

5.1. Stationary Distribution

A probability distribution $\{v_j\}$ is called stationary if

$$v_j = \sum_i v_i P_{ij}. \tag{5.1}$$

For such a distribution we have

$$v_j = \sum_i P_{ij} \sum_k v_k P_{ki} = \sum_k v_k \sum_i P_{ki} P_{ij} = \sum_k v_k P_{kj}^{(2)},$$

and, in general,

$$v_j = \sum_i v_i P_{ij}^{(n)} \qquad (n \geqslant 1). \tag{5.2}$$

If the initial distribution $\{a_j^{(0)}\}$ is stationary, we have

$$a_j^{(n)} = \sum_i a_i^{(0)} P_{ij}^{(n)} = a_j^{(0)}, \tag{5.3}$$

using (5.2); thus the unconditional distribution of X_n is independent of time, and we may therefore say that the process is in statistical equilibrium.

5.2. Limiting Distribution

We have seen that for all i

$$\lim_{n \to \infty} P_{ij}^{(n)} = u_j \geqslant 0. \tag{5.4}$$

Since

$$a_j^{(n)} = \sum_i a_i^{(0)} P_{ij}^{(n)} \to u_j, \tag{5.5}$$

we see that the limiting distribution of X_n is given by $\{u_j\}$.

We have the following important theorem:

THEOREM 5.1. *An irreducible Markov chain has a stationary distribution if, and only if, all its states are persistent nonnull. In this case the stationary distribution is unique and is identical with the limiting distribution* $\{u_j\}$, *so that*

$$u_j = \sum_i u_i P_{ij} \tag{5.6}$$

$$u_j > 0, \qquad \sum_j u_j = 1. \tag{5.7}$$

Proof: If $\{v_j\}$ is a stationary distribution, we have (5.2). If all states are transient or persistent nonnull, then $P_{ij}^{(n)} \to 0$ as $n \to \infty$, and (5.2) shows that no stationary distribution exists in these two cases.

If all states are ergodic, we know that the limiting probabilities $u_j = \lim_{n \to \infty} P_{ij}^{(n)}$ exist. In fact, since by Theorem 2.3 $f_{ij} = 1$, we see from (3.10) that $u_j = 1/\mu_j$. Now we have $\sum_{j=0}^{J} P_{ij}^{(n)} \leqslant 1$, whence, letting $n \to \infty$ we obtain $\sum_{0}^{J} u_j \leqslant 1$. Since J is arbitrary, this gives

$$\sum_{0}^{\infty} u_j \leqslant 1. \tag{5.8}$$

Further, we have

$$P_{ij}^{(m+n)} \geqslant \sum_{k=0}^{K} P_{ik}^{(n)} P_{kj}^{(m)}.$$

Letting $n \to \infty$ in this, we obtain

$$u_j \geqslant \sum_{k} u_k P_{kj}^{(m)}. \tag{5.9}$$

We shall show that the equality holds in (5.9). For, if for some j we have a strict inequality, then

$$1 \geqslant \sum_{j} u_j > \sum_{j} \sum_{k} u_k P_{kj}^{(m)} = \sum_{k} u_k,$$

which is a contradiction. Hence for all j we must have

$$u_j = \sum_{k} u_k P_{kj}^{(m)}. \tag{5.10}$$

In particular, when $m = 1$, this gives $u_j = \sum_{k} u_k P_{kj}$. When $m \to \infty$, this gives $u_j = \left(\sum_{k} u_k \right) u_j$, whence it follows that $\sum_{k} u_k = 1$. Thus the limiting probability distribution $\{u_j\}$ is stationary. If possible, let there be a second stationary distribution $\{v_j\}$; then letting $n \to \infty$ in (5.2) we obtain

$$v_j = \left(\sum_{i} v_i \right) u_j = u_j,$$

so that u_j is unique.

[Note: In the above proof the states of the system are taken to be $0, 1, 2, \ldots$, but the general case requires only a slight modification.]

5.3. Finite Chains

The results which have been derived so far hold whether the number of states is finite or not. However, in the case of a finite chain, the situation is simpler, as stated in the following theorem:

THEOREM 5.2. *In a Markov chain with a finite number of states, there are no null states, and not all states can be transient.*

Proof: Suppose that the chain contains N ($< \infty$) states. If all states are transient, then letting $n \to \infty$ in the relation

$$\sum_{j=1}^{N} P_{ij}^{(n)} = 1 \tag{5.11}$$

we obtain $0 = 1$, which is absurd. This argument applied to the subchain formed by a closed set of persistent null states shows that there cannot be any null states. The theorem is therefore proved.

The following theorem regarding the existence of the limits of $P_{ij}^{(n)}$ as $n \to \infty$ is useful in dealing with examples of finite Markov chains.

THEOREM 5.3. *If for some value of $r > 0$,*

$$P_{jk}^{(r)} > 0 \qquad (j, k = 1, 2, \ldots, N), \tag{5.12}$$

then the limiting probabilities

$$\lim_{n \to \infty} P_{jk}^{(n)} = u_k > 0 \qquad (k = 1, 2, \ldots, N) \tag{5.13}$$

exist independently of the initial suffix j.

Proof: Let $M_k^{(n)}$, $m_k^{(n)}$ denote respectively the maximum and minimum element in the kth column of the matrix $(P_{jk}^{(n)})$. Thus

$$M_k^{(n)} = \max_{1 \leqslant j \leqslant N} P_{jk}^{(n)}, \quad m_k^{(n)} = \min_{1 \leqslant j \leqslant N} P_{jk}^{(n)}. \tag{5.14}$$

We have

$$P_{jk}^{(n+1)} = \sum_{v=1}^{N} P_{jv} P_{vk}^{(n)} \leqslant \sum_{v=1}^{N} P_{jv} M_k^{(n)} = M_k^{(n)},$$

so that

$$M_k^{(n+1)} \leqslant M_k^{(n)} \qquad (n = 1, 2, \ldots); \tag{5.15}$$

similarly,

$$m_k^{(n+1)} \geqslant m_k^{(n)} \qquad (n = 1, 2, \ldots). \tag{5.16}$$

Thus $\{M_k^{(n)}\}$ is a monotone nonincreasing sequence and $\{m_k^{(n)}\}$ is a monotone nondecreasing sequence. Both are bounded, since $0 \leqslant m_k^{(n)} \leqslant M_k^{(n)} \leqslant 1$. Further, we have

$$M_k^{(n+r)} - m_k^{(n+r)} = \max_{j, \ell} \sum_{v=1}^{N} \{P_{jv}^{(r)} - P_{\ell v}^{(r)}\} P_{vk}^{(n)}. \tag{5.17}$$

Let us put

$$
\beta_{j\ell v}^{(r)} =
\begin{cases}
P_{jv}^{(r)} - P_{\ell v}^{(r)} & \text{if } P_{jv}^{(r)} > P_{\ell v}^{(r)} \\
-\{P_{jv}^{(r)} - P_{\ell v}^{(r)}\} & \text{if } P_{jv}^{(r)} \leqslant P_{\ell v}^{(r)}.
\end{cases}
\tag{5.18}
$$

Let J_1 denote the set of values of v such that $P_{jv}^{(r)} > P_{\ell v}^{(r)}$, and J_2 the set of values of v such that $P_{jv}^{(r)} \leqslant P_{\ell v}^{(r)}$. Then

$$
\sum_{v \in J_1} \beta_{j\ell v}^{(r)} - \sum_{v \in J_2} \beta_{j\ell v}^{(r)} = \sum_{v \in J_1} \{P_{jv}^{(r)} - P_{\ell v}^{(r)}\} + \sum_{v \in J_2} \{P_{jv}^{(r)} - P_{\ell v}^{(r)}\}
$$

$$
= \sum_{v=1}^{N} \{P_{jv}^{(r)} - P_{\ell v}^{(r)}\} = 1 - 1 = 0.
\tag{5.19}
$$

Further, by our assumption there exists a $\delta > 0$ such that $P_{jk}^{(r)} \geqslant \delta > 0$, so that

$$
0 < \sum_{v \in J_1} \beta_{j\ell v}^{(r)} = 1 - \sum_{v \in J_2} P_{jv}^{(r)} - \sum_{v \in J_1} P_{\ell v}^{(r)} \leqslant 1 - N\delta.
\tag{5.20}
$$

From (5.19) and (5.20) it follows that

$$
\sum_{v=1}^{N} \{P_{jv}^{(r)} - P_{\ell v}^{(r)}\} P_{vk}^{(n)} = \sum_{v \in J_1} \beta_{j\ell v}^{(r)} P_{vk}^{(n)} - \sum_{v \in J_2} \beta_{j\ell v}^{(r)} P_{vk}^{(n)}
$$

$$
\leqslant \sum_{v \in J_1} \beta_{j\ell v}^{(r)} M_k^{(n)} - \sum_{v \in J_2} \beta_{j\ell v}^{(r)} m_k^{(n)}
$$

$$
= \sum_{v \in J_1} \beta_{j\ell v}^{(r)} \{M_k^{(n)} - m_k^{(n)}\}
\tag{5.21}
$$

$$
\leqslant (1 - N\delta)\{M_k^{(n)} - m_k^{(n)}\}.
$$

From (5.17) and (5.21) we find that

$$
M_k^{(n+r)} - m_k^{(n+r)} \leqslant (1 - N\delta)\{M_k^{(n)} - m_k^{(n)}\}.
\tag{5.22}
$$

Moreover, we have

$$
M_k^{(r)} - m_k^{(r)} = \max_{j,\ell} \{P_{jk}^{(r)} - P_{\ell k}^{(r)}\}
$$

$$
\leqslant \max_{j,\ell} \sum_{v \in J_1} \beta_{j\ell v}^{(r)} \leqslant (1 - N\delta).
\tag{5.23}
$$

Putting $n = r, 2r, \ldots$ successively in (5.22) and using (5.23) we obtain

$$
M_k^{(tr)} - m_k^{(tr)} \leqslant (1 - N\delta)^t \to 0 \qquad \text{as } t \to \infty.
\tag{5.24}
$$

Thus $M_k^{(n)}$ and $m_k^{(n)}$ tend to the same limit u_k (say). Since

$$
0 < \delta \leqslant m_k^{(n)} \leqslant P_{jk}^{(n)} \leqslant M_k^{(n)},
\tag{5.25}
$$

it follows that $P_{jk}^{(n)} \to u_k$ as $n \to \infty$, and that $u_k > 0$, as required.

6. SOME EXAMPLES OF DENUMERABLE MARKOV CHAINS

6.1. Random Walks[2]

Let $\{X_n, n = 0, 1, 2, \ldots\}$ be a sequence of independent discrete random variables, and $S_n = X_0 + X_1 + \cdots + X_n$ $(n = 0, 1, \ldots)$. Then the sequence $\{S_n\}$ is a Markov chain whose transition probabilities are given by

$$P_{ij}(m) = \Pr\{S_{m+1} = j \mid S_m = i\} = \Pr\{X_{m+1} = j - i\},$$

$$(i, j = \ldots, -1, 0, 1, 2, \ldots). \tag{6.1}$$

This chain represents a "random walk" of a particle along a straight line, the magnitude of a "jump" at time n being given by the random variable X_n. If X_0 denotes the initial position of the particle, then its position after n jumps (at time n) is given by S_n. In the case where the X_n are identically distributed, the transition probabilities (6.1) become

$$P_{ij} = p_{j-i}, \tag{6.2}$$

where $p_j = \Pr\{X_n = j\}$ $(j = \ldots, -1, 0, 1, 2, \ldots)$; we have then a homogeneous random walk. Such walks in the general case where the X_n have discrete or continuous distribution will be discussed in Section 8.

When X_n has the binomial distribution

$$\Pr\{X_n = +1\} = p, \qquad \Pr\{X_n = -1\} = q = 1 - p, \tag{6.3}$$

we have the classical random walk. The detailed aspects of this are discussed below.

(a) **Unrestricted Random Walk.** From (6.2) and (6.3) we have

$$P_{i,i+1} = p, \quad P_{i,i-1} = q \quad (i = \ldots, -1, 0, 1, 2, \ldots). \tag{6.4}$$

If $0 < p < 1$, it is clear that the chain is irreducible. We have

$$P_{ij}^{(n)} = \Pr\{X_1 + X_2 + \cdots + X_n = j - i\}$$

$$= \binom{n}{(n+j-i)/2} p^{(n+j-i)/2} q^{(n-j+i)/2}, \tag{6.5}$$

and in particular,

$$P_{00}^{(n)} = \binom{n}{n/2}(pq)^{n/2}$$

if n is even, and $= 0$ if n is odd. By using Stirling's approximation we have

$$P_{00}^{(2n)} \sim \frac{(4pq)^n}{\sqrt{n\pi}}. \tag{6.6}$$

[2] For a detailed treatment of random walks, see Spitzer (1964).

If $p \neq \frac{1}{2}$, then $4pq < 1$, and $\Sigma P_{00}^{(2n)}$ converges faster than the geometric series $\Sigma(4pq)^n$. If $p = \frac{1}{2}$, then $P_{00}^{(2n)} \sim (n\pi)^{-\frac{1}{2}}$, so that $\Sigma P_{00}^{(2n)}$ diverges, but $P_{00}^{(2n)} \to 0$ as $n \to \infty$. We thus see that the states are all persistent null if $p = \frac{1}{2}$, and all transient if $p \neq \frac{1}{2}$. In either case the states have period 2.

By an obvious argument we have for $i, j > 0$

$$P_{ij}^{(n)} = {}^0P_{ij}^{(n)} + \sum_{m=1}^{n-1} P_{i0}^{(m)} \, {}^0P_{0j}^{(n-m)}$$

$$P_{-ij}^{(n)} = \sum_{m=1}^{n-1} P_{-i0}^{(m)} \, {}^0P_{0j}^{(n-m)} = \left(\frac{p}{q}\right)^i \sum_{m=1}^{n-1} P_{i0}^{(m)} \, {}^0P_{0j}^{(n-m)},$$

(6.7)

whence we obtain the identity

$$ {}^0P_{ij}^{(n)} = P_{ij}^{(n)} - \left(\frac{q}{p}\right)^i P_{-ij}^{(n)}, \qquad (i, j > 0). \tag{6.8 a}$$

When $p = q$ (the symmetric case), this gives

$$ {}^0P_{ij}^{(n)} = P_{ij}^{(n)} - P_{-ij}^{(n)}, \tag{6.8 b}$$

which is called the "reflection principle" of D. André.

(b) Random Walk with an Absorbing Barrier. Let

$$P_{ii+1} = p, \; P_{ii-1} = q \quad (p + q = 1) \quad (i \geqslant 1), \; P_{00} = 1. \tag{6.9}$$

Here 0 is an absorbing state and the remaining states are all transient. This chain is the same as that described in (a) except that the states $0, -1, -2, \ldots$ have been "condensed" into a single absorbing state 0. It is then clear that

$$f_{i0}^{(n)} = \sum_{j=1}^{\infty} {}^0P_{ij}^{(n-1)} P_{j0} = q \, {}^0P_{i1}^{(n-1)}$$

$$= q\left[\binom{n-1}{(n-i)/2} p^{(n-i)/2} q^{(n-2+i)/2} - \left(\frac{q}{p}\right)^i \binom{n-1}{(n+i)/2} p^{(n+i)/2} q^{(n-2-i)/2}\right],$$

using (6.8 a). After some simplification this gives

$$f_{i0}^{(n)} = \frac{i}{n}\binom{n}{(n-i)/2} p^{(n-i)/2} q^{(n+i)/2}. \tag{6.10}$$

The probabilities $u_i = \sum_{n}^{\infty} f_{i0}^{(n)}$ satisfy the recurrence relations

$$u_1 = pu_2 + q, \qquad u_i = pu_{i+1} + qu_{i-1} \qquad (i > 1).$$

From these we obtain, remembering that $u_i = (u_1)^i$ $(i \geqslant 1)$,

$$u_i = \begin{cases} 1 & \text{if } p \leqslant q \\ \left(\dfrac{q}{p}\right)^i & \text{if } p \geqslant q. \end{cases} \tag{6.11}$$

(c) Random Walk with Two Absorbing Barriers. Let

$$P_{ii+1} = p, \; P_{ii-1} = q \qquad (p + q = 1) \qquad (1 \leqslant i \leqslant a - 1)$$
$$P_{00} = 1, \; P_{aa} = 1. \tag{6.12}$$

Here there are two absorbing states 0 and a; the remaining states $1, 2, \ldots, a - 1$ are transient. The classical gambler's ruin problem is concerned with the absorption probabilities f_{i0} and f_{ia}.

(d) Random Walk with a Reflecting Barrier. Let

$$P_{ii+1} = p, \; P_{ii-1} = q \qquad (i \geqslant 1)$$
$$P_{00} = q, \; P_{01} = p. \tag{6.13}$$

Here we may imagine a barrier placed at $-\frac{1}{2}$ such that every time the particle moves to the left from 0, it is reflected at the barrier and returns to 0. The chain is clearly irreducible if $0 < p < 1$; to classify its states, consider the system of equations

$$y_i = \sum_1^\infty P_{ij} y_j \qquad (i \geqslant 1).$$

These give $y_i = p y_{i+1} + q y_{i-1}$, which can be written as

$$p(y_{i+1} - y_i) = q(y_i - y_{i-1}) \qquad (i \geqslant 2), \qquad y_1 = p y_2. \tag{6.14}$$

From (6.14) we obtain $y_{i+1} - y_i = y_1 (q/p)^i$ $(i \geqslant 1)$, so that

$$y_i - y_1 = y_1 \left\{ \left(\frac{q}{p}\right) + \left(\frac{q}{p}\right)^2 + \cdots + \left(\frac{q}{p}\right)^{i-1} \right\},$$

$$y_i = \frac{1 - (q/p)^i}{1 - (q/p)} y_1 \qquad (i \geqslant 1). \tag{6.15}$$

This shows that y_i is bounded if, and only if, $p > q$. Thus by Theorem 4.3 the states are all transient if $p > q$, and persistent if $p \leqslant q$.

The equations determining the stationary distribution in the case $p \leqslant q$ are

$$u_j = \sum_0^\infty u_i P_{ij} = p u_{j-1} + q u_{j+1} \qquad (j \geqslant 1)$$

$$u_0 = q u_0 + q u_1. \tag{6.16}$$

Solving (6.16) successively we obtain $u_j = (p/q)^j u_0 \ (j \geqslant 0)$, where

$$u_0 \left\{ 1 + \left(\frac{p}{q} \right) + \left(\frac{p}{q} \right)^2 + \cdots \right\} = 1. \tag{6.17}$$

If $p = q$, the infinite series inside the brackets in (6.17) diverges and consequently $u_0 = 0$, and hence $u_j = 0 \ (j \geqslant 0)$, so that in this case the stationary distribution does not exist. Thus if $p = q$, the states are all persistent null. If, however, $p < q$, then (6.17) gives $u_0 = (1 - p/q) > 0$ and therefore the limiting distribution in this (persistent nonnull) case is given by

$$u_j = \left(1 - \frac{p}{q} \right) \left(\frac{p}{q} \right)^j \qquad (j \geqslant 0). \tag{6.18}$$

(e) Random Walk with Two Reflecting Barriers. If, in addition to the barrier at $-\frac{1}{2}$, there is a second reflecting barrier at $a + \frac{1}{2}$, so that

$$P_{aa} = p, \ P_{a,a-1} = q, \tag{6.19}$$

then we have a chain with a finite number of states $(0, 1, 2, \ldots, a)$. In this case the stationary distribution exists and is in fact the geometric distribution (6.18) truncated at a.

6.2. Branching Processes in Discrete Time[3]

Consider a population in which the individuals of the $(n + 1)$th generation are produced by those of the nth generation in such a way that each individual can, independently of others, produce $0, 1, 2, \ldots$ successors (direct descendants) with probabilities $k_0, k_1, k_2, \ldots$. If we let $X_n =$ number of individuals in the nth generation $(n = 0, 1, 2, \ldots)$, it is clear that $\{X_n\}$ is a Markov chain, and that

$$\sum_{j=0}^{\infty} P_{ij}^{(n)} z^j = \left[\sum_{j=0}^{\infty} P_{1j}^{(n)} z^j \right]^i = [F_n(z)]^i \qquad (i, n \geqslant 0), \tag{6.20}$$

where $F_n(z) = \sum_{0}^{\infty} P_{1j}^{(n)} z^j \ (n \geqslant 0)$, and in particular

$$F_1(z) = \sum_{j=0}^{\infty} k_j z^j = K(z) \ (\text{say}). \tag{6.21}$$

We have

$$P_{1j}^{(n+1)} = \sum_{v=0}^{\infty} k_v \sum_{(j_1 + j_2 + \cdots + j_v = j)} P_{1j_1}^{(n)} P_{1j_2}^{(n)} \cdots P_{1j_v}^{(n)},$$

which gives

$$F_{n+1}(z) = K[F_n(z)]. \tag{6.22}$$

---

[3] A comprehensive account of branching processes has recently been given by Harris (1963).

The transition probabilities of the chain are completely determined by the last three equations. All states are transient except 0, which is an absorbing state; absorption at 0 means the extinction of the population. The probability that extinction occurs at or before the nth generation is given by

$$P_{i0}^{(n)} = \Pr\{X_n = 0 \,|\, X_0 = i\}. \tag{6.23}$$

From (6.20)–(6.22) it is seen that $P_{i0}^{(n)} = (\zeta_n)^i$, where $\zeta_n = P_{10}^{(n)}$ satisfies the relations

$$\zeta_1 = P_0, \zeta_{n+1} = K(\zeta_n) \qquad (n \geqslant 1). \tag{6.24}$$

The probability of ultimate extinction is given by

$$\zeta = \lim_{n \to \infty} \zeta_n, \tag{6.25}$$

and from (6.24) it follows that ζ satisfies the equation $z = K(z)$; ζ is in fact the smallest positive root of this equation. For, let $z > 0$ be an arbitrary root of $z = K(z)$; then since $K(z)$ is an increasing function of z, $\zeta_1 = K(0) < K(z) = z, \zeta_2 = K(\zeta_1) < K(z) = z, \ldots, \zeta_n < z$, which yields, in the limit as $n \to \infty$, $\zeta < z$. The situation is further clarified by the following:

LEMMA 6.1. *Let* $K(z) = \sum_0^\infty k_j z^j$ *be a probability generating function (p.g.f.), and assume that* $k_0 > 0, 0 < K'(1) = \alpha < \infty$. *Then the equation*

$$z = K(z) \tag{6.26}$$

has a root ζ *such that* $0 < \zeta < 1$ *if, and only if,* $\alpha > 1$.

Proof: Consider the function $f(z) = K(z)/z = k_0/z + k_1 + k_2 z + \ldots$ $(0 < z \leqslant 1)$. We have $f(+0) = \infty$, $f(1) = 1$. Moreover, $f''(z) = 2k_0/z^3 + 2k_3 + 6k_4 z + \ldots > 0$. Thus $f'(z)$ is a monotone increasing function, and vanishes at most once in $(0 < z < 1)$, which happens if, and only if, $f'(1) = \alpha - 1 > 0$. If $f'(z) = 0$ at $z = z_0$ $(0 < z_0 < 1)$, then $f(z)$ is monotone decreasing in $(0 < z < z_0)$ and monotone increasing in $(z_0 < z \leqslant 1)$. Since $f(1) = 1$ and $f(z_0) < 1$, there exists exactly one value ζ such that $f(\zeta) = 1, 0 < \zeta < 1$.

Since the states $1, 2, \ldots$ are all transient, $P_{ij}^{(n)} \to 0$ as $n \to \infty$. Thus, irrespective of the value of α, the limiting population size cannot attain any positive finite value. The only possibilities are, therefore, that the population either becomes extinct or "explodes" (becomes infinitely large) at some stage. Using Lemma 6.1, we obtain the following:

THEOREM 6.1. *Let* $\alpha = \sum_1^\infty jk_j$ *be the mean number of direct descendants of an individual in a branching process, and assume that* $0 < \alpha < \infty, k_0 > 0$.

Then if $\alpha \leqslant 1$, the population becomes extinct with probability 1, while if $\alpha > 1$, the population either becomes extinct with probability ζ^i, or explodes with probability $1 - \zeta^i$, where ζ is the smallest positive root of the equation (6.26), and $X_0 = i$ is the initial number in the population.

If N is the number of generations preceding extinction, then in the notation of Section 2, $N = T_{i0} = \min \{n \mid X_n = 0 \mid X_0 = i\}$. Since $P_{i0}^{(n)} = \Pr \{N \leqslant n\}$ we have, from Theorem 6.1, $\Pr \{N < \infty\} = 1$ or ζ^i according as $\alpha \leqslant 1$ or $\alpha > 1$. A second interesting problem is concerned with the total number Z_N of individuals in the population up to the time of extinction. Clearly, $Z_N = X_0 + X_1 + \cdots + X_N$, and the following Theorem (6.2) gives its distribution.

THEOREM 6.2. Let $X_0 = 1$, and $g_j = \Pr \{Z_N = j\}$ $(j = 1, 2, \ldots)$. Then the p.g.f. $G(z) = \sum_1^\infty g_j z^j$ is the unique root of the functional equation

$$G(z) = zK[G(z)] \tag{6.27}$$

such that $0 < G(z) \leqslant 1$ for $0 < z \leqslant 1$. Moreover,

$$\Pr \{Z_N < \infty\} = G(1) = \begin{cases} 1 & \text{if } \alpha \leqslant 1 \\ \zeta & \text{if } \alpha > 1. \end{cases} \tag{6.28}$$

Proof: We have

$$g_1 = k_0$$

$$g_{j+1} = \sum_1^\infty k_\nu \sum_{(j_1 + j_2 + \cdots + j_\nu = j)} g_{j_1} g_{j_2} \cdots g_{j_\nu} \quad (j \geqslant 1), \tag{6.29}$$

whence we obtain

$$G(z) = zk_0 + z \sum_1^\infty k_\nu [G(z)]^\nu = zK[G(z)]. \tag{6.30}$$

Thus $G(z)$ satisfies the functional equation (6.27). Proceeding as in Lemma 6.1 with the function $K(\xi)/\xi$ $(0 < \xi \leqslant 1)$, we see that there is a unique root $\xi = G(z)$ of $K(\xi)/\xi = 1/z$ $(0 < z \leqslant 1)$, such that (i) $0 < G(z) \leqslant 1$ for $0 < z \leqslant 1$, and (ii) as $z \to 1$, $G(z)$ tends to the smallest positive root of the equation $z = K(z)$.

6.3. Two Markov Chains Occurring in Queuing Theory[4]

We shall now consider two examples of Markov chains occurring in queuing theory. In the present case we have

$$P_{0j} = k_j \ (j \geqslant 0), P_{ij} = k_{j-i+1} \quad (i \geqslant 1, j \geqslant i - 1), \tag{6.31}$$

[4] These chains are said to be *imbedded* in the queuing process [see Kendall (1951); also Prabhu (1965)].

where $\{k_j, j = 0, 1, \ldots\}$ is a probability distribution. The transition probability matrix P is

$$
P \equiv
\begin{array}{c|cccccc}
\nearrow & 0 & 1 & 2 & 3 & \cdot & \cdot \\
\hline
0 & k_0 & k_1 & k_2 & k_3 & \cdot & \cdot \\
1 & k_0 & k_1 & k_2 & k_3 & \cdot & \cdot \\
2 & 0 & k_0 & k_1 & k_2 & \cdot & \cdot \\
3 & 0 & 0 & k_0 & k_1 & \cdot & \cdot \\
\cdot & & & & & & \\
\cdot & & & & & & \\
\end{array}
\tag{6.32}
$$

Let us assume that $k_j > 0$ $(j \geqslant 0)$; the chain is then irreducible and aperiodic. To classify its states we calculate the first passage probabilities $f_{00}^{(n)}$. We first note that for $i \geqslant 1$,

$$
f_{i0}^{(1)} = P_{i0} = \begin{cases} k_0 & \text{if } i = 1 \\ 0 & \text{if } i > 1, \end{cases}
\tag{6.33}
$$

$$
f_{i0}^{(2)} = \sum_{v=1}^{\infty} P_{iv} P_{v0} = P_{i1} k_0 = \begin{cases} k_0 k_1 & \text{if } i = 1 \\ k_0^2 & \text{if } i = 2 \\ 0 & \text{if } i > 2. \end{cases}
$$

Now, let

$$
K(z) = \sum_{0}^{\infty} k_j z^j, \quad \text{and} \quad [K(z)]^n = \sum_{0}^{\infty} k_j^{(n)} z^j.
$$

From

$$
\frac{d}{dz}[K(z)]^{n+1} = (n + 1)[K(z)]^n K'(z)
$$

we obtain the identity

$$
\sum_{v=0}^{j} v k_v k_{j-v}^{(n)} = \frac{j}{n+1} k_j^{(n+1)} \quad (j \geqslant 0).
\tag{6.34}
$$

We can write $f_{i0}^{(1)} = i k_{1-i}$, $f_{i0}^{(2)} = \frac{1}{2} i k_{2-i}^{(2)}$, and since

$$
f_{i0}^{(n+1)} = \sum_{v=1}^{\infty} P_{iv} f_{v0}^{(n)} = \sum_{v \neq 0} k_{v-i+1} f_{v0}^{(n)},
\tag{6.35}
$$

it follows by induction, using (6.34), that

$$f_{i0}^{(n)} = \begin{cases} \dfrac{i}{n} k_{n-i}^{(n)} & (n \geqslant i) \\[2mm] 0 & (n < i). \end{cases} \qquad (6.36)$$

From this we obtain

$$f_{00}^{(1)} = P_{00} = k_0 \qquad (6.37)$$

$$f_{00}^{(n)} = \sum_{v=1}^{\infty} P_{0v} f_{v0}^{(n-1)} = \sum_{v=0}^{n-1} k_v \frac{v}{n-1} k_{n-1-v}^{(n-1)} = \frac{1}{n} k_{n-1}^{(n)} \qquad (n \geqslant 1).$$

The mean recurrence time of 0 is given by

$$\mu_0 = \sum_{1}^{\infty} n f_{00}^{(n)} = \sum_{1}^{\infty} k_{n-1}^{(n)}. \qquad (6.38)$$

The results (6.37) and (6.38) lead to the following theorems:

THEOREM 6.3. *The Markov chain with the transition probability matrix* (6.32) *is irreducible and aperiodic. Let*

$$A = \sum_{1}^{\infty} \frac{1}{n} k_{n-1}^{(n)} \qquad B = \sum_{1}^{\infty} k_{n-1}^{(n)}. \qquad (6.39)$$

Then its states are

(i) transient if $A < 1$,

(ii) persistent null if $A = 1$, $B = \infty$, and   (6.40)

(iii) persistent nonnull if $A = 1$, $B < \infty$.

THEOREM 6.4. *In the persistent nonnull case the stationary distribution has the* p.g.f.

$$U(z) = \frac{B^{-1} K(z)(1-z)}{K(z) - z}. \qquad (6.41)$$

Proof: The equations determining the stationary distribution are

$$u_j = u_0 k_j + \sum_{i=1}^{j+1} u_i k_{j-i+1} \qquad (j \geqslant 0). \qquad (6.42)$$

Let $U(z) = \Sigma u_j z^j$; then multiplying (6.42) by z^j and adding over $j = 0, 1, \ldots,$ we obtain

$$U(z) = u_0 K(z) + \frac{K(z)}{z} [U(z) - u_0],$$

$$U(z) = \frac{u_0 K(z)(1-z)}{K(z) - z}. \qquad (6.43)$$

Since $u_0 = \mu_0^{-1} = B^{-1} < \infty$, we have (6.41).

In queuing theory it is reasonable to assume that the mean $\alpha = \Sigma jk_j$ exists, that is, $0 < \alpha < \infty$. In this case it is possible to rederive the above results in a more elegant manner. We note that a first passage from i to 0 can occur only through $i - 1, i - 2, \ldots, 1$; moreover, since P_{ij} depends only on the difference $j - i$, the first passage time $T_{i,i-1}$ is independent of i. It follows that T_{i0} is the sum of i independent random variables, each having the same distribution as T_{10}. Hence

$$F_{i0}(z) = \sum_{1}^{\infty} f_{i0}^{(n)} z^n = [\xi(z)]^i, \tag{6.44}$$

where $\xi(z) = F_{10}(z)$. However, since

$$f_{10}^{(1)} = k_0, \qquad f_{10}^{(n+1)} = \sum_{\nu=1}^{\infty} k_\nu f_{\nu 0}^{(n)} \tag{6.45}$$

we see that $\xi(z)$ satisfies the functional equation

$$\xi = zK(\xi). \tag{6.46}$$

Applying Theorem 6.2 we find readily that

$$f_{10} = F_{10}(1) = \begin{cases} 1 & \text{if } \alpha \leqslant 1 \\ \zeta & \text{if } \alpha > 1. \end{cases} \tag{6.47}$$

Moreover, if $\alpha \leqslant 1$, we have

$$\mu_{10} = F'_{10}(1) = \begin{cases} (1 - \alpha)^{-1} & \text{if } \alpha < 1 \\ \infty & \text{if } \alpha = 1. \end{cases} \tag{6.48}$$

From (6.37) we have $F_{00}(z) = F_{10}(z)$. The above results can be summarized as follows:

THEOREM 6.5. *Let $0 < \Sigma jk_j = \alpha < \infty$. Then the states of the Markov chain (6.32) are transient if $\alpha > 1$, persistent null if $\alpha = 1$, and persistent nonnull if $\alpha < 1$. In the persistent nonnull case we have $u_0 = 1 - \alpha$, and*

$$U(z) = \frac{(1 - \alpha)K(z)(1 - z)}{K(z) - z}. \tag{6.49}$$

Proof: From (6.37) we have $f_{00}^{(n)} = f_{10}^{(n)} \ (n \geqslant 1)$, so that $F_{00}(z) = \xi(z)$, and hence $f_{00} = f_{10}$, $\mu_0 = \mu_{10}$. The theorem now follows from (6.47), (6.48), and (6.43).

6.4. The Dual Chain

This second Markov chain arising in queuing theory can be considered as a dual of the one considered in the last section, as will be clear from the theorem below. Here

$$P_{i0} = \alpha_i, \ P_{ij} = k_{i-j+1} \qquad (i \geqslant 0, \quad 0 \leqslant j \leqslant i + 1), \tag{6.50}$$

where $\{k_j\}$ is again a probability distribution, $\alpha_i = k_{i+1} + k_{i+2} + \dots$, and we assume that $k_j > 0$ $(j \geqslant 0)$, $0 < \alpha < \Sigma j k_j < \infty$. The chain is irreducible and aperiodic. Its transition probability matrix is given by

$$
P \equiv
\begin{array}{c|cccccc}
\nearrow & 0 & 1 & 2 & 3 & . & . & . \\
\hline
0 & \alpha_0 & k_0 & 0 & 0 & . & . & . \\
1 & \alpha_1 & k_1 & k_0 & 0 & . & . & . \\
2 & \alpha_2 & k_2 & k_1 & k_0 & . & . & . \\
. & . & . & . & . & . & . & . \\
. & . & . & . & . & . & . & . \\
\end{array}
\tag{6.51}
$$

We have, for $j \geqslant 1$,

$$
{}^0 P_{0j}^{(1)} = P_{0j} = k_j \quad \text{if } j = 1, \quad = 0 \quad \text{if } j > 1
$$

$$
{}^0 P_{0j}^{(2)} = \sum_{v=1}^{\infty} P_{0v} P_{vj} = k_0 k_{2-j} = \frac{j}{2} k_{2-j}^{(2)},
$$

and proceeding as in the last section, we obtain

$$
{}^0 P_{0j}^{(n)} =
\begin{cases}
\dfrac{j}{n} k_{n-j}^{(n)} & (n \geqslant j) \\[2mm]
0 & (n < j).
\end{cases}
\tag{6.52}
$$

We thus see that the expression for ${}^0 P_{0j}^{(n)}$ is identical with that for $f_{j0}^{(n)}$ of the last example. Further, we have

$$
f_{00}^{(1)} = P_{00} = \alpha_0
$$

$$
f_{00}^{(n+1)} = \sum_{j=1}^{\infty} {}^0 P_{0j}^{(n)} P_{j0} = \sum_1^{\infty} \alpha_j^0 P_{0j}^{(n)} \quad (n \geqslant 1),
$$

and using (6.44),

$$
F_{00}(z) = \sum_1^{\infty} f_{00}^{(n)} z^n = z\alpha_0 + z \sum_1^{\infty} \alpha_j \xi^j
$$

$$
= z \frac{1 - K(\xi)}{1 - \xi} = \frac{z - \xi}{1 - \xi},
\tag{6.53}
$$

where $\xi = \xi(z)$ satisfies (6.46). It follows that

$$
f_{00} = F_{00}(1) =
\begin{cases}
1 & \text{if } \alpha \geqslant 1 \\
\alpha & \text{if } \alpha < 1
\end{cases}
\tag{6.54}
$$

$$\mu_0 = F'_{00}(1) = \begin{cases} (1 - \zeta)^{-1} & \text{if } \alpha > 1 \\ \infty & \text{if } \alpha = 1. \end{cases} \tag{6.55}$$

We now establish the following:

THEOREM 6.6.   *The Markov chain* (6.51) *is irreducible and aperiodic. Its states are all transient if* $\alpha < 1$, *persistent null if* $\alpha = 1$, *and persistent nonnull if* $\alpha > 1$. *In the case* $\alpha > 1$ *the stationary distribution is given by*

$$u_j = (1 - \zeta)\zeta^j \qquad (j = 0, 1, \ldots), \tag{6.56}$$

where ζ *is the smallest positive root of the equation* $K(z) = z$.

Proof: The first part of the theorem is an immediate consequence of (6.54) and (6.55). For the second part we note that when $\alpha > 1$, $u_j = (1 - \zeta)\zeta^j$ is a solution of the equations (5.6), and there cannot be a second solution.

7. MARKOV CHAINS WITH A CONTINUOUS INFINITY OF STATES

7.1. Definition

In this section we consider the case of a Markov chain $\{X_n\}$ where the range of values of X_n is $(-\infty, \infty)$. We restrict ourselves to homogeneous chains. The function

$$P_n(x; y) = \Pr\{X_{m+n} \leqslant y \,|\, X_m = x\} \tag{7.1}$$

defines the nth order transition probability distribution function (p.d.f.). In particular, let

$$P_1(x; y) = P(x; y) = \Pr\{X_{m+1} \leqslant y \,|\, X_m = x\}. \tag{7.2}$$

We have

$$P_{m+n}(x; y) = \int_{-\infty}^{\infty} d_z \; \Pr\{X_m \leqslant z \,|\, X_0 = x\} \; \Pr\{X_{m+n} \leqslant y \,|\, X_m = z\},$$

whence we obtain Chapman–Kolmogorov equations

$$P_{m+n}(x; y) = \int_{-\infty}^{\infty} d_z P_m(x; z) P_n(z; y). \tag{7.3}$$

As in the case of a denumerable chain, we can investigate the existence of the stationary distribution [see, for instance, Doob (1953)], and also the first passage problem. However, it will be found more useful to develop special methods to deal with the particular cases likely to arise, and therefore in the remainder of this section we consider two examples.

7.2. A Waiting Time Problem

Consider a single server queuing system in which the customers arrive at times $t = 0, a, 2a, \ldots$, and are served in the order of their arrival.

Let the service time of a customer be a random variable with the distribution $dB(v) = \mu e^{-\mu v}\,dv\ (0 < v < \infty)$. Let W_n be the waiting time of the nth customer, that is, the time he has to wait for his service to commence $(n = 0, 1, 2, \ldots)$; we have then the recurrence relations

$$W_{n+1} = \begin{cases} W_n + v_n - a & \text{if } W_n + v_n > a \\ 0 & \text{if } W_n + v_n \leqslant a, \end{cases} \qquad (7.4)$$

where v_n denotes the service time of the nth customer. These relations show that $\{W_n\}$ is a Markov chain;[5] its transition d.f. is given by

$$\begin{aligned} P(x\,;\,y) &= \Pr\{W_{n+1} \leqslant y\,|\,W_n = x\} \\ &= \Pr\{W_{n+1} = 0\,|\,W_n = x\} + \Pr\{0 < W_{n+1} \leqslant y\,|\,W_n = x\} \\ &= \Pr\{x + v_n - a \leqslant 0\} + \Pr\{0 < x + v_n - a \leqslant y\} \\ &= \Pr\{x + v_n - a \leqslant y\} = B(y + a - x). \end{aligned} \qquad (7.5)$$

The higher order transition p.d.f.'s can be obtained by using the Chapman–Kolmogorov equations (7.3), which in this case give

$$\begin{aligned} F_{n+1}(0\,;\,x) &= \int_{0-}^{x+a} d_y F_n(0\,;\,y) B(a + x - y) \\ &= \int_{0}^{x+a} F_n(0\,;\,y)\mu e^{-\mu(a+x-y)}\,dy \qquad (n \geqslant 1). \end{aligned} \qquad (7.6)$$

Since

$$F_1(0\,;\,x) = B(x + a) = 1 - e^{-\mu(x+a)} \qquad (x \geqslant 0),$$

we obtain from (7.6),

$$\begin{aligned} F_2(0\,;\,x) &= \int_{0}^{x+a} dy\,\mu e^{-\mu(a+x-y)}[1 - e^{-\mu(y+a)}] \\ &= 1 - e^{-\mu(x+a)} - e^{-\mu(x+2a)}\mu(x + a), \\ F_3(0\,;\,x) &= \int_{0}^{x+a} dy\,\mu e^{-\mu(a+x+y)}\{1 - e^{-\mu(y+a)} - e^{-\mu(y+2a)}\mu(y + a)\} \\ &= 1 - e^{-\mu(x+a)} - e^{-\mu(x+2a)}\mu(x + a) \\ &\qquad - e^{-\mu(x+3a)}\frac{\mu^2}{2}(x + 3a)(x + a), \end{aligned}$$

and by induction,

$$F_n(0\,;\,x) = 1 - \sum_{r=1}^{n} e^{-\mu(x+ra)}\frac{\mu^{r-1}}{(r-1)!}(x + ra)^{r-2}(x + a). \qquad (7.7)$$

---

[5] The fundamental work on such chains was done by Lindley (1952); see also the references cited in footnote 4.

The d.f. of the waiting time of the nth customer is thus given by (7.7). Further we have,

$$\lim_{n \to \infty} F_n(0; x) = 1 - \sum_{r=1}^{\infty} e^{-\mu(x+ra)} \frac{\mu^{r-1}}{(r-1)!} (x+ra)^{r-2}(x+a). \tag{7.8}$$

To evaluate the infinite sum on the right-hand side of (7.8), consider the series

$$\sum_{n=0}^{\infty} e^{-\mu(x+na)} \frac{\mu^n}{n!} (x+na)^n. \tag{7.9}$$

We have

$$e^{-\mu(x+na)} \frac{\mu^n}{n!} (x+na)^n \sim \frac{e^{-\mu(x+na)}(\mu an)^n e^{x/a}}{\sqrt{2\pi} n^{n+\frac{1}{2}} e^{-n}}$$

$$= e^{-(x/a)(\mu a - 1)} \cdot \frac{[e^{-(\mu a - 1)}(\mu a)]^n}{\sqrt{2\pi n}}. \tag{7.10}$$

If $\mu a \neq 1$, we have $e^{-(\mu a - 1)}\mu a < 1$, so that the series (7.9) converges faster than the geometric series with the ratio $e^{-(\mu a - 1)}\mu a$; if $\mu a = 1$, the general term of the series (7.9) is $\sim (2\pi n)^{-\frac{1}{2}}$, so that the series diverges. We have

$$\sum_{n=0}^{\infty} e^{-\mu(x+na)} \frac{\mu^n}{n!} (x+na)^n = \begin{cases} (1 - \mu a)^{-1} & \text{if } \mu a < 1 \\ e^{-\mu x(1-\zeta)}(1 - \mu a\zeta)^{-1} & \text{if } \mu a > 1, \end{cases} \tag{7.11}$$

where ζ is the smallest positive root of the equation $e^{-\mu a(1-z)} = z$ (by Lemma 6.1, $0 < \zeta < 1$ since $\mu a > 1$). For proof see Complement 30. Now

$$\sum_{n=1}^{\infty} e^{-\mu(x+na)} \frac{\mu^{n-1}}{(n-1)!} (x+na)^{n-2}(x+a)$$

$$= \sum_{n=1}^{\infty} e^{-\mu(x+na)} \frac{\mu^{n-1}}{(n-1)!} \{(x+na)^{n-1} - (n-1)a(x+na)^{n-2}\}$$

$$= \sum_{n=0}^{\infty} e^{-\mu(x'+na)} \frac{\mu^n}{n!} (x'+na)^n - \mu a \sum_{n=0}^{\infty} e^{-\mu(x''+na)} \frac{\mu^n}{n!} (x''+na)^n,$$

where $x' = x + a$, $x'' = x + 2a$. Using (7.11) we find that the last expression is

$$= \begin{cases} \dfrac{1}{1 - \mu a} - \dfrac{\mu a}{1 - \mu a} = 1 & \text{if } \mu a \leqslant 1 \\[2ex] \dfrac{\exp[-\mu(1 - \zeta)(x + a)]}{1 - \mu a\zeta} - \mu a \dfrac{\exp[-\mu(1 - \zeta)(x + 2a)]}{1 - \mu a\zeta} \\[2ex] \qquad\qquad = \zeta e^{-\mu(1-\zeta)x} & \text{if } \mu a > 1. \end{cases} \tag{7.12}$$

Thus the limiting distribution (7.8) of the waiting time is given by

$$\lim_{n \to \infty} \Pr\{W_n \leqslant x | W_0 = 0\} = \begin{cases} 1 - \zeta e^{-\mu(1-\zeta)x} & \text{if } \mu a > 1 \\ 0 & \text{if } \mu a \leqslant 1. \end{cases} \quad (7.13)$$

When $\mu a \leqslant 1$, the above result implies that as $n \to \infty$, $W_n \to \infty$ with probability one.

7.3. A Stochastic Difference Equation

Let $\{\varepsilon_n, n = 0, 1, \ldots\}$ be a sequence of mutually independent and identically distributed random variables, and $\{X_n, n = 0, 1, 2, \ldots\}$ a second sequence defined by the relation

$$X_n = \rho X_{n-1} + \varepsilon_{n-1} \ (n = 1, 2, \ldots), \qquad X_0 = 0, \quad (7.14)$$

where ρ is a constant. The equation (7.14) is called a stochastic difference equation of the first order; clearly, the sequence $\{X_n\}$ is a Markov chain, whose transition p.d.f. can be expressed in terms of the d.f. of ε_n. Solving (7.14) successively for $X_1, X_2, \ldots$, we obtain

$$X_n = \varepsilon_{n-1} + \rho \varepsilon_{n-2} + \rho^2 \varepsilon_{n-3} + \cdots + \rho^{n-1} \varepsilon_0,$$

or since the ε_r are identically distributed,[6]

$$X_n \sim \sum_{r=0}^{n-1} \rho^r \varepsilon_r \qquad (n \geqslant 1). \quad (7.15)$$

To study the behavior of X_n as $n \to \infty$, let us assume that $E(\varepsilon_n) = 0$, and $\text{Var}(\varepsilon_n) = \sigma^2 < \infty$. Then

$$\text{Var}\left(\sum_{r=0}^{\infty} \rho^r \varepsilon_r\right) = \sigma^2 \sum_{0}^{\infty} \rho^{2r} < \infty$$

if $|\rho| < 1$; so in this case the series $\sum_{0}^{\infty} \rho^r \varepsilon_r$ converges with probability one, and

$$\lim_{n \to \infty} X_n \sim \sum_{r=0}^{\infty} \rho^r \varepsilon_r. \quad (7.16)$$

If, however, $|\rho| \geqslant 1$, and the ε_n are uniformly bounded, the series does not converge, that is, $X_n \to \infty$ with probability one.

8. SUMS OF INDEPENDENT RANDOM VARIABLES

8.1. Fluctuation Theory

Let $\{X_n, n = 1, 2, \ldots\}$ be a sequence of independent and identically distributed random variables assuming values in $(-\infty, \infty)$, and put $S_0 = 0$, $S_n = X_1 + X_2 + \cdots + X_n \ (n \geqslant 1)$. Then the sequence $\{S_n\}$

---

[6] For two random variables X, Y, we write $X \sim Y$ if they have the same distribution.

is a Markov chain of the random walk type briefly described in Section 6. We now discuss the fluctuation theory of this chain due to Chung and Fuchs (1951).

The value x is *possible* if for every $\delta > 0$ there exists an n such that $\Pr\{|S_n - x| < \delta\} > 0$.

The value x is *recurrent* if for every $\delta > 0$ we have

$$\Pr\{|S_n - x| < \delta \text{ i.o.}\} = 1, \qquad (8.1)$$

where we have written "i.o." for infinitely often, that is, for an infinity of values of n.

THEOREM 8.1.   *The set R of all recurrent values is a closed additive group.*

Proof: That R is closed is implied in the definition. To prove the additive property, we shall show that if $x \in R$ and $y \in R$, then $x - y \in R$. If $x - y \notin R$, then we shall have

$$q = \Pr\{|S_n - (x - y)| < 2\delta \text{ for a finite number of } n \text{ only}\} > 0$$

for some $\delta > 0$. Since a recurrent value is also a possible value, there is a $k > 0$ such that

$$p = \Pr\{|S_k - y| < \delta\} > 0.$$

Now,

$$\Pr\{|S_n - x| < \delta \text{ for a finite number of } n \text{ only}\}$$

$$> \Pr\{|S_k - y| < \delta, |S_{n+k} - S_k - (x - y)| < 2\delta \text{ for a finite number of } n$$

$$\text{only}\}$$

$$(8.2)$$

$$= \Pr\{|S_k - y| < \delta\} \Pr\{S_n - (x - y)| < 2\delta \text{ for a finite number of } n \text{ only}\}$$

$$= pq > 0,$$

since $S_{n+k} - S_k = X_{k+1} + X_{k+2} + \cdots + X_{n+k}$ has the same distribution as S_n and is independent of S_k. However, (8.2) contradicts the fact that x is recurrent.

THEOREM 8.2.   *Either no value is recurrent or all possible values are recurrent.*

Proof: The only closed additive groups of real numbers are (i) the empty set, (ii) the set of all real numbers, and (iii) the set of all numbers $n\lambda$ ($n = 0, \pm 1, \pm 2, \ldots$), where λ is a real number. From Theorem 8.1 it follows that R falls into one of these three categories. If R is not empty, then $0 \in R$. If x is a possible value, then proceeding as in (8.2) we find that $0 - x = -x \in R$, and hence $0 - (-x) = x \in R$. Thus in this case all possible values are recurrent.

THEOREM 8.3.   *A necessary and sufficient condition for recurrent values to exist is that*

$$U(h) \equiv \sum_{n=1}^{\infty} \Pr\{|S_n| < h\} = \infty \qquad \text{for } h > 0. \qquad (8.3)$$

Proof: In view of Theorem 8.2 we need investigate only whether or not 0 is recurrent. If $0 \in R$, then we must have (8.3); for if $U(h) < \infty$, then by the Borel–Cantelli lemma $\Pr\{|S_n| < h \text{ i.o.}\} = 0$, which means that $0 \notin R$, a contradiction. Thus the condition (8.3) is necessary. To prove its sufficiency we shall first prove that (8.3) implies

$$q(2h) = \Pr\{|S_n| \geqslant 2h \qquad (n = 1, 2, \ldots)\} = 0. \qquad (8.4)$$

Let

$$r(h) = \Pr\{|S_n| < h \text{ for a finite number of } n \text{ only}\}; \qquad (8.5)$$

then

$$1 \geqslant r(h) \geqslant \sum_{k=1}^{\infty} \Pr\{|S_k| < h, \ |S_n - S_k| \geqslant 2h \qquad (n = k+1, k+2, \ldots)\}$$

$$= \sum_{k=1}^{\infty} \Pr\{|S_k| < h\} \Pr\{|S_n| \geqslant 2h \qquad (n = 1, 2, \ldots)\}$$

$$= U(h)q(2h).$$

This contradicts (8.3) unless $q(2h) = 0$.

Now,

$$r(h) \leqslant \sum_{m > 1/h} \sum_{k=1}^{\infty} \Pr\{|S_k| < h - \frac{1}{m}, \ |S_n| \geqslant h \ (n = k+i, k+2, \ldots)\} + q(h)$$

$$\leqslant \sum_{m > 1/h} \sum_{k=1}^{\infty} \Pr\{|S_k| < h - \frac{1}{m}\} \Pr\{|S_n - S_k| \geqslant \frac{1}{m} (n = k+1, k+2, \ldots)\}$$

$$= \sum_{m > 1/h} U\left(h - \frac{1}{m}\right) q\left(\frac{1}{m}\right) = 0.$$

This proves that $0 \in R$.

It is interesting to note the significance of the above results, and compare them with those of Section 2. The result $q(h) = 0$ implies that the system (that is, the particle performing the random walk) will eventually enter the interval $(-h, h)$, that is, if we define the first entrance time

$$T_h = \min\{n \,|\, |S_n| < h\}; \qquad (8.6)$$

then in the recurrent case

$$\Pr\{T_h < \infty\} = 1. \qquad (8.7)$$

This is the analogue of the result $f_{jj} = 1$ for j recurrent. Further, let us define

$$N_h^{(n)} = \begin{cases} 1 & \text{if } |S_n| < h \\ 0 & \text{if } |S_n| \geqslant h, \end{cases} \tag{8.8}$$

then $N_h = N_h^{(1)} + N_h^{(2)} + \cdots$ is the total number of times the system visits $(-h, h)$. Clearly, $U(h) = E(N_h)$, and Theorem 8.3 therefore implies that recurrent values exist if, and only if, on the average, the system visits any such interval an infinite number of times. Again, this corresponds to $\sum_1^\infty P_{jj}^{(n)} = \infty$ for j recurrent.

We shall now prove that for a positive integer m,

$$U(m) \leqslant 2mU(1), \tag{8.9}$$

where the inequality is taken to mean that $U(1) = \infty$ if $U(m) = \infty$. Let $T_v = \min \{n \,|\, v \leqslant S_n < v + 1\}$. Then we have, for $n \geqslant 1$,

$$\Pr \{v \leqslant S_n < v + 1\}$$

$$= \sum_{k=1}^n \int_v^{v+1} \Pr \{T_v = k, \quad y < S_k < y + dy, \quad v \leqslant S_n < v + 1\}$$

$$= \sum_{k=1}^n \int_v^{v+1} \Pr \{T_v = k, \quad y < S_k < y + dy\} \Pr \{v \leqslant y + S_{n-k} < v + 1\},$$

whence, by adding over $n = 1, 2, \ldots$, we obtain

$$\sum_{n=1}^\infty \Pr \{v \leqslant S_n < v + 1\} \leqslant \Pr \{T_v < \infty\} \sup_{v \leqslant y < v+1} \sum_{n=1}^\infty \Pr \{v \leqslant y + S_n < v + 1\}. \tag{8.10}$$

Now, since the interval $[v, v + 1)$ is contained in $(y - 1, y + 1)$ for $v \leqslant y < v + 1$, we have

$$\Pr \{v \leqslant y + S_n < v + 1\} \leqslant \Pr \{y - 1 < y + S_n < y + 1\} \tag{8.11}$$
$$= \Pr \{-1 < S_n < 1\}.$$

From (8.10) and (8.11) it follows that

$$\sum_{n=1}^\infty \Pr \{v \leqslant S_n < v + 1\} \leqslant \sum_{n=1}^\infty \Pr \{-1 < S_n < 1\} = U(1), \tag{8.12}$$

and hence

$$U(m) = \sum_{v=-m}^{m-1} \sum_{n=1}^\infty \Pr \{v \leqslant S_n < v + 1\} \leqslant 2mU(1),$$

as required.

THEOREM 8.4. *If $E|X_n| < \infty$, then recurrent values exist if, and only if, $E(X_n) = 0$.*

Proof:[7] If $E(X_n) = \mu \neq 0$, the strong law of large numbers gives

$$\Pr\left\{\lim_{n\to\infty}\frac{S_n}{n} = \mu\right\} = 1, \tag{8.13}$$

and hence (8.1) cannot be true, and recurrent values do not exist. On the other hand, if $E(X_n) = 0$, we shall prove that $U(1) = \infty$, so that by Theorem 8.3 recurrent values exist. If b is a positive integer, we have from (8.9),

$$U(1) \geqslant \frac{1}{2m}U(m) \geqslant \frac{1}{2m}\sum_{n=1}^{mb}\Pr\{|S_n| < m\}$$

$$\geqslant \frac{1}{2m}\sum_{n=1}^{mb}\Pr\{|S_n| < n/b\}.$$

However, since $E(X_n) = 0$, the weak law of large numbers gives

$$\lim_{n\to\infty}\Pr\left\{|S_n| < \frac{n}{b}\right\} = 1, \tag{8.14}$$

so that

$$U(1) \geqslant \liminf_{m\to\infty}\frac{1}{2m}\sum_{n=1}^{bm}1 = \frac{b}{2}. \tag{8.15}$$

Since b is arbitrary, this gives $U(1) = \infty$, as desired.

The above theorem has the following interesting interpretation. If $E(X_n) = \mu > 0$, then the strong law of large numbers (8.13) implies that $\Pr\{S_n < 0 \text{ i.o.}\} = 0$; while if $\mu < 0$, then $\Pr\{S_n > 0 \text{ i.o.}\} = 0$. Thus if $E(X_n) \neq 0$, then the system drifts to $+\infty$ or $-\infty$ according as $E(X_n) > 0$ or < 0. If, however, $E(X_n) = 0$, then

$$\Pr\{S_n > 0 \text{ i.o.}\} = \Pr\{S_n < 0 \text{ i.o.}\} = 1, \tag{8.16}$$

that is, the system "oscillates." For, ignoring the trivial case $\Pr\{X = 0\} = 1$ in which 0 is the only possible and recurrent value, we must have two values $a > 0$, $b < 0$ which are recurrent. Then for $\delta < \min\{a, -b\}$ we have

$$\Pr\{S_n > 0 \text{ i.o.}\} \geqslant \Pr\{|S_n - a| < \delta \text{ i.o.}\} = 1,$$

$$\Pr\{S_n < 0 \text{ i.o.}\} \geqslant \Pr\{|S_n - b| < \delta \text{ i.o.}\} = 1,$$

which lead to (8.16) [see Rosenblatt (1952)].

---

[7] This proof is due to Chung and Ornstein (1962).

8.2. A Problem in Sequential Analysis

An important problem arising in Wald's (1947) sequential analysis is concerned with the random variable $N = N(a, b)$, where

$$N = \min \{n \,|\, S_n \leqslant -b \quad \text{or} \quad S_n \geqslant a\} \quad (0 < a, b < \infty); \tag{8.17}$$

N is the first exit time from the interval $(-b, a)$. In what follows we ignore the trivial case where $\Pr \{X_n = 0\} = 1$.

THEOREM 8.5. *N is a "proper" random variable, with finite moments of all orders, that is,*

(i) $\Pr \{N < \infty\} = 1$ (8.18)

(ii) $E(N^k) < \infty$ $(k = 1, 2, \ldots)$.   (8.19)

Proof: (i) We shall show, more specifically, that there exist constants A and δ independent of n, such that $A > 0$, $0 < \delta < 1$ and

$$\Pr \{N \geqslant n\} \leqslant A\delta^n. \tag{8.20}$$

Let $c = a + b$, and r be an arbitrary positive integer. Let $S'_1 = X_1 + X_2 + \cdots + X_r$, $S'_2 = X_{r+1} + \cdots + X_{2r}, \ldots, S'_k = S_{(k-1)r+1} + \cdots + S_{kr}, \ldots$; we have then

$$\Pr \{N \geqslant kr\} \leqslant \Pr \{|S'_1| < c, |S'_2| < c, \ldots |S'_{k-1}| < c\} = p^{k-1},$$

where $p = \Pr \{|S'_k| < c\}$ is independent of k. Hence

$$\Pr \{N \geqslant n\} \leqslant p^{[n/r]-1} \leqslant p^{(n/r)-2} = p^{-2}(p^{1/r})^n, \tag{8.21}$$

which is of the form (8.20). It remains to prove that $0 < p < 1$. Obviously, $p > 0$; if $p = 1$, then $E(S'_k)^2 = rE(X_i^2) + r(r-1)[E(X_i)]^2$, which can be made to exceed c^2 with a proper choice of r, since $E(X_i^2) > 0$. It follows that $p < 1$.

(ii) For $t > 0$, and all k, we have $n^k < e^{tn}$ for sufficiently large n. Hence for large m,

$$\sum_{n=m}^{\infty} n^k \Pr \{N = n\} \leqslant \sum_{m}^{\infty} e^{tn} \Pr \{N \geqslant n\} \leqslant A \sum_{m}^{\infty} (\delta e^t)^n < \infty,$$

if we choose t so that $\delta e^t < 1$. Thus

$$E(N^k) = \sum_{1}^{\infty} n^k \Pr \{N = n\} < \infty.$$

THEOREM 8.6 (WALD'S EQUATION). *If $E|X_n| < \infty$, then*

$$E(S_N) = E(X_n)E(N). \tag{8.22}$$

Proof: We have

$$
\begin{aligned}
E(S_N) &= \sum_{n=1}^{\infty} E(S_N | N = n) \Pr\{N = n\} \\
&= \sum_{n=1}^{\infty} \sum_{i=1}^{n} \Pr\{N = n\} E(X_i | N = n) \\
&= \sum_{i=1}^{\infty} \sum_{n=i}^{\infty} \Pr\{N = n\} E(X_i | N = n) \\
&= \sum_{i=1}^{\infty} \Pr\{N \geqslant i\} E(X_i | N \geqslant i).
\end{aligned}
\tag{8.23}
$$

Now, since the event $\{N \geqslant i\}$ depends only on $X_1, X_2, \ldots, X_{i-1}$, we obtain

$$
E(S_N) = E(X_n) \sum_{i=1}^{\infty} \Pr\{N \geqslant i\} = E(X_n) E(N) < \infty. \tag{8.24}
$$

The interchange of the order of summation in (8.23) is justified, since

$$
\left| \sum_{i=1}^{\infty} \sum_{n=i}^{\infty} E(X_i | N = n) \Pr\{N = n\} \right| \leqslant \sum_{i=1}^{\infty} \sum_{n=i}^{\infty} E(|X_i| | N = n) \Pr\{N = n\}
$$

$$
= E|X_i| E(N) < \infty.
$$

Wald's Fundamental Identity. Let

$$
\begin{aligned}
K_n(x) &= \Pr\{S_n \leqslant x\} \qquad (n = 1, 2, \ldots) \\
K_1(x) &= K(x) = \Pr\{X_n \leqslant x\}.
\end{aligned}
\tag{8.25}
$$

The moment generating function (m.g.f.)

$$
\phi(\theta) = \int_{-\infty}^{\infty} e^{\theta x}\, dK(x) \tag{8.26}
$$

exists if, and only if, $\phi(\sigma) < \infty$, where $\sigma = Re(\theta)$. We shall assume that $\phi(\sigma) < \infty$ in a real interval surrounding the origin, say $\beta < \sigma < \alpha$, where $-\infty \leqslant \beta < 0 < \alpha \leqslant \infty$. Under certain conditions (as, for instance, in Wald's lemma, see Complement 31) there is a unique real value θ_0 in $\beta < \sigma < \alpha$ such that $\phi(\theta)$ has a minimum at $\theta = \theta_0$.

The so-called fundamental identity of Wald is the following:

$$
E\{e^{\theta S_N} [\phi(\theta)]^{-N}\} = 1, \tag{8.27}
$$

valid in the region where $\phi(\theta)$ exists, and $|\phi(\theta)| \geqslant 1$; we shall deduce this from the more general identity (8.31) due to Miller (1961) and Kemperman (1961). For this we define

$$
F_0(x) = 1 \qquad \text{for } x < 0, \quad = 1 \qquad \text{for } x \geqslant 0
$$

$$
\begin{aligned}
F_n(x) &= \Pr\{S_n \leqslant x; N \geqslant n\} \\
&= \Pr\{-b < S_k < a \quad (k = 1, 2, \ldots, n-1); \quad S_n \leqslant x\} \quad (n \geqslant 1);
\end{aligned}
\tag{8.28}
$$

$F_n(x)$ is the d.f. of S_n conditional on an exit from $(-b, a)$ not having occurred up to the time $n - 1$. The series

$$F(z, \theta) = \sum_{n=0}^{\infty} z^n \int_{-b}^{a} e^{\theta x} \, dF_n(x) \tag{8.29}$$

converges for all finite θ and $|z| < [\phi(\theta_0)]^{-1}$, since

$$\left| z^n \int_{-b}^{a} e^{\theta x} \, dF_n(x) \right| \leq |z|^n \int_{-b}^{a} \exp\left[x(\sigma - \theta_0) + \theta_0 x\right] dK_n(x)$$

$$\leq \begin{cases} |z|^n e^{a(\sigma - \theta_0)}[\phi(\theta_0)]^n & \text{if } \sigma \geq \theta_0 \\ |z|^n e^{-b(\sigma - \theta_0)}[\phi(\theta_0)]^n & \text{if } \sigma \leq \theta_0. \end{cases} \tag{8.30}$$

THEOREM 8.7 (A GENERALIZATION OF WALD'S IDENTITY). *We have*

$$E(e^{\theta S_N} z^N) = 1 + [z\phi(\theta) - 1]F(z, \theta), \tag{8.31}$$

valid for all θ for which $\phi(\theta)$ exists and for $|z| < [\phi(\theta_0)]^{-1}$.

Proof: We have

$$E(e^{\theta S_N} z^N) = \sum_{n=1}^{\infty} z^n \left(\int_{-\infty}^{-b} + \int_{a}^{\infty} \right) e^{\theta x} \, dF_n(x)$$

$$= \sum_{n=1}^{\infty} z^n \left(\int_{-\infty}^{\infty} - \int_{-b}^{a} \right) e^{\theta x} \, dF_n(x) \tag{8.32}$$

$$= \sum_{n=1}^{\infty} z^n \int_{-\infty}^{\infty} e^{\theta x} \, dF_n(x) - [F(z, \theta) - 1],$$

where the series on the right-hand side converges absolutely for all θ for which $\beta < \sigma < \alpha$ and for $|z| < [\phi(\sigma)]^{-1}$, since

$$\left| z^n \int_{-\infty}^{\infty} e^{\theta x} \, dF_n(x) \right| \leq |z|^n \int_{-\infty}^{\infty} e^{\sigma x} \, dF_n(x) = |z|^n [\phi(\sigma)]^n.$$

Now we have

$$F_n(x) = \int_{-b}^{a} K(x - y) \, dF_{n-1}(y) \qquad (n \geq 1), \tag{8.33}$$

whence

$$\int_{-\infty}^{\infty} e^{\theta x} \, dF_n(x) = \int_{-\infty}^{\infty} e^{\theta x} \, dK(x) \int_{-b}^{a} e^{\theta y} \, dF_{n-1}(y)$$

$$= \phi(\theta) \int_{-b}^{a} e^{\theta y} \, dF_{n-1}(y).$$

Hence

$$E(e^{\theta S_N} z^N) = \sum_{n=1}^{\infty} z^n \phi(\theta) \int_{-b}^{a} e^{\theta y}\, dF_{n-1}(y) - F(z, \theta) + 1$$

$$= 1 + [z\phi(\theta) - 1]F(z, \theta),$$

which proves (8.31). As regards the region of validity, we note that $E(e^{\theta S_N} z^N) < \infty$ for all θ for which $\beta < \sigma < \alpha$ and for $|z| < [\phi(\sigma)]^{-1}$, while $F(z, \theta)$ is an entire function of θ, and a regular function of z for $|z| < [\phi(\theta_0)]^{-1}$. Thus the right-hand side of (8.31) may be taken to define the left-hand side for $|z| < [\phi(\theta_0)]^{-1}$ and for those values of θ for which $\phi(\theta)$ exists.

COROLLARY. *Wald's identity* (8.27) *holds, provided that* $|\phi(\theta)| > \phi(\theta_0)$ *and* $\beta < \sigma < \alpha$.

Proof: In the identity (8.31) set $z = [\phi(\theta)]^{-1}$, and note that $\beta < \sigma < \alpha$ and $|\phi(\theta)| > \phi(\theta_0)$,

$$E\{e^{\theta S_N}[\phi(\theta)]^{-N}\} = 1 + \lim_{z \to [\phi(\theta)]^{-1}} [z\phi(\theta) - 1]F(z, \theta).$$

The Case of a Single Barrier. When either a or b tends to ∞ we have a single barrier. We consider the case where $a = \infty$, $b < \infty$, and

$$N \equiv N(b) = \min\{n\,|\,S_n \leqslant -b\}. \tag{8.34}$$

Obviously, Theorem 8.5 does not apply to this case, and we therefore have $\Pr\{N < \infty\} \leqslant 1$ (see Theorem 8.8 below). However, Theorem 8.7 remains valid, each side of the identity (8.31) being regarded as analytic continuation of the other beyond the common range of validity.

THEOREM 8.8. *If* $E|X_n| < \infty$, *then*

$$\Pr\{N(b) < \infty\} \begin{cases} = 1 & \text{if } E(X_n) \leqslant 0 \\ < 1 & \text{if } E(X_n) > 0. \end{cases} \tag{8.35}$$

Proof: If $E(X_n) \neq 0$, then the strong law of large numbers implies the desired result. If $E(X_n) = 0$, then by Theorem 8.4 the values of S_n are all recurrent and (8.35) follows (cf. remarks at the end of the proof of Theorem 8.4).

9. COMPLEMENTS AND PROBLEMS
Section 2

1. Prove that $g_{ij} = f_{ij}$ or 0 according as j is persistent or transient.

2. Use (2.9) to prove that the series $\sum_0^{\infty} P_{ij}^{(n)} < \infty$ or $= \infty$ according as $g_{ij} = 0$ or > 0.

3. Let N_{ij} be the number of times the system enters the state j from the initial state i; in particular, N_{ii} is the number of returns to i. Show that for a transient state i,

$$\Pr\{N_{ii} = r\} = (1 - f_{ii})(f_{ii})^r \qquad (r = 0, 1, \ldots) \tag{9.1}$$

$$E(N_{ii}) = \sum_1^\infty P_{ii}^{(n)} < \infty. \tag{9.2}$$

4. Show that $(x_i = f_{i0}, i = 1, 2, \ldots)$ is the minimal nonnegative solution of the equations

$$x_i = P_{i0} + \sum_{j=1}^\infty P_{ij} x_j \qquad (i = 1, 2, \ldots). \tag{9.3}$$

[We have

$$f_{i0}^{(1)} = P_{i0}, \quad f_{i0}^{(n+1)} = \sum_1^\infty P_{ij} f_{j0}^{(n)} \qquad (n > 1);$$

adding these equations we find that the sums

$$\sum_1^\infty f_{i0}^{(n)} = f_{i0} \qquad (i = 1, 2, \ldots)$$

satisfy (9.3). To prove the minimal property, let $(x_1, x_2, \ldots)$ be any arbitrary nonnegative solution of (9.3). Then we have

$$x_i \geqslant P_{i0} = f_{i0}^{(1)}$$

$$x_i \geqslant P_{i0} + \sum_1^\infty P_{ij} f_{j0}^{(1)} = f_{i0}^{(1)} + f_{i0}^{(2)},$$

and by induction $x_i \geqslant f_{i0}^{(1)} + f_{i0}^{(2)} + \cdots + f_{i0}^{(n)}$ $(n \geqslant 1)$. In the limit as $n \to \infty$, $x_i \geqslant f_{i0}$.]

5. Proceeding as in (2.9), and considering last exit times, prove that if $j \to i$,

$$\lim_{N \to \infty} \frac{\sum\limits_0^N P_{ij}^{(n)}}{\sum\limits_0^N P_{ii}^{(n)}} = {}^iP_{ij}^* < \infty \qquad (j \neq i). \tag{9.4}$$

6. If i is persistent, we have seen that the series $\sum\limits_0^\infty P_{ii}^{(n)}$ diverges. However, one might be interested in the limit

$$\lim_{N \to \infty} \frac{\sum\limits_0^N P_{ii}^{(n)}}{\sum\limits_0^N P_{jj}^{(n)}} \tag{9.5}$$

for two persistent states i, j. Show that for any two states i, j, this limit is equal to

$$\frac{1 + {}^{j}P_{ii}^{*}}{1 + {}^{i}P_{jj}^{*}} \tag{9.6}$$

[see Chung (1960)].

Section 3

7. Show that for every pair i, j of states, the limits

$$\Pi_{ij} = \lim_{N \to \infty} \frac{1}{N} \sum_{1}^{N} P_{ij}^{(n)} \tag{9.7}$$

exist, and satisfy the equations $\sum_{j} \Pi_{ij} \leqslant 1$, and

$$\Pi_{ij} = \sum_{k} \Pi_{ik}\Pi_{kj} = \sum_{k} P_{ik}\Pi_{kj} = \sum_{k} \Pi_{ik}P_{kj}. \tag{9.8}$$

Section 4

8. Prove that for any i, f_{ij} has the same value (say x_i) for all $j \in C_k$, and therefore $P_{ij}^{(n)} \to x_i/\mu_j$ as $n \to \infty$.

9. *Absorption in a Closed Set.* Let D be the set of all transient states, and C a closed set of persistent states. As a generalization of the first entrance times T_{ij}, let us define

$$T_i(C) = \min \{n \,|\, X_n \in C \,|\, X_0 = i\}, \quad i \in D. \tag{9.9}$$

Prove that the probabilities

$$x_i = \Pr \{T_i(C) < \infty\} \tag{9.10}$$

satisfy the system of equations

$$x_i = \sum_{v \in C} P_{iv} + \sum_{j \in D} P_{ij}x_j \quad (i \in D). \tag{9.11}$$

10. Let $y_i^{(n)} = \Pr \{X_n \in D \,|\, X_0 = i\}$ $(i \in D, n = 1, 2, \ldots)$. Show that the limits $y_i = \lim_{n \to \infty} y_i^{(n)}$ exist, and satisfy the system of equations

$$y_i = \sum_{j \in D} P_{ij}y_j \quad (i \in D). \tag{9.12}$$

11. If D contains only a finite number of states, show that the system (9.12) admits of no solution, and consequently (9.11) has a unique solution. [For problems 9–11, see Feller (1957), pp. 362–364.]

12. *Doubly Stochastic Matrices.* If, in addition to the property $\sum_{j} P_{ij} = 1$, we have $\sum_{i} P_{ij} = 1$, then the matrix P is said to be doubly stochastic. Show that a finite chain with a doubly stochastic matrix has no transient states; if it is irreducible and aperiodic, then $P_{ij}^{(n)} \to N^{-1}$, where N is the number of states. On the other hand, if an irreducible infinite chain has a doubly stochastic matrix, then its states are either null or transient.

[Letting $n \to \infty$ in $\sum_{i=1}^{N} P_{ij}^{(n)} = 1$, we obtain $1 = \sum_{1}^{N} \lim P_{ij}^{(n)}$, so that for a given j, $\lim P_{ij}^{(n)}$ cannot be zero for all i. Thus a finite chain has no transient states (by Theorem 5.2 it has no null states). Moreover, in the irreducible aperiodic case this gives $\lim P_{ij}^{(n)} = N^{-1}$. In the case of an infinite irreducible chain, if the states are all persistent nonnull, we would have for arbitrary N,

$$1 \geqslant \sum_{1}^{N} \lim P_{ij}^{(n)} \to N u_j, \tag{9.13}$$

which gives $u_j = 0$, a contradiction.]

Section 5

13. *Inverse Probabilities.* Consider a homogeneous Markov chain with the absolute distribution $\{a_j^{(n)}\}$, where $a_j^{(n)} > 0$. Let

$$Q_{ji}(n, m) = \Pr \{X_m = i \,|\, X_n = j\} \qquad (n > m)$$

$$= \frac{\Pr \{X_m = i, X_n = j\}}{\Pr \{X_n = j\}} = \frac{a_i^{(m)} P_{ij}^{(n-m)}}{a_j^{(n)}}. \tag{9.14}$$

Prove that $Q_{ji}(n, m)$ determine the transition probabilities of a Markov chain.

14. If the original Markov chain is irreducible, with a stationary distribution $\{u_j\}$, then

$$Q_{ji}(n, m) = \frac{u_i}{u_j} P_{ij}^{(n-m)} \qquad (n > m), \tag{9.15}$$

so that the derived chain is homogeneous.

15. *Stationary Measure.* If the sequence $\{v_j\}$ is such that $v_j > 0$ and $v_j = \sum_{i=0}^{\infty} v_i P_{ij} (j \geqslant 0)$, then $\{v_j\}$ is called a stationary measure. Note that Σv_j may diverge, so that such a measure is more general than a stationary distribution. Show that if the states of an irreducible Markov chain are persistent, then there is a unique stationary measure $\{v_j\}$ given by

$$v_0 = 1, \quad v_j = {}^0P_{0j}^* < \infty \qquad (j = 1, 2, \ldots). \tag{9.16}$$

[Derman (1954)].

Section 6

16. *Classical Random Walk in Two and Three Dimensions.* Proceeding as in Section 6.1 show that in the symmetric random walk in two dimensions the particle eventually returns to its initial position with probability one, while in three dimensions there is a positive probability that it does not do so (Polya).

17. *A Nonhomogeneous Random Walk.* Let

$$P_{00} = q_0, \qquad P_{01} = p_0$$

$$P_{i,i-1} = q_i, \; P_{i,i+1} = p_i \qquad (i = 1, 2, \ldots), \tag{9.17}$$

where $p_i = 1 - q_i$ $(i \geqslant 1)$. Further, let $L_i = (q_1 q_2 \cdots q_i)(p_1 p_2 \cdots p_i)^{-1}$ $(i \geqslant 1)$. Show that the states are (i) transient if the series $\Sigma L_i < \infty$, (ii) persistent null if $\Sigma L_i = \infty$, $\Sigma (P_i L_i)^{-1} = \infty$, and (iii) persistent nonnull if $\Sigma L_i = \infty$, $\Sigma (P_i L_i)^{-1} < \infty$. Find the stationary distribution in the last case.

18. If $P_{i0} = q_i$, $P_{ii+1} = p_i = 1 - q_i$ $(i = 0, 1, \ldots)$, show that $f_{00}^{(n)} = Q_{n-1} - Q_n$, where

$$Q_0 = 1, \qquad Q_n = (1 - q_0)(1 - q_1) \cdots (1 - q_{n-1}) \qquad (n \geqslant 1), \tag{9.18}$$

and also that $^0 P_{0j}^{(n)} = Q_j$ $(n = j)$, $= 0$ $(n \neq j)$. Hence or otherwise show that the states are (i) transient if $\Sigma q_i < \infty$, (ii) persistent null if $\Sigma q_i = \infty$, $\Sigma Q_n = \infty$, and (iii) persistent nonnull if $\Sigma q_i = \infty$, $0 < \mu = \Sigma Q_n < \infty$. In the last case the stationary distribution is given by $u_j = Q_j \mu^{-1}$ $(j \geqslant 0)$.

19. Let $P_{0j} = a_j$ $(j \geqslant 0)$, $P_{i,i-1} = 1$ $(i \geqslant 1)$. Show that all states are persistent, null, or nonnull according as $\mu = \Sigma n a_n = \infty$ or $< \infty$. In the latter case the stationary distribution is given by $u_j = \mu^{-1}(a_j + a_{j+1} + \cdots)$ $(j \geqslant 0)$.

20. Show that for a branching process, we have the Chapman–Kolmogorov equations

$$F_{m+n}(z) = F_m[F_n(z)] \qquad (m, n \geqslant 1). \tag{9.19}$$

21. Show that if the number of direct descendants has a geometric distribution (possibly with a modified initial term), so has the number of individuals in any generation.

22. If each individual produces at most one successor, so that $k_0 > 0$, $k_1 = 1 - k_0 > 0$, $k_j = 0$ $(j > 1)$, then show that (i) $\zeta_n = \Pr\{X_n = 0 \mid X_0 = 1\} = 1 - k_1^n$ $(n \geqslant 1)$, and (ii) $g_j = k_0 k_1^{j-1}$ $(j \geqslant 1)$.

23. If the number of direct descendants has the Poisson distribution $k_j = e^{-\lambda}\lambda^j/j!$ $(j = 0, 1, \ldots)$, show that $g_j = e^{-j\lambda}(j\lambda)^{j-1}/j!$ $(j = 1, 2, \ldots)$. For large j, $g_j \sim (2\pi)^{-\frac{1}{2}} e^{j(1-\lambda)}\lambda^{j-1}j^{-\frac{3}{2}}$. Moreover, if $\lambda > 1$, the probability of ultimate extinction is $\zeta \sim 1 - 2(\lambda - 1)\lambda^{-2}$ [Otter (1949)].

24. Prove Theorem 6.1 by using the result in Complement 4.

[The probabilities $f_{i0} = \Pr\{N < \infty \mid X_0 = i\}$ $(i \geqslant 1)$ are the minimal nonnegative solution of the equations (9.3).]

25. Let $Z_n = X_0 + X_1 + \cdots + X_n$ $(n = 0, 1, 2, \ldots)$ be the total number of individuals in the first n generations of a branching process, with $X_0 = 1$. Show that the p.g.f. $G_n(z)$ of Z_n satisfies the recurrence relations

$$G_1(z) = zK(z), \quad G_{n+1}(z) = zK[G_n(z)] \qquad (n \geqslant 1). \tag{9.20}$$

[Good (1948).]

26. *Extension of Lemma 6.1.* If the p.g.f. $K(z) = k_0 + k_1 z + k_2 z^2 + \cdots$ converges for all $z \geqslant 0$, and if $K(z)/z \to \infty$ as $z \to \infty$, then lemma 6.1 can be extended as follows: Apart from the obvious root $z = 1$, the equation $K(z) = z$ has a second root ζ such that $0 < \zeta < 1$ if $\alpha > 1$, and $1 < \zeta < \infty$ if $\alpha < 1$. These two roots coincide, that is, $\zeta = 1$ if, and only if, $\alpha = 1$. Here $\alpha = K'(1)$, and it is assumed that $0 < \alpha < \infty$.

27. For the Markov chain of example 6.3, show that

$$\sum_{n=0}^{\infty} \sum_{j=0}^{\infty} P_{ij}^{(n)} \theta^n z^j = \frac{z^{i+1}(1 - \xi) - \theta K(z)(1 - z)\xi^i}{(1 - \xi)[z - \theta K(z)]} \tag{9.21}$$

$(|\theta| < 1, |z| \leqslant 1)$, where $\xi = \xi(\theta)$ is the root of the functional equation $z = \theta K(z)$ such that $0 < \xi \leqslant 1$ for $0 < z \leqslant 1$.

28. For the Markov chain of example 6.4, show that

$$\sum_{n=0}^{\infty} \sum_{i=0}^{\infty} P_{ij}^{(n)} \theta^n z^i = \frac{(1 - \theta)(1 - z)z^{j+1} + \theta[z - K(z)]\xi^j(1 - \xi)}{(1 - \theta)(1 - z)[z - \theta K(z)]} \tag{9.22}$$

$(|\theta| < 1, |z| < 1)$, ξ being the same as in problem 27.

29. For the Markov chain with the transition probability matrix

↗	0	1	2	3	.	.	.
0	k_0	k_1	k_2	k_3	.	.	.
1	k_0	k_1	k_2	k_3	.	.	.
.	.	.	.	.	.	.	.
.	.	.	.	.	.	.	.
s	k_0	k_1	k_2	k_3	.	.	.
$s + 1$	0	k_0	k_1	k_2	.	.	.
$s + 2$	0	0	k_0	k_1	.	.	.
.	.	.	.	.	.	.	.

$$P \equiv \qquad \tag{9.23}$$

the notation being the same as in example 6.3, show that the states are ergodic if and only if $\rho \leqslant s$, and the stationary distribution is given by

$$U(z) = \frac{\sum\limits_{i=0}^{s-1} u_i(z^s - z^i)}{z^s - K(z)} K(z), \tag{9.24}$$

where the unknown quantities $u_0, u_1, \ldots, u_{s-1}$ can be determined uniquely under certain conditions [Bailey (1954)].

Section 7

30. *Proof of (7.11).*

$$\sum_{n=0}^{\infty} e^{-\mu(x+na)} \frac{\mu^n}{n!} (x+na)^n = \begin{cases} (1 - \mu a)^{-1} & \text{if } \mu a < 1. \\ e^{-\mu x(1-\zeta)}(1 - \mu a \zeta)^{-1} & \text{if } \mu a > 1. \end{cases} \tag{9.25}$$

The case $\mu a > 1$ corresponds to Jensen's formula, valid for complex values of μ, a such that $|e^{-(\mu a - 1)} \mu a| < 1$.

The left-hand side of (9.25) is the constant term in the expansion of

$$f(z) = \sum_{n=0}^{\infty} \exp\left[-\mu(x+na) + \mu z(x+na)\right] z^{-n}$$

$$= \exp\left[-\mu x(1-z)\right] \sum_{n=0}^{\infty} \left[\frac{e^{-\mu a(1-z)}}{z}\right]^n$$

$$= \exp\left[-\mu x(1-z)\right] \sum_{n=0}^{\infty} \left[\frac{K(z)}{z}\right]^n,$$

where $K(z) = e^{-\mu a(1-z)}$ is the p.g.f. of the Poisson distribution with mean μa. Obviously, $K(z)$ satisfies the conditions of problem 26, so that the equation $K(z) = z$ has a root ζ such that $0 < \zeta < 1$ if $\mu a > 1$ and $1 < \zeta < \infty$ if $\mu a < 1$. Considering the second case, let α_1, α_2 be two real numbers such that $1 < \alpha_1 < \zeta_1$, and $K(\alpha_1) < K(\alpha_2) < \alpha_1$ [which is possible since $K(z)$ is continuous in z]; then in the annulus $\alpha_1 < |z| < \alpha_2$, we have $|K(z)| < K(\alpha_2) < \alpha_1 < |z|$, so that $|K(z)/z| < 1$ and

$$f(z) = \frac{ze^{-\mu x(1-z)}}{z - K(z)} \qquad (\alpha_1 < |z| < \alpha_2). \tag{9.26}$$

The constant term in $f(z)$ is given by

$$\frac{1}{2\pi i} \int_{|z| \leqslant \alpha_1} \frac{f(z)}{z} dz = \frac{1}{2\pi i} \int_{|z| \leqslant \alpha_1} \frac{e^{-\mu x(1-z)}}{z - K(z)} dz. \tag{9.27}$$

Since $|K(z)| < |z|$ for $|z| = \alpha_1$, by Rouche's Theorem, $z = 1$ is the only pole of the integrand in (9.27) within the circle $|z| \leqslant \alpha_1$ and the integral has therefore the value

$$\lim_{z \to 1} (z-1)\frac{e^{-\mu x(1-z)}}{z - K(z)} = (1 - \mu a)^{-1}. \tag{9.28}$$

For $\mu a > 1$, we have $0 < \zeta < 1$ and proceeding as above, we find that $f(z)$ is given by (9.26) for $\alpha_1 < |z| < \alpha_2$, where $\zeta < \alpha_1 < 1$ and $K(\alpha_1) < K(\alpha_2) < \alpha_1$. Thus the constant term in $f(z)$ is given by

$$\lim_{z \to \zeta} (z - \zeta)\frac{e^{-\mu x(1-z)}}{z - K(z)} = \frac{e^{-\mu x(1-\zeta)}}{1 - \mu a \zeta}. \tag{9.29}$$

Section 8

31. *Wald's Lemma.* Let X be a random variable such that (a) $E(X)$ exists and $\neq 0$, (b) the m.g.f. $\phi(\theta) = E(e^{\theta X}) < \infty$ for all real θ, and (c) there exists a $\delta > 0$ such that $\Pr \{e^X < 1 - \delta\} > 0$ and $\Pr \{e^X > 1 + \delta\} > 0$. Then the equation $\phi(\theta) = 1$ has a unique root $\theta_0 \neq 0$.

32. Putting $\theta = \theta_0$ in Wald's identity we obtain

$$E(e^{\theta_0 S_N}) = 1. \tag{9.30}$$

Let

$$E_0 = E(e^{\theta_0 S_N}|S_N \leqslant -b), \qquad E_1 = E(e^{\theta_0 S_N}|S_N \geqslant a) \tag{9.31}$$

be the conditional expected values of $e^{\theta_0 S_N}$ under the restrictions $S_N \leqslant -b$ and $S_N \geqslant a$ respectively. Using (9.30) prove that

$$\Pr \{S_N \leqslant -b\} = \frac{E_1 - 1}{E_1 - E_0}. \tag{9.32}$$

33. If $\phi(\theta)$ exists for all real values of θ, prove that Wald's identity (8.27) can be differentiated under the expectation sign any number of times with respect to θ at any value θ in the domain $|\phi(\theta)| \geqslant 1$. Differentiating (8.27) once and putting $\theta = 0$, we obtain $E(S_N) = E(X_n)E(N)$ as in Theorem 8.6; hence

$$E(N) = \frac{E(S_N)}{E(X_n)} \qquad \text{if } E(X_n) \neq 0. \tag{9.33}$$

If $E(X_n) = 0$, a second differentiation of (8.27) gives

$$E(N) = \frac{E(S_N^2)}{E(X_n^2)}. \tag{9.34}$$

34. Consider the classical gambler's ruin problem where two players A and B with capitals a and b play a series of games for unit stakes, with probabilities p and q of winning each game, the series being continued until one of them is ruined. Let X_n be A's gain in the nth game, so that $a + S_n$ is his capital at the end of the nth game, and the number of games played is given by

$$N = \min \{n \mid a + S_n = 0 \quad \text{or} \quad a + S_n = a + b\}$$
$$= \min \{n \mid S_n = -a \quad \text{or} \quad S_n = b\}. \tag{9.35}$$

Using (9.32) and (9.33) prove that the probability of A's ruin is given by

$$\Pr \{S_N = -a\} = \begin{cases} \dfrac{1 - (p/q)^b}{1 - (p/q)^{a+b}} & \text{if } p \neq q \\[3mm] \dfrac{a}{a + b} & \text{if } p = q = \frac{1}{2}, \end{cases} \tag{9.36}$$

and the expected duration of the game by

$$E(N) = \begin{cases} \dfrac{b}{p - q} - \dfrac{a + b}{p - q} \dfrac{1 - (p/q)^b}{1 - (p/q)^{a+b}} & \text{if } p \neq q \\[3mm] ab & \text{if } p = q = \frac{1}{2}. \end{cases} \tag{9.37}$$

35. *Walter Bartky's Multiple Sampling Scheme.* In this scheme, an initial sample of M_0 units is examined; if the number X_0 of defectives in this sample is such that $X_0 \leqslant c$, the lot is accepted and if $X_0 \geqslant c + a$, the lot is rejected. But if $c < X_0 < c + a$, additional samples of size M are examined according to the following procedure. Let X_n be the number of defectives in the nth additional sample, and $S_n = X_1 + X_2 + \cdots + X_n$. Then if $X_0 + S_n = c + n$ the lot is accepted, and if $X_0 + S_n \geqslant c + n + a$ it is rejected, while if $c + n < X_0 + S_n < c + n + a$, an additional sample is examined ($n = 1, 2, \ldots$). Clearly, additional samples will be required if, and only if, $X_0 = c + i$ ($i = 1, 2, \ldots, a - 1$), and the number of additional samples required is given by

$$N = \min \{n \mid X_0 + S_n = c + n \quad \text{or } X_0 + S_n \geqslant c + n + a\}$$
$$= \min \{n \mid S_n' = -i \quad \text{or } S_n' \geqslant a - i\} \tag{9.38}$$

if $X_0 = c + i$ and $S_n' = S_n - n$. If p is the fraction defective in an infinite lot and $q = 1 - p$, show that the probability of eventually accepting the lot is

$$\Pi = \sum_{m \leqslant c} \binom{N_0}{m} p^m q^{N_0 - m} + \frac{h_a}{g_a} \tag{9.39}$$

and the expected number of additional samples is

$$E = \frac{h_a}{g_a} (g_1 + g_2 + \cdots + g_{a-1}) - (h_1 + h_2 + \cdots + h_{a-1}), \tag{9.40}$$

where $g_1, g_2, \ldots$ and $h_1, h_2, \ldots$ are functions of p, and are defined by the following:

$$\frac{1}{K(x) - x} = g_1 + g_2 x + g_3 x^2 + \ldots,$$

$$\frac{\sum_{i=1}^{a-1} \binom{M_0}{c+1} p^{c+i} q^{M_0 - c - i} x^i}{K(x) - x} = h_1 + h_2 x + h_3 x^2 + \ldots, \qquad (9.41)$$

$$K(x) = (q + px)^M.$$

[Walter Bartky (1943).]

36. Let $\Pr\{X_n = j\} = k_j$ $(j = 0, 1, \ldots)$ and $K(z) = \sum_{j=0}^{\infty} k_j z^j$. Show that if $N = \min\{n \mid i + S_n \leqslant n\}$, then the p.g.f. of N is given by ξ^i, where ξ is the root of the functional equation $\xi = zK(\xi)$ such that $0 < \xi \leqslant 1$ for $0 < z \leqslant 1$.

37. Let $\Pr\{X_n = j\} = k_j > 0 (-r \leqslant j \leqslant s)$, $M(z) = \sum_{-r}^{s} k_j z^j$, and $N = \min\{n \mid S_n \geqslant a\}$ where a is a positive integer. Show that

$$\Pr\{N < \infty\} = \sum_{k=1}^{s} \zeta_k^{-a} \prod_{j \neq k} \left(\frac{1 - \zeta_j}{\zeta_k - \zeta_j} \right), \qquad (9.42)$$

where $\zeta_1, \zeta_2, \ldots, \zeta_s$ are the roots of the equation $M(z) = 1$ such that $|\zeta_k| \geqslant |\zeta_1|$ $(k = 1, 2, \ldots, s)$.

38. Let the d.f. of X_n be such that

$$dK(x) = ce^{\mu x} \, dx \; (x < 0), \qquad (9.43)$$

where $c > 0$, $\mu > 0$, and let $N = \min\{n \mid u + S_n \leqslant 0\}$. Show that

$$E(z^N) = \frac{1}{\mu}(\mu + \xi)e^{\xi u}, \qquad (9.44)$$

where $\xi = \xi(z)$ is the unique root of $z\phi(\theta) = 1$, with $Re(\xi) < 0$, $\phi(\theta)$ being the m.g.f. of X_n [Kemperman, (1961)].

10. REFERENCES

Bailey, Norman T. J. ON QUEUING PROCESSES WITH BULK SERVICE. *J. Roy. Stat. Soc.*, B **16** (1954), pp. 80–87.

Bartky, Walter. MULTIPLE SAMPLING WITH CONSTANT PROBABILITY. *Ann. Math. Statist.*, **14** (1943), pp. 363–377.

Chung, K. L. MARKOV CHAINS WITH STATIONARY TRANSITION PROBABILITIES. Berlin: Springer, 1960.

———, and Fuchs, W. H. J. ON THE DISTRIBUTION OF VALUES OF SUMS OF RANDOM VARIABLES. *Mem. Amer. Math. Soc.,* **6** (1951), pp. 1–12.

———, and Ornstein, Donald. ON THE RECURRENCE OF SUMS OF RANDOM VARIABLES. *Bull. Amer. Math. Soc.,* **68** (1962), pp. 30–32.

Derman, C. A SOLUTION TO A SET OF FUNDAMENTAL EQUATIONS IN MARKOV CHAINS. *Proc. Amer. Math. Soc.,* **5** (1954), pp. 332–334.

Doeblin, W. SUR DEUX PROBLÈMES DE M. KOLMOGOROFF CONCERNANT LES CHAINES DÉNOMBRABLES. *Bull. Soc. Math. de France,* **66** (1939), pp. 1–11.

Doob, J. L. STOCHASTIC PROCESSES. New York: Wiley, 1953.

Feller, W. AN INTRODUCTION TO PROBABILITY THEORY AND ITS APPLICATIONS. 2nd ed. New York: Wiley, 1957.

Foster, F. G. ON THE STOCHASTIC MATRICES ASSOCIATED WITH CERTAIN QUEUING PROCESSES. *Ann. Math. Statist.,* **24** (1953), pp. 355–360.

Fréchet, M. RECHERCHES THÉORIQUES MODERNES SUR LE CALCUL DES PROBABILITÉS. Vol. 2. Paris: Gauthier-Villars, 1938.

Good, I. J. THE NUMBER OF INDIVIDUALS IN A CASCADE PROCESS. *Proc. Cam. Phil. Soc.,* **45** (1948), pp. 360–363.

Harris, T. E. THE THEORY OF BRANCHING PROCESSES. Berlin: Springer, 1963.

Hostinsky, B. MÉTHODES GÉNÉRALES DU CALCUL DE PROBABILITÉS. Paris: Gauthier-Villars, 1931.

Kemeny, J. G. and Snell, J. L. FINITE MARKOV CHAINS. New York: Van Nostrand, 1960.

Kemperman, J. H. B. THE PASSAGE PROBLEM FOR A STATIONARY MARKOV CHAIN. Chicago: University of Chicago Press, 1961.

Kendall, David G. SOME PROBLEMS IN THE THEORY OF QUEUES. *J. Roy. Stat. Soc.,* **B 13** (1951), pp. 151–185.

Kolmogorov, A. ANFANGSGRÜNDE DER THEORIE DER MARKOFFSCHEN KETTEN MIT UNENDLICH VIELEN MÖGLICHEN ZUSTÄNDEN. *Math. Sbornik, N.S.,* **1** (1936), pp. 607–610.

Lindley, D. V. THE THEORY OF QUEUES WITH A SINGLE SERVER. *Proc. Cam. Phil. Soc.,* **48** (1952), pp. 277–289.

Miller, H. D. A GENERALIZATION OF WALD'S IDENTITY WITH APPLICATIONS TO RANDOM WALKS. *Ann. Math. Statist.,* **32** (1961), pp. 549–560.

Otter, Richard. THE MULTIPLICATIVE PROCESS. *Ann. Math. Statist.,* **20** (1949), pp. 206–224.

Prabhu, N. U. QUEUES AND INVENTORIES. New York: Wiley, 1965.

Romanovsky, V. I. DISCRETE MARKOV CHAINS (in Russian). Moscow: Gostekhizdat, 1949.

Rosenblatt, M. ON THE OSCILLATION OF SUMS OF RANDOM VARIABLES. *Trans. Amer. Math. Soc.,* **72** (1952), pp. 165–178.

Spitzer, Frank. PRINCIPLES OF RANDOM WALK. New York: Van Nostrand, 1964.

Wald, Abraham. SEQUENTIAL ANALYSIS. New York: Wiley, 1947.

CHAPTER **3**

Diffusion Processes

1. INTRODUCTION

The stochastic process $X(t)$ $(t \geqslant 0)$ is said to be a Markov process if, for every finite set of values, $t_1 < t_2 < \cdots < t_r < t$ $(r \geqslant 1)$ we have

$$\Pr\{X(t)|X(t_1), X(t_2), \ldots, X(t_r)\} = \Pr\{X(t)|X(t_r)\}. \qquad (1.1)$$

Let the possible values (or the states) of $X(t)$ belong to the real line $(-\infty < x < \infty)$, and let

$$F(x_0, \tau; x, t) = \Pr\{X(t) \leqslant x|X(\tau) = x_0\}. \qquad (1.2)$$

As in Chapter 2, Section 1, we can interpret $F(x_0, \tau; x, t)$ as the probability that the system will be in a state included in $(-\infty, x]$, given that it was at x_0 at time τ; $F(x_0, \tau; x, t)$ is called the transition distribution function (d.f.) of $X(t)$. We have

$$F(x_0, \tau; x, t) \geqslant 0$$
$$F(x_0, \tau; -\infty, t) = 0, \qquad F(x_0, \tau; \infty, t) = 1; \qquad (1.3)$$

further, $F(x_0, \tau; x, t)$ satisfies the Chapman-Kolmogorov equations

$$F(x_0, \tau; x, t) = \int_{-\infty}^{\infty} d_y F(x_0, \tau; y, s) F(y, s; x, t) \qquad (\tau < s < t). \qquad (1.4)$$

We define

$$F(x_0, t; x, t) = \delta(x_0, x) = \begin{cases} 0 & \text{if } x < x_0 \\ 1 & \text{if } x \geqslant x_0. \end{cases} \qquad (1.5)$$

87

If the partial derivative

$$f(x_0, \tau; x, t) = \frac{\partial}{\partial x} F(x_0, \tau; x, t) \tag{1.6}$$

exists, then $f(x_0, \tau; x, t)$ is called the transition frequency function (fr.f.) of $X(t)$. This satisfies the Chapman-Kolmogorov equations

$$f(x_0, \tau; x, t) = \int_{-\infty}^{\infty} f(x_0, \tau; y, s) f(y, s; x, t)\, dy \qquad (\tau < s < t). \tag{1.7}$$

We have

$$f(x_0, t; x, t) = \delta(x - x_0), \tag{1.8}$$

where $\delta(x)$ is Dirac's delta function, that is, $\delta(x) = 0$ if $x \neq 0$,

$$\int_{-\infty}^{\infty} \delta(x)\, dx = 1. \tag{1.9}$$

If $F(x_0, \tau; x, t)$ is a function of the difference $t - \tau$, the process $X(t)$ is said to be time homogeneous. In this case we can simplify the notation to

$$F(x_0; x, t) = \Pr\{X(t) \leqslant x \mid X(0) = x_0\}. \tag{1.10}$$

The transition fr.f. can then be denoted as $f(x_0; x, t)$. Let

$$F_0(x) = \Pr\{X(0) \leqslant x\} \tag{1.11}$$

be the initial d.f.; then the unconditional (absolute) d.f. of $X(t)$ is given by

$$F(x) = \Pr\{X(t) \leqslant x\}$$

$$= \int_{-\infty}^{\infty} dF_0(y) F(y; x, t). \tag{1.12}$$

In this chapter we shall discuss Markov processes of the continuous type, in which the system changes its state continually, but only small changes of state occur during small intervals of time. Thus for any $\delta > 0$ we have

$$\Pr\{|X(t) - X(s)| > \delta \mid X(s) = x\} = o(t - s) \qquad (s < t); \tag{1.13}$$

in terms of the transition distribution function, this can be written as

$$\text{(a)} \quad \lim_{\Delta t \to 0} \frac{1}{\Delta t} \int_{|y - x| > \delta} d_y F(x, t; y, t + \Delta t) = 0. \tag{1.14}$$

We shall impose two further restrictions. For any $\delta > 0$, the limits

$$\text{(b)} \quad \lim_{\Delta t \to 0} \frac{1}{\Delta t} \int_{|y - x| \leqslant \delta} (y - x) d_y F(x, t; y, t + \Delta t) = a(x, t) \tag{1.15}$$

(c) $\lim_{\Delta t \to 0} \dfrac{1}{\Delta t} \int_{|y-x| \leqslant \delta} (y - x)^2 d_y F(x, t; y, t + \Delta t) = b(x, t) > 0$ (1.16)

exist, the convergence being uniform in x. In view of (a), the conditions (b) and (c) imply that the means (over time) of the mean and variance of the displacement during $(t, t + \Delta t)$ are finite. [See also the remarks at the end of Section 2.] A process satisfying (a), (b), and (c) is called a diffusion process.

We consider two examples of diffusion processes obtained from discrete time models by a limiting technique.

EXAMPLE 1.1. In the unrestricted random walk problem discussed in Chapter 2, Section 6, the transition probabilities are given by

$$P_{ij}^{(n)} = v(j - i, n) \qquad (-\infty < i, j < \infty), \tag{1.17}$$

where

$$v(x, n) = \binom{n}{\frac{n + x}{2}} p^{(n + x)/2}\, q^{(n - x)/2}. \tag{1.18}$$

Here x is the displacement of the particle (performing the random walk) in n steps. From (1.18) we find that the mean and variance of this displacement is given by

$$E(x) = n(p - q), \qquad \text{Var}\,(x) = 4npq. \tag{1.19}$$

Now let us assume that (i) each step has length Δx, and (ii) the time between any two consecutive steps is Δt. Then, during $(0, t)$

$$\text{expected displacement} = \frac{t}{\Delta t}(p - q)\Delta x = t(p - q)\frac{\Delta x}{\Delta t},$$

$$\text{variance of displacement} = \frac{t}{\Delta t}4pq(\Delta x)^2 = 4tpq\frac{(\Delta x)^2}{\Delta t}. \tag{1.20}$$

In order to get meaningful results when $\Delta x \to 0$, $\Delta t \to 0$, we must therefore have

$$\frac{(\Delta x)^2}{\Delta t} \to \text{a limit}, \qquad p - q = \Delta x; \tag{1.21}$$

if we set

$$\frac{(\Delta x)^2}{\Delta t} = 2D, \quad p = \frac{1}{2} + \frac{c}{2D}\Delta x, \quad q = \frac{1}{2} - \frac{c}{2D}\Delta x, \tag{1.22}$$

where c and D are constants, it is clear that the conditions (1.21) will be satisfied. From (1.20) it will then follow that the mean and variance of the displacement during $(0, t)$ tend respectively to $m(t)$ and $\sigma^2(t)$, where

$$m(t) = 2ct, \quad \sigma^2(t) = 2Dt. \tag{1.23}$$

Thus the binomial distribution $v(x, n)$ of displacements (1.18) will then tend to $f(x, t)dx$, where

$$f(x, t) = \frac{1}{\sqrt{2\pi\sigma(t)}} \exp\left[-\frac{1}{2\sigma^2(t)}[x - m(t)]^2\right]. \tag{1.24}$$

However, we have the recurrence relations

$$v(j, n + 1) = pv(j - 1, n) + qv(j + 1, n),$$

or, in our new units

$$v(x, t + \Delta t) = pv(x - \Delta x, t) + qv(x + \Delta x, t). \tag{1.25}$$

Substituting for p and q from (1.22), and proceeding to the limit, we find from (1.25) that

$$f(x, t) + \Delta t \frac{\partial f}{\partial t} + o(\Delta t)$$

$$= \left(\frac{1}{2} + \frac{c}{2D}\Delta x\right)\left[f(x, t) - \Delta x\frac{\partial f}{\partial x} + \frac{1}{2}(\Delta x)^2\frac{\partial^2 f}{\partial x^2}\right]$$

$$+ \left(\frac{1}{2} - \frac{c}{2D}\Delta x\right)\left[f(x, t) + \Delta x\frac{\partial f}{\partial x} + \frac{1}{2}(\Delta x)^2\frac{\partial^2 f}{\partial x^2}\right] + o(\Delta x)^2,$$

whence

$$\frac{\partial f}{\partial t} = -\frac{c}{D}\frac{(\Delta x)^2}{\Delta t}\frac{\partial f}{\partial x} + \frac{1}{2}\frac{(\Delta x)^2}{\Delta t}\frac{\partial^2 f}{\partial x^2} + o(1),$$

or

$$\frac{\partial f}{\partial t} = -2c\frac{\partial f}{\partial x} + D\frac{\partial^2 f}{\partial x^2}. \tag{1.26}$$

We thus find that the fr.f. $f(x, t)$ satisfies the partial differential equation (1.26).

EXAMPLE 1.2 (The Ehrenfest Model of Diffusion). Consider the finite Markov chain whose transition probabilities are given by

$$P_{i,i-1} = \frac{1}{2}\left(1 + \frac{i}{a}\right), \quad P_{i,i+1} = \frac{1}{2}\left(1 - \frac{i}{a}\right) \quad (-a < i < a),$$
$$\tag{1.27}$$
$$P_{a,a-1} = 1, \quad P_{-a,-a+1} = 1,$$

and $P_{ij} = 0$ for all other combinations of i, j. We have here a nonhomogeneous random walk, which also describes a model for heat exchange between two bodies. We have

$$P_{ij}^{(n+1)} = P_{i,j-1}^{(n)} P_{j-1,j} + P_{i,j+1}^{(n)} P_{j+1,j}$$

$$= \frac{a-j+1}{2a} P_{i,j-1}^{(n)} + \frac{a+j+1}{2a} P_{i,j+1}^{(n)}. \tag{1.28}$$

Let us now choose the units of distance and time as in the last example, and let $\Delta x \to 0$, $\Delta t \to 0$, and $a \to \infty$ in such a way that

$$\frac{(\Delta x)^2}{\Delta t} = 2D, \quad a\Delta t \to \beta^{-1} \quad (\beta > 0). \tag{1.29}$$

Then

$$\sum_{x_1 < j\Delta < x_2} P_{ij}^{(n)} \to \int_{x_1}^{x_2} f(x_0; y, t) \, dy \quad (i\Delta x = x_0), \tag{1.30}$$

where $f(x_0; x, t)$ satisfies the differential equation obtained from (1.28) in the limit. Thus, let $j\Delta x = x$, $n\Delta t = t$, and write $f(x, t) \equiv f(x_0; x, t)$ for convenience; then

$$f(x, t + \Delta t) = \frac{a-j+1}{2a} f(x - \Delta x, t) + \frac{a+j+1}{2a} f(x + \Delta x, t).$$

Proceeding as in (1.25) we obtain

$$f(x, t) + \Delta t \frac{\partial f}{\partial t} + o(\Delta t)$$

$$= \frac{a-j+1}{2a} \left[f(x, t) - \Delta x \frac{\partial f}{\partial x} + \tfrac{1}{2}(\Delta x)^2 \frac{\partial^2 f}{\partial x^2} \right]$$

$$+ \frac{a+j+1}{2a} \left[f(x, t) + \Delta x \frac{\partial f}{\partial x} + \tfrac{1}{2}(\Delta x)^2 \frac{\partial^2 f}{\partial x^2} \right] + o(\Delta x)^2,$$

or

$$\Delta t \frac{\partial f}{\partial t} + o(\Delta t) = \frac{1}{a} \frac{\partial}{\partial x} (xf) + \left(1 + \frac{1}{a} \right)(\Delta x)^2 \frac{\partial^2 f}{\partial x^2} + o(\Delta x)^2,$$

which gives the desired equation

$$\frac{\partial f}{\partial t} = \beta \frac{\partial}{\partial x} (xf) + D \frac{\partial^2 f}{\partial x^2}. \tag{1.31}$$

For further examples of limiting processes of the type described above, see Kac (1947).

2. THE KOLMOGOROV EQUATIONS

The differential equation derived in each of the examples of the last section is called the diffusion equation (or Fokker-Planck equation) of the continuous time process, which is the limit of the Markov chain. We shall now prove that every Markov process of the diffusion type satisfies a similar equation.

THEOREM 2.1.   *Let the Markov process $X(t)$ satisfy the conditions (a), (b), and (c); moreover, let us assume that the transition frequency function $f(x, t) \equiv f(x_0, \tau; x, t)$ exists, and is such that the derivatives*

$$\frac{\partial}{\partial t} f(x, t), \quad \frac{\partial}{\partial x}[a(x, t) f(x, t)], \quad \frac{\partial^2}{\partial x^2}[b(x, t) f(x, t)] \tag{2.1}$$

exist and are continuous. Then $f(x, t)$ satisfies the differential equation

$$\frac{\partial f}{\partial t} = -\frac{\partial}{\partial x}[a(x, t) f(x, t)] + \frac{1}{2}\frac{\partial^2}{\partial x^2}[b(x, t) f(x, t)]. \tag{2.2}$$

Proof: Let $Q(x)$ be an arbitrary function which is continuous and has continuous derivatives $Q'(x)$ and $Q''(x)$. Further, let $Q(x) = 0$ outside the interval $[a, b]$. Then from continuity we find that $Q(x)$, $Q'(x)$, and $Q''(x)$ vanish at $x = a$ and $x = b$. Now consider the integral

$$
\begin{aligned}
I &= \int_{-\infty}^{\infty} Q(y)\frac{\partial}{\partial t} f(y, t)\, dy \\[4pt]
&= \frac{\partial}{\partial t}\int_{a}^{b} Q(y) f(x_0, \tau; y, t)\, dy \\[4pt]
&= \lim_{\Delta t \to 0}\int_{a}^{b} dy\, Q(y)\frac{f(x_0, \tau; y, t + \Delta t) - f(x_0, \tau; y, t)}{\Delta t} \\[4pt]
&= \lim_{\Delta t \to 0} (\Delta t)^{-1}\Bigg\{\int_{a}^{b} dy\, Q(y)\int_{-\infty}^{\infty} f(x_0, \tau; x, t) f(x, t; y, t + \Delta t)\, dx \\[4pt]
&\qquad\qquad\qquad\qquad\qquad\qquad\qquad - \int_{a}^{b} dx\, Q(x) f(x_0, \tau; x, t)\Bigg\} \\[4pt]
&= \lim_{\Delta t \to 0} (\Delta t)^{-1}\int_{-\infty}^{\infty} dx\, f(x_0, \tau; x, t)\Bigg\{\int_{a}^{b} f(x, t; y, t + \Delta t)Q(y)\, dy - Q(x)\Bigg\},
\end{aligned}
\tag{2.3}
$$

the interchange of order of integration being obviously justified. Now, sine $Q(x)$ is bounded in $[a, b]$ we find, using the condition (a), that

$$\int_{|y-x|>\delta} f(x, t; y, t + \Delta t)Q(y)\, dy = o(\Delta t), \tag{2.4}$$

so that we can write (2.3) as

$$I = \lim_{\Delta t \to 0} (\Delta t)^{-1} \int_{-\infty}^{\infty} dx f(x_0, \tau; x, t).$$

$$\left\{ \int_{|y-x| \leqslant \delta} f(x, t; y, t + \Delta t) Q(y) \, dy - Q(x) \right\}.$$

(2.5)

Expanding $Q(y)$ in the neighborhood of x, we obtain

$$Q(y) = Q(x) + (y - x)Q'(x) + \tfrac{1}{2}(y - x)^2 Q''(x) + o(y - x)^2.$$

(2.6)

Using (2.6) and the conditions (a), (b), and (c) we find that

$$\int_{|y-x| \leqslant \delta} f(x, t; y, t + \Delta t) Q(y) \, dy - Q(x)$$

$$= \int_{|y-x| \leqslant \delta} dy f(x, t; y, t + \Delta t)[Q(x) + (y - x)Q'(x) + \tfrac{1}{2}(y - x)^2 Q''(x)$$

$$+ o(y - x)^2] - Q(x)$$

$$= o(\Delta t) + Q'(x) \int_{|y-x| \leqslant \delta} (y - x) f(x, t; y, t + \Delta t) \, dy$$

$$+ \tfrac{1}{2} Q''(x) \int_{|y-x| \leqslant \delta} [(y - x)^2 + o(y - x)^2] f(x, t; y, t + \Delta t) \, dy,$$

and therefore, that

$$I = \int_{-\infty}^{\infty} dx f(x_0, \tau; x, t)[Q'(x)a(x, t) + \tfrac{1}{2}Q''(x)b(x, t)].$$

(2.7)

Integration by parts now gives

$$\int_{-\infty}^{\infty} (af)Q'(x) \, dx = [af Q]_a^b - \int_a^b Q(x) \frac{\partial}{\partial x}(af) \, dx$$

$$= -\int_b^b Q(x) \frac{\partial}{\partial x}(af) \, dx$$

(2.8)

and

$$\int_{-\infty}^{\infty} (bf)Q''(x) \, dx = [bf Q']_a^b - \int_a^b Q'(x) \frac{\partial}{\partial x}(bf) \, dx$$

$$= \int_a^b Q(x) \frac{\partial^2}{\partial x^2}(bf) \, dx.$$

(2.9)

Substituting (2.8) and (2.9) in (2.7) we obtain

$$I = \int_{-\infty}^{\infty} \left\{ -\frac{\partial}{\partial x}(af) + \frac{1}{2} \frac{\partial^2}{\partial x^2}(bf) \right\} Q(x) \, dx.$$

(2.10)

Since I has been defined as in (2.3), we therefore obtain the identity

$$\int_{-\infty}^{\infty}\left\{\frac{\partial f}{\partial t}+\frac{\partial}{\partial x}(af)-\frac{1}{2}\frac{\partial^2}{\partial x^2}(bf)\right\}Q(x)\,dx=0. \tag{2.11}$$

Here the integrand is a continuous function of x, and $Q(x)$ is arbitrary. It follows that

$$\frac{\partial f}{\partial t}+\frac{\partial}{\partial x}(af)-\frac{1}{2}\frac{\partial^2}{\partial x^2}(bf)=0, \tag{2.12}$$

which is the required equation.

In the proof of Theorem 2.1 we considered the transitions of the process $X(t)$ during the consecutive intervals $(\tau,t]$, $(t,t+\Delta t]$. By considering the intervals $(\tau-\Delta\tau,\tau]$, $(\tau,t]$ we obtain a second diffusion equation for the process. This is given by the following theorem:

THEOREM 2.2. *Let the Markov process $X(t)$ satisfy the conditions* (a), (b), *and* (c). *Further, let us assume that the derivatives*

$$\frac{\partial}{\partial x_0}F(x_0,\tau;x,t),\qquad \frac{\partial^2}{\partial x_0^2}F(x_0,\tau;x,t) \tag{2.13}$$

exist and are continuous in x_0,τ,x,t. Then $F(x_0,\tau;x,t)$ satisfies the differential equation

$$\frac{\partial}{\partial\tau}F(x_0,\tau;x,t)=-a(x_0,\tau)\frac{\partial}{\partial x_0}F(x_0,\tau;x,t)$$
$$-\tfrac{1}{2}b(x_0,\tau)\frac{\partial^2}{\partial x_0^2}F(x_0,\tau;x,t). \tag{2.14}$$

Proof: We have

$$\frac{F(x_0,\tau-\Delta\tau;x,t)-F(x_0,\tau;x,t)}{\Delta\tau}$$

$$=(\Delta\tau)^{-1}\int_{-\infty}^{\infty}d_yF(x_0,\tau-\Delta\tau;y,\tau)\{F(y,\tau;x,t)-F(x_0,\tau;x,t)\} \tag{2.15}$$

$$=I_1+I_2,$$

where

$$I_1=(\Delta\tau)^{-1}\int_{|y-x|>\delta},\qquad I_2=(\Delta\tau)^{-1}\int_{|y-x|\leqslant\delta}, \tag{2.16}$$

the integrands in (2.16) being the same as in (2.15). We have

$$|I_1|\leqslant\frac{2}{\Delta\tau}\int_{|y-x|>\delta}d_yF(x_0,\tau-\Delta\tau;y,\tau)\to 0\qquad\text{as }\Delta\tau\to 0 \tag{2.17}$$

on account of (a). Further, $F(y, \tau; x, t)$, treated as a function of y, can be expanded in the neighborhood of x_0, on account of the condition (2.13); thus

$$F(y, \tau; x, t) = F(x_0, \tau; x, t) + (y - x_0)\frac{\partial F}{\partial x_0}$$

$$+ \tfrac{1}{2}(y - x)^2\frac{\partial^2 F}{\partial x_0^2} + o(y - x)^2. \qquad (2.18)$$

Substituting (2.18) in I_2, we obtain

$$I_2 = \frac{\partial F}{\partial x_0}\cdot\frac{1}{\Delta\tau}\int_{|y-x|\leqslant\delta} (y - x_0)d_y F(x_0, \tau - \Delta\tau; y, \tau)$$

$$+ \frac{\partial^2 F}{\partial x_0^2}\frac{1}{\Delta\tau}\int_{|y-x|\leqslant\delta} [\tfrac{1}{2}(y - x_0)^2 + o(y - x)^2]d_y F(x_0, \tau - \Delta\tau; y, \tau) \quad (2.19)$$

$$\rightarrow \frac{\partial F}{\partial x_0}a(x_0, \tau) + \frac{1}{2}\frac{\partial^2 F}{\partial x_0^2}b(x_0, \tau) \qquad \text{as } \Delta\tau \rightarrow 0.$$

It follows that the left-hand derivative

$$-\frac{\partial}{\partial\tau}F(x_0, \tau; x, t) = \lim_{\Delta\tau\rightarrow 0}\frac{F(x_0, \tau - \Delta\tau; x, t) - F(x_0, \tau; x, t)}{\Delta\tau} \qquad (2.20)$$

exists, and is given by the last expression in (2.19). Similarly, the right-hand derivative is given by (2.19). We have thus proved the theorem.

The diffusion equations (2.2) and (2.14) are also called respectively the forward and backward equations of Kolmogorov, who derived them systematically in 1931. The existence and uniqueness of the solutions of these equations, having the properties of a transition fr.f. or d.f., were proved by Feller (1936). In simple cases it is possible to obtain the solutions by the usual methods, as we shall show in the following examples.

EXAMPLE 2.1 (The Wiener–Einstein Process). This is a time-homogeneous process whose transition fr.f. $f(x_0; x, t)$ satisfies the differential equation

$$\frac{\partial f}{\partial t} = D\frac{\partial^2 f}{\partial x^2} \qquad (2.21)$$

(D being a positive constant), with the boundary conditions

$$f(x_0; x, t) \rightarrow 0, \qquad \frac{\partial}{\partial x}f(x_0; x, t \rightarrow 0 \qquad \text{as } x \rightarrow \pm\infty. \qquad (2.22)$$

From example 1.1 we see that (2.21) can be obtained from a symmetric random walk model. Let $\phi(x_0; \theta, t)$ be the characteristic function (c.f.) of

$f(x_0; x, t)$, so that

$$\phi(x_0; \theta, t) = \int_{-\infty}^{\infty} e^{i\theta x} f(x_0; x, t)\, dx, \qquad (2.23)$$

and from (1.8),

$$\phi(x_0; \theta, 0) = e^{i\theta x_0}. \qquad (2.24)$$

Using the conditions (2.22) we find that

$$\int_{-\infty}^{\infty} e^{i\theta x} \frac{\partial f}{\partial x}\, dx = \left[e^{i\theta x} f \right]_{-\infty}^{\infty} - i\theta \int_{-\infty}^{\infty} e^{i\theta x} f(x_0; x, t)\, dx$$
$$= -i\theta \phi(x_0; \theta, t), \qquad (2.25)$$

and

$$\int_{-\infty}^{\infty} e^{i\theta x} \frac{\partial^2 f}{\partial x^2}\, dx = \left[e^{i\theta x} \frac{\partial f}{\partial x} \right]_{-\infty}^{\infty} - i\theta \int_{-\infty}^{\infty} e^{i\theta x} \frac{\partial f}{\partial x}\, dx$$
$$= -i\theta(-i\theta\phi) = -\theta^2 \phi(x_0; \theta, t). \qquad (2.26)$$

Multiplying both sides of (2.21) by $e^{i\theta x}$, integrating over $(-\infty, \infty)$, and using (2.26), we obtain

$$\frac{\partial \phi}{\partial t} = -D\theta^2 \phi, \qquad (2.27)$$

a differential equation for the c.f. $\phi \equiv \phi(x_0; \theta, t)$. The solution of (2.27) is readily found to be

$$\phi(x_0; \theta, t) = A e^{-Dt\theta^2}, \qquad (2.28)$$

where the constant A is determined by (2.24). Thus $A = \phi(x_0; \theta, 0) = e^{i\theta x_0}$,

$$\phi(x_0; \theta, t) = e^{i\theta x_0 - Dt\theta^2}. \qquad (2.29)$$

Clearly, ϕ is the c.f. of a Gaussian (normal) distribution with mean x_0 and variance $2Dt$. The uniqueness property of characteristic functions then gives

$$f(x_0; x, t) = \frac{1}{\sqrt{4\pi Dt}} \exp\left[-\frac{1}{4Dt}(x - x_0)^2 \right] \qquad (-\infty < x < \infty) \qquad (2.30)$$

for the transition fr.f. of the Wiener–Einstein process. From (2.30) we see that the process is also spatially homogeneous.

EXAMPLE 2.2 (The Ornstein–Uhlenbeck Process). The differential equation of this process is given by

$$\frac{\partial f}{\partial t} = \beta \frac{\partial}{\partial x}(xf) + D\frac{\partial^2 f}{\partial x^2}, \qquad (2.31)$$

the boundary conditions being

$$xf(x_0; x, t) \to 0, \qquad \frac{\partial}{\partial x} f(x_0; x, t) \to 0 \qquad \text{as } x \to \pm\infty \qquad (2.32)$$

(cf. example 1.2). To solve (2.31) let us again introduce the c.f. $\phi(x_0; \theta, t)$ defined by (2.24). We have

$$\int_{-\infty}^{\infty} e^{i\theta x} \frac{\partial}{\partial x}(xf)\, dx = \left[e^{i\theta x} xf \right]_{-\infty}^{\infty} - i\theta \int_{-\infty}^{\infty} e^{i\theta x} xf\, dx$$

$$= -\theta \frac{\partial}{\partial \theta} \int_{-\infty}^{\infty} e^{i\theta x} f\, dx = -\theta \frac{\partial \phi}{\partial \theta}. \qquad (2.33)$$

Using (2.33) and (2.26), and proceeding as in the last example, we obtain the differential equation

$$\frac{\partial \phi}{\partial t} + \beta\theta \frac{\partial \phi}{\partial \theta} = -D\theta^2 \phi. \qquad (2.34)$$

To solve (2.34) we consider the system of equations

$$\frac{dt}{1} = \frac{d\theta}{\beta\theta} = -\frac{d\phi}{D\theta^2 \phi}. \qquad (2.35)$$

These give the solutions

$$\theta e^{-\beta t} = c_1, \qquad \phi \exp\left(\frac{D\theta^2}{2\beta}\right) = c_2,$$

where c_1 and c_2 are constants; eliminating one of these two constants we obtain

$$\phi \exp\left(\frac{D\theta^2}{2\beta}\right) = \psi(\theta e^{-\beta t}), \qquad (2.36)$$

where the function ψ is determined from

$$e^{i\theta x_0} = \phi(x_0; \theta, 0) = \exp\left(-\frac{D\theta^2}{2\beta}\right)\psi(\theta),$$

or

$$\psi(\theta) = \exp\left(i\theta x_0 + \frac{D\theta^2}{2\beta}\right). \qquad (2.37)$$

From (2.36) and (2.37) we find that

$$\phi(x_0; \theta, t) = \exp\left[i\theta m(t) - \tfrac{1}{2}\theta^2 \sigma^2(t)\right], \qquad (2.38)$$

where

$$m(t) = x_0 e^{-\beta t}, \qquad \sigma^2(t) = \frac{D}{\beta}(1 - e^{-2\beta t}). \qquad (2.39)$$

From (2.38) we obtain the transition fr.f. $f(x_0; x, t)$ as

$$f(x_0; x, t) = \frac{1}{\sqrt{2\pi}\sigma(t)} \exp\left\{-\frac{1}{2\sigma^2(t)}[x - m(t)]^2\right\}. \qquad (2.40)$$

The process $X(t)$ is therefore Gaussian, with mean $m(t)$ and variance $\sigma^2(t)$ as given by (2.39). (The processes discussed in these examples are again considered in the next section.)

We remark here that the condition (a) is sometimes replaced by the weaker condition

$$(a')\ \lim_{\Delta t \to 0} \frac{1}{\Delta t} \int_{|y-x|>\delta} (y - x)^2\, d_y F(x, t; y, t + \Delta t) = 0. \qquad (2.41)$$

The conditions (b) and (c) can then be replaced by

$$(b')\ \lim_{\Delta t \to 0} \frac{1}{\Delta t} \int_{-\infty}^{\infty} (y - x)\, d_y F(x, t; y, t + \Delta t) = a(x, t) \qquad (2.42)$$

$$(c')\ \lim_{\Delta t \to 0} \frac{1}{\Delta t} \int_{-\infty}^{\infty} (y - x)^2\, d_y F(x, t; y, t + \Delta t) = b(x, t). \qquad (2.43)$$

In applications the functions $a(x, t)$ and $b(x, t)$ can be easily obtained from (b') and (c') (if the limits exist), once it is verified that (a') holds.

3. THE BROWNIAN MOTION

The erratic movement of small particles suspended in fluids, caused by the impacts of the molecules of the fluid, is called Brownian motion, after the botanist Robert Brown, who noticed it in 1827. The statistical treatment of this topic was first given by Einstein and Smoluchowski; we shall outline here the theory as developed by Uhlenbeck and Ornstein (1930) [see also Doob (1942)]. Actually, we shall consider here the one-dimensional version of the theory.

Let $U(t)$ be the velocity of the particle at time t; from physical considerations it is clear that $U(t)$ is a Markov process of the diffusion type. The equation of motion is given by

$$\frac{dU}{dt} = -\beta U + f(t) \qquad (3.1)$$

(the Langevin equation), where $-\beta U$ is the systematic part, which is caused by friction, $f(t)$ is the random part, and it is assumed that these two parts are independent. Clearly, (3.1) assumes the existence of the derivative dU/dt (finite acceleration of the particle); however, as we shall see later, this assumption is not valid. We therefore replace (3.1) by the equation

$$dU(t) = -\beta U(t)\,dt + dF(t), \tag{3.2}$$

where we assume that the process $F(t)$ is Gaussian, with

$$E\{F(t+s) - F(s)\} = 0$$

$$E\{F(t+s) - F(s)\}^2 = 2Dt \tag{3.3}$$

$$E\{F(t_2) - F(t_1)\}\{F(s_2) - F(s_1)\} = 0 \qquad (t_1 < t_2 \leqslant s_1 < s_2).$$

From (3.2) we obtain

$$\int_t^{t+\Delta t} dU(s) = -\beta \int_t^{t+\Delta t} U(s)\,ds + \int_t^{t+\Delta t} dF(s)$$

or,

$$\Delta U \equiv U(t+\Delta t) - U(t) = -\beta U(t)\Delta t + \int_t^{t+\Delta t} dF(s) + o(\Delta t). \tag{3.4}$$

Taking mean values of both sides of (3.4) for a fixed $U(t)$, and using (3.3) we obtain

$$E\{\Delta U \mid U(t) = u\} = -\beta u \Delta t + \int_t^{t+\Delta t} E\,dF(s) + o(\Delta t)$$

$$= -\beta u \Delta t, \tag{3.5}$$

and

$$E\{(\Delta U)^2 \mid U(t) = u\} = \beta^2 u^2 (\Delta t)^2 + \int_t^{t+\Delta t} \int_t^{t+\Delta t} E[dF(s)\,dF(s')] + o(\Delta t)$$

$$= \beta^2 u^2 (\Delta t)^2 + 2D \int_t^{t+\Delta t} ds + o(\Delta t) \tag{3.6}$$

$$= \beta^2 u^2 (\Delta t)^2 + 2D\Delta t + o(\Delta t).$$

From (3.5) and (3.6) it follows that

$$\lim_{\Delta t \to 0} \frac{1}{\Delta t} E\{\Delta U \mid U(t) = u\} = -\beta u$$

$$\lim_{\Delta t \to 0} \frac{1}{\Delta t} E\{(\Delta U)^2 \mid U(t) = u\} = 2D. \tag{3.7}$$

In the notation of Section 2, we therefore have

$$a(u,t) = -\beta u, \qquad b(u,t) = 2D. \tag{3.8}$$

Thus the transition fr.f. $g(u_0; u, t)$ of $U(t)$ satisfies the differential equation

$$\frac{\partial g}{\partial t} = -\beta \frac{\partial}{\partial u}(ug) + D \frac{\partial^2 g}{\partial u^2}, \tag{3.9}$$

which is the same as discussed in example 2.2. It follows that the velocity $U(t)$ is the Ornstein-Uhlenbeck process; this is stated in Theorem 3.1. The limiting behavior of the process as $t \to \infty$ is described by Theorem 3.2. If the position of the particle at time t is denoted by $X(t)$, we have the relation

$$\frac{dX}{dt} = U(t), \tag{3.10}$$

which, on integration, yields the $X(t)$ process; this is investigated in Theorem 3.3.

THEOREM 3.1. *The transition fr.f.* $g(u_0; u, t)$ *of the velocity* $U(t)$ *is given by*

$$g(u_0; u, t) = \frac{1}{\sqrt{2\pi}\sigma(t)} \exp\left\{-\frac{1}{2\sigma^2(t)}[u - m(t)]^2\right\} \quad (-\infty < u < \infty), \tag{3.11}$$

where $m(t) = u_0 e^{-\beta t}$ *and* $\sigma^2(t) = D(1 - e^{-2\beta t})/\beta$.

THEOREM 3.2. *The limiting distribution of* $U(t)$ *as* $t \to \infty$ *has the* fr.f. *given by*

$$g_0(u) = \frac{1}{\sqrt{2\pi}\sigma_0} \exp\left(-\frac{u^2}{2\sigma_0^2}\right) \quad (-\infty < u < \infty) \tag{3.12}$$

(*the Maxwell distribution of velocities*), *where* $\sigma_0^2 = D/\beta$.

Proof: As $t \to \infty$ we find that

$$m(t) \to 0, \qquad \sigma^2(t) \to \frac{D}{\beta} = \sigma_0^2 \tag{3.13}$$

and therefore

$$\frac{1}{\sqrt{2\pi}\sigma(t)} \exp\left\{-\frac{1}{2\sigma^2(t)}[u - m(t)]^2\right\} \to \frac{1}{\sqrt{2\pi}\sigma} \exp\left(-\frac{u^2}{2\sigma_0^2}\right). \tag{3.14}$$

If $U(0)$ has the Maxwell distribution, then the (unconditional) distribution of $U(t)$ is given by the fr.f.

$$g(u) = \int_{-\infty}^{\infty} \frac{1}{\sqrt{2\pi}\sigma_0} \exp\left(-\frac{u_0^2}{2\sigma_0^2}\right) \frac{1}{\sqrt{2\pi}\sigma(t)} \exp\left[-\frac{1}{2\sigma^2(t)}(u - u_0 e^{-\beta t})^2\right] du_0$$

$$= \frac{1}{2\pi\sigma_0\sigma(t)} \exp\left(-\frac{u^2}{2\sigma_0^2}\right) \int_{-\infty}^{\infty} \exp\left[-\frac{1}{2\sigma^2(t)}(u_0 - ue^{-\beta t})^2\right] du_0 \tag{3.15}$$

$$= \frac{1}{\sqrt{2\pi}\sigma_0} \exp\left(-\frac{u^2}{2\sigma_0^2}\right) = g_0(u).$$

We thus see that the Maxwell distribution is stationary in the sense that if $U(s)$ has this distribution, then $U(s + t)(t > 0)$ has the same distribution. Now let us consider $U(s)$, $U(s + t)$, and assume that $U(s)$ has the Maxwell distribution; the joint distribution of $U(s)$, $U(s + t)$ is given by $f_1(u, v)\, du\, dv$, where

$$f_1(u, v) = \frac{1}{\sqrt{2\pi}\sigma_0} \exp\left(-\frac{u^2}{2\sigma_0^2}\right) \frac{1}{\sqrt{2\pi}\sigma(t)} \exp\left[-\frac{1}{2\sigma^2(t)}(v - ue^{-\beta t})^2\right]$$

$$= \frac{1}{2\pi\sigma_0^2\sqrt{1 - \rho^2}} \exp\left[-\frac{1}{2\sigma_0^2(1 - \rho^2)}(v^2 - 2\rho vu + u^2)\right], \tag{3.16}$$

where $\rho = e^{-\beta t}$. This shows that $U(s)$, $U(s + t)$ have a bivariate Gaussian distribution with zero means, and

$$\text{Var}\,\{U(s)\} = \text{Var}\,\{U(s + t)\} = \sigma_0^2$$

$$\text{Covar}\,\{U(s), U(s + t)\} = \sigma_0^2\, e^{-\beta|t|}. \tag{3.17}$$

It follows that

$$\text{Var}\,\{U(s + t) - U(s)\} = 2\sigma_0^2(1 - e^{-\beta|t|}) \sim 2\sigma_0^2\beta|t| \tag{3.18}$$

for small t, and

$$\text{Var}\left\{\frac{U(s + t) - U(s)}{|t|}\right\} \sim \frac{2\sigma_0^2\beta}{|t|} \to \infty \qquad \text{as } t \to 0. \tag{3.19}$$

Therefore, the derivative dU/dt does not exist, as was remarked earlier.

THEOREM 3.3. *For a given* $X(0) = x_0$, *the position* $X(t)$ $(t > 0)$ *of the particle at time t has a Gaussian distribution with*

$$E\{X(t)\} = x_0, \text{Var}\,\{X(t)\} = \frac{2\sigma_0^2}{\beta^2}(e^{-\beta t} - 1 + \beta t). \tag{3.20}$$

Proof: From (3.10) we obtain

$$X(t) - X(0) = \int_0^t U(s)\, ds, \tag{3.21}$$

where it can be shown that the Riemann integral of $u(s)$ exists.[1] Therefore, we can put

$$X(t) - X(0) = \lim_{n \to \infty} \sum_{j=1}^n \frac{t}{n} U\left(j\frac{t}{n}\right). \tag{3.22}$$

Since $U(t/n)$, $U(2t/n)$, $\ldots$, $U(nt/n)$ have an n-variate Gaussian distribution,

[1] See Complement 6.

it follows that $X(t) - X(0)$ has also a Gaussian distribution if it can be shown that its variance is nonzero. Now let us assume that $U(t)$ has the Maxwell distribution; then we obtain

$$E\{X(t) - X(0)\} = \int_0^t E\{U(s)\} \, ds = 0 \qquad (3.23)$$

$$
\begin{aligned}
E\{X(t) - X(0)\}^2 &= \int_0^t \int_0^t E\{U(s)U(s')\} \, ds \, ds' \\
&= \int_0^t \int_0^t \sigma_0^2 e^{-\beta|s'-s|} \, ds \, ds' \\
&= 2\sigma_0^2 \int_{s=0}^t \int_{s'=s}^t e^{-\beta(s'-s)} \, ds \, ds' \\
&= \frac{2\sigma_0^2}{\beta} \int_0^t [1 - e^{-\beta(t-s)}] \, ds \\
&= \frac{2\sigma_0^2}{\beta^2} (e^{-\beta t} - 1 + \beta t).
\end{aligned}
\qquad (3.24)
$$

For a given $X(0) = x_0$, the results (3.23) and (3.24) give (3.20). The theorem is therefore proved.

The older theory, due to Einstein and Smoluchowski, started with the diffusion equation of example 2.1 for the process $X(t)$, and arrived at the Gaussian process with mean 0 and variance $2D't$ (the Wiener-Einstein process). Theorem 3.3 shows that this latter process described the Brownian motion only for large t, since in this case $\mathrm{Var}\{X(t)\} \sim 2\sigma_0^2 t/\beta$. However, for small t we have $\mathrm{Var}\{X(t)\} \sim \sigma_0^2 t^2$, and

$$\frac{1}{t} E\{[X(t) - X(0)]^2 \,|\, X(0) = x_0\} \sim \sigma_0^2 t \to 0 \qquad \text{as } t \to 0, \qquad (3.25)$$

so that the diffusion equation does not apply.

4. FIRST PASSAGE TIMES

In this section we consider a time-homogeneous diffusion process $X(t)$ with the transition d.f. $F(x_0; x, t)$. Let $X(0) = x_0$, $-\infty \leqslant b < x_0 < a \leqslant \infty$, and set

$$T \equiv T_{ab}(x_0) = \inf\{t \,|\, X(t) \leqslant b \quad \text{or} \quad X(t) \geqslant a\}. \qquad (4.1)$$

The random variable T is the first passage time of $X(t)$ from the interval (b, a); let its d.f. be denoted by

$$G(x_0, t) = \Pr\{T \leqslant t\} \qquad (t \geqslant 0). \qquad (4.2)$$

The usual method for obtaining this d.f. is to consider a truncated process

$Y(t)$ defined as follows: $Y(0) = x_0$, and

$$Y(t) = \begin{cases} X(t) & \text{if } T > t \\ X(T) & \text{if } T \leqslant t \end{cases} \tag{4.3}$$

Thus $Y(t)$ coincides with the given process $X(t)$ until $X(t)$ leaves the interval (b, a), after which $Y(t)$ is identically equal to $X(T)$. Let

$$H(x_0; y, t) = \Pr\{Y(t) \leqslant y \,|\, Y(0) = x_0\}; \tag{4.4}$$

then

$$\Pr\{T > t\} = \int_b^a d_y H(x_0; y, t),$$

so that

$$G(x_0, t) = 1 - \int_b^a d_y H(x_0; y, t). \tag{4.5}$$

If $X(t)$ is a diffusion process, then it can be proved (under certain conditions) that so is the truncated process $Y(t)$; solving the diffusion equation of $Y(t)$ with appropriate initial and boundary conditions, we obtain $H(x_0; y, t)$. Substitution in (4.5) then yields the d.f. $G(x_0, t)$ of the first passage time T.

If $a = \infty$, we can write (4.1) as

$$T_b(x_0) = \inf\{t \,|\, X(t) \leqslant b\} \qquad (x_0 > b); \tag{4.6}$$

and if $b = -\infty$, then

$$T_a(x_0) = \inf\{t \,|\, X(t) \geqslant a\} \qquad (x_0 < a), \tag{4.7}$$

where $X(0) = x_0$ in both cases. We first prove the following theorem [cf. Siegert (1951)]:

THEOREM 4.1. *Let T be the first passage time*

$$T = \inf\{t \,|\, X(t) \leqslant 0\}, \ X(0) = x_0 > 0. \tag{4.8}$$

Then if $X(t)$ is a symmetric process, that is, if its transition d.f. is such that

$$F(x_0; x, t) = 1 - F(-x_0; -x, t), \tag{4.9}$$

we have

$$G(x_0; 0, t) = \Pr\{T \leqslant t\} = 2F(x_0; 0, t).$$

If the partial derivative $\partial F / \partial t$ exists, then it follows that T has the fr.f. given by

$$g(x_0; 0, t) = \frac{\partial}{\partial t} G(x_0; 0, t) = 2 \frac{\partial F}{\partial t} F(x_0; 0, t). \tag{4.11}$$

Proof: An enumeration of all paths from x_0 to 0 gives

$$F(x_0; 0, t) = \int_0^t d_\tau G(x_0; 0, \tau) F(0; 0, t - \tau). \tag{4.12}$$

However, from (4.9) we find that $F(0;0,t) = 1 - F(0;0,t)$, or $F(0;0,t) = \frac{1}{2}$. Substituting this in (4.12) we obtain

$$F(x_0;0,t) = \frac{1}{2}\int_0^t d_\tau G(x_0;0,\tau) = \frac{1}{2}G(x_0;0,t), \tag{4.13}$$

which is the result (4.10).

EXAMPLE 4.1. The Wiener–Einstein process, for which

$$f(x_0;x,t) = \frac{1}{\sqrt{4\pi\,Dt}}\exp\left[-\frac{1}{4Dt}(x-x_0)^2\right], \tag{4.14}$$

is clearly a symmetric process, since

$$f(x_0;x,t) = f(-x_0;-x,t). \tag{4.15}$$

The first passage time T from x_0 (>0) to 0 has therefore the d.f. given by

$$G(x_0;0,t) = 2\int_{-\infty}^0 \frac{1}{\sqrt{4\pi\,Dt}}\exp\left[-\frac{1}{4Dt}(x-x_0)^2\right]dx$$

$$= 2\int_{-\infty}^{-x_0/\sqrt{2Dt}} \frac{1}{\sqrt{2\pi}}e^{-\frac{1}{2}y^2}\,dy. \tag{4.16}$$

This shows that T has a continuous distribution with the fr.f.

$$g(x_0;0,t) = \frac{\partial}{\partial t}G(x_0;0,t) = \frac{1}{\sqrt{2\pi}}\exp\left(-\frac{x_0^2}{4Dt}\right)\frac{x_0}{\sqrt{2Dt^3}}$$

$$= \frac{x_0}{t}f(x_0;0,t). \tag{4.17}$$

In the case of a single barrier, Fortet (1943) has proved that under certain conditions, the distribution of the first passage time T has a frequency function. Let us consider the case where $b = -\infty$, and T is defined by (4.7). Put

$$G(x_0;a,t) = \text{Pr}\,\{T_a(x_0) \leqslant t\} \tag{4.18}$$

and

$$g(x_0;a,t) = \frac{\partial}{\partial t}G(x_0;a,t), \tag{4.19}$$

where $x_0 < a$, and $t \geqslant 0$. For some suitable θ, we now define the Laplace transforms (L.T.)

$$f^*(x_0;x,\theta) = \int_0^\infty e^{-\theta t}f(x_0;x,t)\,dt \tag{4.20}$$

$$g^*(x_0;a,\theta) = \int_0^\infty e^{-\theta t}g(x_0;a,t)\,dt. \tag{4.21}$$

We have then the following:

THEOREM 4.2. *If $x_0 < a < x$, then*

$$g^*(x_0; a, \theta) = \frac{f^*(x_0; x, \theta)}{f^*(a; x, \theta)}. \tag{4.22}$$

Proof : An enumeration of possible paths from x_0 to x gives

$$f(x_0; x, t) = \int_0^t g(x_0; a, \tau) f(a, x, t - \tau) \, d\tau. \tag{4.23}$$

Hence we obtain

$$\int_0^\infty e^{-\theta t} f(x_0; x, t) \, dt = \int_0^\infty g(x_0; a, \tau) \, d\tau \int_\tau^\infty e^{-\theta t} f(a; x, t - \tau) \, dt$$
$$= \int_0^\infty e^{-\theta \tau} g(x_0; a, \tau) \, d\tau \int_0^\infty e^{-\theta t} f(a; x, t) \, dt, \tag{4.24}$$

which leads to the required result (4.22).

Suppose that the L.T. $f^*(x_0; x, \theta)$ of the transition fr.f. $f(x_0; x, t)$ can be determined in a simple way; substituting this in the right-hand side of (4.22) and inverting the transform, we can then obtain the fr.f. $g(x_0; a, t)$ of T. Theorem 4.2 thus gives a formal solution of the first passage problem. Another method of solution makes use of the backward diffusion equation

$$\frac{\partial f}{\partial t} = a(x_0) \frac{\partial f}{\partial x_0} + \tfrac{1}{2} b(x_0) \frac{\partial^2 f}{\partial x_0^2}, \tag{4.25}$$

where, since the process $X(t)$ has been assumed to be time homogeneous, the functions $a(x_0)$ and $b(x_0)$ are independent of t. The following theorem is due to Siegert (1951) and Darling and Siegert (1953).

THEOREM 4.3. *Suppose that $X(t)$ satisfies the diffusion equation (4.25) with the conditions*

$$f(x_0; x, t) \to 0 \qquad \text{as } x_0 \to \pm \infty,$$
$$f(x_0; x, 0) = \delta(x - x_0). \tag{4.26}$$

Then the L.T. of the fr.f. of T is given by

$$g^*(x_0; a, \theta) = \frac{u(x_0)}{u(a)} \qquad (x_0 < a), \tag{4.27}$$

where $u(x_0) \equiv u(x_0; \theta)$ is a solution of the equation

$$\theta w = a(x) \frac{\partial w}{\partial x_0} + \tfrac{1}{2} b(x_0) \frac{\partial^2 w}{\partial x^2} \tag{4.28}$$

such that $u(-\infty) = 0$.

Proof: Taking Laplace transforms of both sides of (4.25) and noting that

$$\int_0^\infty e^{-\theta t}\frac{\partial f}{\partial t}\,dt = \left[e^{-\theta t}f\right]_0^\infty + \theta\int_0^\infty e^{-\theta t}f(x_0\,;\,x,t)\,dt \tag{4.29}$$

$$= \theta f^*(x_0\,;\,x,0) \qquad (x_0 \neq x)$$

on account of the conditions (4.26), we find that the L.T. $f^*(x_0\,;\,x,\theta) \equiv w(x_0,\theta)$ satisfies the equation

$$\theta w = a(x_0)\frac{\partial w}{\partial x_0} + \tfrac{1}{2}b(x_0)\frac{\partial^2 w}{\partial x_0^2}. \tag{4.30}$$

It is seen that $-w$ is the Green's solution over the interval $(-\infty < x_0 < \infty)$. Therefore, if $u(x_0)$ and $v(x_0)$ are two linearly independent solutions of (4.30), with

$$u(-\infty) = 0,\ v(\infty) = 0, \tag{4.31}$$

then, except for a constant factor, we have

$$f^*(x_0\,;\,x,\theta) = \begin{cases} u(x_0)v(x) & \text{if } x_0 < x \\ u(x)v(x_0) & \text{if } x_0 > x. \end{cases} \tag{4.32}$$

Substituting (4.32) in (4.27) we find that

$$g^*(x_0\,;\,a,\theta) = \frac{u(x_0)v(x)}{u(a)v(x)} = \frac{u(x_0)}{u(a)}, \tag{4.33}$$

in agreement with (4.27).

Darling and Siegert (1953) have extended this theorem to the case of two boundaries.

EXAMPLE 4.2. Let us again consider the Wiener–Einstein Process and let T be the first passage time from the origin to a point a $(a > 0)$. The equation (4.28) in this case is

$$\theta w = D\frac{\partial^2 w}{\partial x^2}. \tag{4.34}$$

Clearly, $u(x) = \exp\left(\sqrt{\dfrac{\theta}{D}}x\right)$ and $v(x) = \exp\left(-\sqrt{\dfrac{\theta}{D}}x\right)$ are two linearly independent solutions of (4.34), and therefore

$$g^*(0\,;\,a,\theta) = \frac{u(0)}{u(a)} = \exp\left(-\sqrt{\frac{\theta}{D}}a\right). \tag{4.35}$$

The inverse of this transform is known to be

$$g(0\,; a, t) = \frac{a}{\sqrt{4\pi Dt^3}} \exp\left(-\frac{a^2}{4Dt}\right) \qquad (t \geqslant 0). \qquad (4.36)$$

However, considerations of symmetry show that the random variable T has the same distribution as the first passage time a to 0; therefore (4.36) follows from the result (4.17). From (4.35) we find that

$$\Pr\{T < \infty\} = \lim_{\theta \to 0+} g^*(0\,; a, \theta) = 1, \qquad (4.37)$$

so that the process crosses the barrier at a eventually.

EXAMPLE 4.3. The backward equation of the Ornstein–Uhlenbeck process is

$$\frac{\partial f}{\partial t} = -\beta x \frac{\partial f}{\partial x_0} + D\frac{\partial^2 f}{\partial x_0^2}, \qquad (4.38)$$

so that the equation (4.30) becomes

$$\theta w = -\beta x \frac{\partial w}{\partial x} + D\frac{\partial^2 w}{\partial x^2}. \qquad (4.39)$$

The substitution $w = \exp(\frac{1}{4}x^2)y(x)$ reduces (4.39) to the equation

$$\frac{d^2 y}{dx^2} - (\tfrac{1}{4}x^2 + \theta - \tfrac{1}{2})y = 0 \qquad (4.40)$$

[Whittaker and Watson (1927)], for which two linearly independent solutions are $D_{-\theta}(x)$ and $D_{-\theta}(-x)$, where $D_a(x)$ is the Weber function. Therefore the required solutions of (4.39) are $u(x) = e^{x^2/4}D_{-\theta}(-x)$ and $v(x) = e^{x^2/4}D_{-\theta}(x)$, and (4.27) gives

$$g^*(x_0\,; a, \theta) = \exp\left(\frac{x^2}{4} - \frac{a^2}{4}\right)D_{-\theta}(-x_0)/D_{-\theta}(-a). \qquad (4.41)$$

5. COMPLEMENTS AND PROBLEMS

Section 1

1. It is sometimes assumed that a diffusion process is continuous with probability one, but this has not been proved rigorously [the condition (a) is necessary for continuity]. See Feller (1954).

2. Recent investigations of diffusion processes are based on the theory of semigroups; for a bibliography, see Bharucha–Reid (1960).

3. Consider the branching process described in Chapter 2, Section 7. Let the number of direct descendants have mean μ and variance σ^2. Assume that $\mu > 1$, and put $\mu = 1 + \Delta x$, where $\Delta x =$ unit of time $= \Delta t =$ unit of time. Show that when $\Delta x \to 0$, the c.f. $F_n(e^{i\theta \Delta x}) \to \phi(t, \theta)$, where $\phi(t, \theta)$ satisfies the differential equation

$$\frac{\partial \phi}{\partial t} = (\theta + \tfrac{1}{2}i\theta^2 \sigma^2)\frac{\partial \phi}{\partial \theta}. \tag{5.1}$$

[Feller (1951)].

Section 2

4. Show that the diffusion equation

$$\frac{\partial f}{\partial t} = -2c\frac{\partial f}{\partial x} + D\frac{\partial^2 f}{\partial x^2} \tag{5.2}$$

subject to the conditions (2.22), has the solution

$$f(x_0; x, t) = \frac{1}{\sqrt{4\pi Dt}}\exp\left[-\frac{1}{4Dt}(x - x_0 - ct)^2\right]. \tag{5.3}$$

5. Consider the equation

$$\frac{\partial f}{\partial t} = -\alpha\frac{\partial}{\partial x}(xf) + \beta\frac{\partial^2}{\partial x^2}(xf) \tag{5.4}$$

with the condition $f(x_0; 0, t) = 0$. Show that the c.f. $\phi(x_0; \theta, t)$ of $f(x_0; x, t)$ satisfies an equation of the type (5.1) with $\alpha = 1$, $\beta = \tfrac{1}{2}\sigma^2$. Show that the solution of (5.4) is

$$f(x_0; x, t) = \gamma\left(\frac{m}{x}\right)^{\frac{1}{2}} e^{-\gamma(x+m)} I_1\left(2\gamma\sqrt{xm}\right) \qquad (0 < x < \infty), \tag{5.5}$$

where $I_1(x)$ is the Bessel function

$$I_1(x) = \sum_{n=0}^{\infty} \frac{(x/2)^{2n+1}}{n!(n+1)!}, \tag{5.6}$$

$m = x_0 e^{\alpha t}$ and $\gamma = \alpha/\beta(e^{\alpha t} - 1)$. Show also that the mean and variance of the process are m and $2e^{\alpha t}/\gamma$ respectively [Feller (1951)].

Section 3

6. Show that if

$$V(t) = t^{\frac{1}{2}}U\left(\frac{1}{2\beta}\log t\right), \tag{5.7}$$

the transformed process is the Wiener–Einstein process. Since this latter process is known to be continuous with probability one, it follows that

$U(t)$ is also continuous with probability one. Therefore $U(t)$ is Riemann-integrable over any interval $(0, t)$ with probability one [Doob (1942)].

7. Show that for $s_1 < s_2 \leqslant t_1 < t_2$,

$$\text{Covar}\,\{X(t_2) - X(t_1), X(s_2) - X(s_1)\}$$

$$= \int_{t_1}^{t_2} \int_{s_1}^{s_2} E\{u(t)u(s)\}\, dt\, ds \tag{5.8}$$

$$= \frac{\sigma_0^2}{\beta^2}(e^{-\beta t_1} - e^{-\beta t_2})(e^{\beta s_2} - e^{\beta s_1}).$$

As $t_1 \to \infty$, this covariance tends to zero [Doob (1942)].

8. Show that the joint distribution of $X(t) - X(0)$, and $U(t)$ is Gaussian with zero means,

$$\text{Var}\,\{X(t) - X(0)\} = \frac{2\sigma_0^2}{\beta^2}(e^{-\beta t} - 1 + \beta t), \qquad \text{Var}\,\{U(t)\} = \sigma_0^2, \quad (5.9)$$

and

$$\text{Covar}\,\{X(t) - X(0), U(t)\} = \frac{\sigma_0^2}{\beta}(1 - e^{-\beta t}) \tag{5.10}$$

[Doob (1942)].

9. If there is an external force $K(x)$ acting on the particle, the equation of motion is

$$\frac{dU}{dt} = -\beta U(t) + f(t) + \frac{1}{m}K(x). \tag{5.11}$$

Show that (5.7) leads to the diffusion equation of the type

$$\frac{\partial f}{\partial t} = -\beta\frac{\partial}{\partial x}(Kf) + D\frac{\partial^2 f}{\partial x^2} \tag{5.12}$$

for the transition fr.f. of the $X(t)$ process. In particular, when $K(x) = -w^2 x$, we have the case of a harmonically bound particle [see Chandrasekhar (1943), Uhlenbeck and Ornstein (1930), Wang and Uhlenbeck (1945)].

Section 4

10. Show that for the Wiener–Einstein process, if the origin is an absorbing barrier, the transition fr.f. is given by

$$f(x_0 ; x, t) = \frac{1}{\sqrt{4\pi Dt}}\left\{\exp\left[-\frac{1}{4Dt}(x - x_0)^2\right] - \exp\left[-\frac{1}{4Dt}(x + x_0)^2\right]\right\} \tag{5.13}$$

while, if the origin is a reflecting barrier, then

$$f(x_0; x, t) = \frac{1}{\sqrt{4\pi Dt}} \left\{ \exp\left[-\frac{1}{4Dt}(x - x_0)^2 \right] + \exp\left[-\frac{1}{4Dt}(x + x_0)^2 \right] \right\} (5.14)$$

[cf. Chandrasekhar (1943)].

11. Using (4.10), show that for the Wiener–Einstein process $X(t)$ with $X(0) = 0$,

$$\text{Pr} \left\{ \sup_{0 \leqslant \tau \leqslant t} X(\tau) \geqslant x \right\} = 2\text{Pr} \{ X(t) \geqslant x \}. \qquad (5.15)$$

12. From (5.5) show that the probability that the population [see remarks following equation (5.4)] becomes extinct before time t is given by

$$\delta(t) = 1 - \int_0^\infty f(x_0; x, t)\, dx = e^{-\gamma m}, \qquad (5.16)$$

and the probability of ultimate extinction, by

$$\lim_{t \to \infty} \delta(t) = \begin{cases} 1 & \text{if } \alpha \leqslant 0 \\ e^{-\alpha x_0/\beta} & \text{if } \alpha > 0 \end{cases} \qquad (5.17)$$

[Feller (1951)].

13. Let the diffusion process be symmetric, and

$$^0f(x_0; x, t)dx$$

$$= \text{Pr} \{ X(\tau) > 0 \qquad (0 \leqslant \tau \leqslant t), x < X(t) < x + dx \,|\, X(0) = x_0 \} \quad (5.18)$$

$(x_0 > 0)$ the zero-avoiding transition frequency function. Show that

$$^0f(x_0; x, t) = f(x_0; x, t) - f(-x_0; x, t) \qquad (5.19)$$

(the reflection principle of D. André). In particular, for the Wiener–Einstein process, (5.19) gives (5.13).

6. REFERENCES

Bharucha-Reid, A. T. ELEMENTS OF THE THEORY OF MARKOV PROCESSES AND THEIR APPLICATIONS. New York: McGraw-Hill, 1960.

Chandrasekhar, S. STOCHASTIC PROBLEMS IN PHYSICS AND ASTRONOMY. *Reviews of Mod. Phys.*, **15** (1943), pp. 1–89.

Darling, D. A. and Siegert, A. J. F. THE FIRST PASSAGE PROBLEM FOR A CONTINUOUS MARKOV PROCESS. *Ann. Math. Statist.*, **24** (1953), pp. 624–639.

Doob, J. L. THE BROWNIAN MOTION AND STOCHASTIC EQUATIONS. *Ann. Math.*, **2** (1942), pp. 351–369.

Feller, W. ZUR THEORIE DER STOCHASTISCHEN PROZESSE. *Math. Ann.*, **113** (1936), pp. 113–160.

Feller, W. DIFFUSION PROCESSES IN GENETICS. *Proc. 2nd Berkeley Symposium.* Berkeley, Calif.: University of California Press, 1951.

———. DIFFUSION PROCESSES IN ONE DIMENSION. *Trans. Amer. Math. Soc.,* **77,** (1954), pp. 1–31.

Fortet, R. LES FONCTIONS ALÉATOIRE DU TYPE DE MARKOFF ASSOCIÉES A CERTAINES ÉQUATIONS LINÉAIRES AUX DÉRIVÉES PARTIELLES DU TYPE PARABOLIQUE. *J. Math. Pures Appl.,* **22** (1943), pp. 177–243.

Kac, M. RANDOM WALK AND THE THEORY OF BROWNIAN MOTION. *Amer. Math. Monthly,* **54** (1947), pp. 369–417.

Kolmogorov, A. ÜBER DIE ANALYTISCHEN METHODEN IN DER WAHRSCHEINLICHKEITS-RECHNUNG. *Math. Ann.,* **104** (1931), pp. 415–458.

Siegert, A. J. F. ON THE FIRST PASSAGE TIME PROBABILITY PROBLEM. *Phys. Rev.,* **81** (1951), pp. 617–623.

Uhlenbeck, G. E. and Ornstein, L. S. ON THE THEORY OF BROWNIAN MOTION. *Phys. Rev.,* **36** (1930), pp. 823–841.

Wang, Ming Chen and Uhlenbeck, G. E. ON THE THEORY OF BROWNIAN MOTION II. *Rev. Mod. Phys.,* **17** (1945), pp. 323–342.

Wax, Nelson. SELECTED PAPERS ON NOISE AND STOCHASTIC PROCESSES. New York: Dover, 1954. (This contains the papers by Chandrasekhar, Kac, Uhlenbeck and Ornstein, Wang and Uhlenbeck, and Doob cited above.)

Whittaker, E. T. and Watson, G. N. MODERN ANALYSIS. New York: Cambridge University Press, 1927.

CHAPTER 4

Discontinuous Markov Processes

1. INTRODUCTION

In the last chapter we studied Markov processes of the diffusion type, in which changes of state occur continually, the changes being small over small intervals of time. In contrast to these, we have discontinuous processes, where changes of state can occur by sudden jumps. The foundations of the theory of such processes were laid by Kolmogorov (1931), who treated the denumerable case, and Feller [(1936), (1940)], who extended Kolmogorov's results to the general case; both authors were concerned with the *purely discontinuous* process, where the state remains unchanged between jumps. Moyal (1957) considered the general discontinuous process in which changes of state can occur by jumps of a specified kind, as well as otherwise (for instance, by jumps of some other kind).

In this chapter we shall investigate purely discontinuous processes, following the analytic approach of Kolmogorov and Feller. An alternative treatment based on the properties of sample functions, was given by Doeblin (1939), and Doob [(1942), (1945); see also (1953)]. More recent developments are based on the theory of semigroups [for a bibliography see Bharucha–Reid (1960)].

Let the states (possible values) of the process $X(t)$ belong to the real line $(-\infty < x < \infty)$. Let the transition distribution function (d.f.) $F(x_0, \tau; x, t)$ be defined by

$$F(x_0, \tau; x, t) = \Pr\{X(t) \leqslant x \,|\, X(\tau) = x_0\} \qquad (\tau < t), \qquad (1.1)$$

and

$$F(x_0, t; x, t) = \delta(x_0; x) = \begin{cases} 0 & \text{if } x < x_0 \\ 1 & \text{if } x \geqslant x_0. \end{cases} \tag{1.2}$$

We impose the continuity condition on $F(x_0, \tau; x, t)$:

$$\lim_{\tau \to t-0} F(x_0, \tau; x, t) = \lim_{t \to \tau+0} F(x_0, \tau; x, t) = \delta(x_0; x). \tag{1.3}$$

The function $F(x_0, \tau; x, t)$ satisfies the Chapman–Kolmogorov equations

$$F(x_0, \tau; x, t) = \int_{-\infty}^{\infty} d_y F(x_0, \tau; y, s) F(y, s; x, t) \qquad (\tau < s < t). \tag{1.4}$$

Finally, we note that

$$F(x_0, \tau; x, t) \geqslant 0$$
$$F(x_0, \tau; -\infty, t) = 0, \qquad F(x_0, \tau; \infty, t) = 1. \tag{1.5}$$

We now define a purely discontinuous process as one in which (1) if $X(t) = x$, then there is a probability $1 - p(x, t)\Delta t + o(\Delta t)$ that there is no change of state (that is, $X(t)$ remains constant during $[t, t + \Delta t]$), and (2) if there is a change of state, then the distribution function of $X(t + \Delta t)$ is given by $\pi(x; y, t) + o(1)$. More specifically, we have

$$F(x, t; y, t + \Delta t) = \{1 - p(x, t)\Delta t\} \, \delta(x; y)$$
$$+ \Delta t p(x, t) \, \pi(x; y, t) + o(\Delta t). \tag{1.6}$$

The function $p(x, t)$ is thus the "jump rate," and $\pi(x; y, t)$ is the conditional d.f. of the magnitude of a jump given that it has occurred. We have

$$\pi(x; -\infty, t) = 0, \qquad \pi(x; \infty, t) = 1. \tag{1.7}$$

Our study of the purely discontinuous process defined by (1.6) is based on the two systems of integro-differential equations (called the Kolmogorov–Feller equations), analogous to the two diffusion equations. These are discussed in the next section.

2. THE KOLMOGOROV–FELLER EQUATIONS

THEOREM 2.1. *Let $X(t)$ be a purely discontinuous Markov process, for which the functions $p(x, t)$ and $\pi(x; y, t)$ are defined by (1.6). Let $p(x, t)$ be finite, nonnegative, and continuous in x, t, and let $\pi(x; y, t)$ be continuous in t. Moreover, let us assume that $p(x, t)$ is bounded. Then we have the forward equation*

$$\frac{\partial}{\partial t} F(x_0, \tau; x, t) = -\int_{-\infty}^{x} p(y, t) \, d_y \, F(x_0, \tau; y, t)$$
$$+ \int_{-\infty}^{\infty} p(y, t) \, \pi(y; x, t) \, d_y \, F(x_0, \tau; y, t), \tag{2.1}$$

and the backward equation

$$\frac{\partial}{\partial \tau} F(x_0, \tau; x, t) = p(x_0, \tau) F(x_0, \tau; x, t)$$

$$-p(x_0, \tau) \int_{-\infty}^{\infty} d_y \, \pi(x_0; y, \tau) F(y, \tau; x, t). \tag{2.2}$$

Proof: We shall first consider the backward equation (2.2). The Chapman–Kolomogorov equations give

$$F(x_0, \tau - \Delta\tau; x, t) = \int_{-\infty}^{\infty} d_y F(x_0, \tau - \Delta\tau; y, \tau) F(y, \tau; x, t); \tag{2.3}$$

substituting for $F(x_0, \tau - \Delta\tau; y, \tau)$ from (1.6), we can write this as

$$F(x_0, \tau - \Delta\tau; x, t)$$

$$= \int_{-\infty}^{\infty} d_y \{[1 - p(x_0, \tau - \Delta\tau)\Delta\tau]\delta(x_0; y) + \Delta\tau p(x_0, \tau - \Delta\tau)\pi(x_0; y, \tau - \Delta\tau)$$

$$+ o(\Delta\tau)\} F(y, \tau; x, t)$$

$$= [1 - p(x_0, \tau - \Delta\tau)\Delta\tau]F(x_0, \tau; x, t) \tag{2.4}$$

$$+ \Delta\tau p(x_0, \tau - \Delta\tau) \int_{-\infty}^{\infty} d_y \pi(x_0; y, \tau - \Delta\tau) F(y, \tau; x, t) + o(\Delta\tau).$$

From (2.4) we obtain

$$-\frac{F(x_0, \tau - \Delta\tau; x, t) - F(x_0, \tau; x, t)}{\Delta\tau} = p(x_0, \tau - \Delta\tau) F(x_0, \tau; x, t)$$

$$-p(x_0, \tau - \Delta\tau) \int_{-\infty}^{\infty} d_y \pi(x_0; y, \tau - \Delta\tau) F(y, \tau; x, t) + \frac{o(\Delta\tau)}{\Delta\tau}. \tag{2.5}$$

Since $p(x_0, \tau - \Delta\tau) \to p(x_0, \tau)$ and $\pi(x_0; y, \tau - \Delta\tau) \to \pi(x_0; y, \tau)$ because of continuity, we find from (2.5) that the left-hand derivative $\partial F/\partial \tau$ of $F(x_0, \tau; x, t)$ exists, and is given by (2.2). Now, we have

$$F(x_0, \tau; x, t) = \int_{-\infty}^{\infty} d_y F(x_0, \tau; y, \tau + \Delta\tau) F(y, \tau + \Delta\tau; x, t)$$

$$= [1 - p(x_0, \tau)\Delta\tau]F(x_0, \tau + \Delta\tau; x, t) \tag{2.6}$$

$$+ \Delta\tau p(x_0, \tau) \int_{-\infty}^{\infty} d_y \pi(x_0; y, \tau) F(y, \tau + \Delta\tau; x, t) + o(\Delta\tau).$$

Equations (2.4) and (2.6) show that $F(x_0, \tau; x, t)$ is continuous in τ. Therefore, proceeding as in (2.5), we find that the right-hand derivative $\partial F/\partial \tau$ exists, and is given by (2.2). We have thus established the backward equation of the process.

The forward equation can also be proved similarly, but needs a slightly more careful treatment. In particular, the boundedness of $p(y, t)$ guarantees the existence of the two integrals in (2.1). The proof of Theorem 2.1 is thus complete.

It should be noted, however, that the boundedness of $p(x, t)$ is a severe restriction on the process, and is not always satisfied in practice. In the general case, the backward equation (2.2) is found to hold, but the forward equation (2.1) has to be replaced by the inequality

$$\frac{\partial F}{\partial t} \geqslant -\int_{-\infty}^{x} p(y, t)\, d_y F(x_0, \tau; y, t)$$

$$+ \int_{-\infty}^{\infty} p(y, t)\pi(y; x, t)\, d_y F(x_0, \tau; y, t). \tag{2.7}$$

Nevertheless, the various steps in the above proof indicate that the equation (2.1) is *plausible*. In actual applications it is always worthwhile establishing these two equations, starting from the basic assumptions, instead of quoting from Theorem 2.1.

If the equations (2.1) and (2.2) are accepted, then there arises the question regarding the existence and uniqueness of their solutions. A partial answer to this question is provided by the following theorems due to Feller (1940).

THEOREM 2.2. *Let*

$$P_0(x_0, \tau; x, t) = \delta(x_0; x) \exp\left[-\int_{\tau}^{t} p(x_0, s)\, ds\right] \tag{2.8}$$

$$P_n(x_0, \tau; x, t) = \int_{\tau}^{t} p(x_0, \sigma) \exp\left[-\int_{\tau}^{\sigma} p(x_0, s)\, ds\right] d\sigma.$$

$$\int_{-\infty}^{\infty} P_{n-1}(y, \sigma; x, t)\, d_y \pi(x_0; y, \sigma) \qquad (n \geqslant 1), \tag{2.9}$$

and

$$P(x_0, \tau; x, t) = \sum_{n=0}^{\infty} P_n(x_0, \tau; x, t). \tag{2.10}$$

Then $P(x_0, \tau; x, t)$ is a transition distribution function satisfying the initial condition (1.3), the Chapman–Kolmogorov equations, and the basic assumption (1.6).

Proof: If we put

$$S_n(x_0, \tau; x, t) = \sum_{k=0}^{n} P_k(x_0, \tau; x, t) \qquad (n \geqslant 0), \tag{2.11}$$

we have to prove that as $n \to \infty$, $S_n \equiv S_n(x_0, \tau; x, t)$ converges to a function with the stated properties. From (2.8) and (2.9) we obtain the relation

$$S_n(x_0, \tau; x, t) = \delta(x_0; x) \exp\left[-\int_\tau^t p(x_0, s)\, ds\right]$$

$$+ \int_\tau^t p(x_0, \sigma) \exp\left[-\int_\tau^\sigma p(x_0, s)\, ds\right] d\sigma \int_{-\infty}^\infty S_{n-1}(y, \sigma; x, t)\, d_y\pi(x_0; y, \sigma)$$

(2.12)

$$(n \geqslant 1).$$

We have $0 \leqslant S_0 = P_0(x_0, \tau; x, t) \leqslant 1$. Assuming that $0 \leqslant S_{n-1} \leqslant 1$ for some n, we find from (2.12) that

$$0 \leqslant S_n \leqslant \exp\left[-\int_\tau^t p(x_0, s)\, ds\right] + \int_\tau^t p(x_0, \sigma) \exp\left[-\int_\tau^\sigma p(x_0, s)\, ds\right] d\sigma = 1.$$

(2.13)

It follows by induction that $0 \leqslant S_n \leqslant 1$ for all n. Since all the terms $P_k(x_0, \tau; x, t)$ in (2.11) are nonnegative, we have $S_n \geqslant S_{n-1}$. Therefore, $S_n \to P(x_0, \tau; x, t)$, where $0 \leqslant P(x_0, \tau; x, t) \leqslant 1$. It is obvious that $P(x_0, \tau; x, t)$ has the properties of a distribution function. We proceed to prove the remaining properties.

(i) We have

$$\lim_{\tau \to t-0} P_n(x_0, \tau; x, t) = \lim_{t \to \tau+0} P_n(x_0, \tau; x, t)$$

$$= \begin{cases} \delta(x_0; x) & \text{if } n = 0 \\ 0 & \text{if } n \geqslant 1, \end{cases}$$

(2.14)

which shows that $P(x_0, \tau; x, t)$ satisfies the initial condition (1.3).

(ii) We shall prove that

$$P_n(x_0, \tau; x, t) = \sum_{k=0}^n \int_{-\infty}^\infty d_y P_k(x_0, \tau; y, s) P_{n-k}(y, s; x, t) \quad (\tau < s < t, n \geqslant 0).$$

(2.15)

For $n = 0$, this reduces to the definition (2.8). Assuming (2.15) to be true for some n, we find that

$$\sum_{k=0}^{n+1} \int_{-\infty}^\infty d_z P_k(x_0, \tau; z, s) P_{n+1-k}(z, s; x, t)$$

$$= \exp\left[-\int_\tau^s p(x_0, \theta)\, d\theta\right] P_{n+1}(x_0, s; x, t)$$

$$+ \sum_{k=1}^{n+1} \int_{-\infty}^\infty \int_\tau^s p(x_0, \sigma) \exp\left[-\int_\tau^\sigma p(x_0, \theta)\, d\theta\right] d\sigma.$$

$$\int_{-\infty}^{\infty} d_z P_{k-1}(y, \sigma; z, s) \, d_y \pi(x_0, y, \sigma) P_{n+1-k}(z, s; x, t)$$

$$= \exp\left[-\int_{\tau}^{s} p(x_0, \theta) \, d\theta\right] P_{n+1}(x_0, s; x, t)$$

$$+ \int_{\tau}^{s} p(x_0, \sigma) \exp\left[-\int_{\tau}^{\sigma} p(x_0, \theta) \, d\theta\right] d\sigma \int_{-\infty}^{\infty} P_n(y, \sigma; x, t) \, d_y \pi(x_0; y, \sigma)$$

$$= \left\{\exp\left[-\int_{\tau}^{s} p(x_0, \theta) \, d\theta\right] \int_{s}^{t} p(x_0, \sigma) \exp\left[-\int_{s}^{\sigma} p(x_0, \theta) \, d\theta\right] d\sigma\right.$$

$$\left. + \int_{\tau}^{s} p(x_0, \sigma) \exp\left[-\int_{\tau}^{\sigma} p(x_0, \theta) \, d\theta\right] d\sigma\right\} \int_{-\infty}^{\infty} P_n(y, \sigma; x, t) \, d_y \pi(x_0; y, \sigma)$$

$$= \int_{\tau}^{t} p(x_0, \sigma) \exp\left[-\int_{\tau}^{\sigma} p(x_0, \theta) \, d\theta\right] d\sigma \int_{-\infty}^{\infty} P_n(y, \sigma; x, t) \, d_y \pi(x_0; y, \sigma)$$

$$= P_{n+1}(x_0, \tau; x, t),$$

and the result (2.15) therefore follows by induction. Summing (2.15) over $n = 0, 1, 2, \ldots$, we find that

$$P(x_0, \tau; x, t) = \int_{-\infty}^{\infty} d_y P(x_0, \tau; y, s) P(y, s; x, t), \tag{2.16}$$

which is the Chapman–Kolmogorov equation.

(iii) We have

$$\frac{\delta(x_0; x) - P_0(x_0, t; x, t + \Delta t)}{\Delta t}$$

$$= \delta(x_0; x) \frac{1 - \exp\left[-\int_{t}^{t+\Delta t} p(x_0, s) \, ds\right]}{\Delta t} \tag{2.17}$$

$$\rightarrow \delta(x_0; x) p(x_0, t) \qquad \text{as } \Delta t \to 0.$$

Also, since

$$\sum_{n=1}^{\infty} P_n(x_0, \tau; \infty, t) \leqslant 1 - P_0(x_0, \tau; \infty, t),$$

we find that

$$\limsup_{\Delta t \to 0} \frac{1}{\Delta t} \sum_{1}^{\infty} P_n(x_0, t; \infty, t + \Delta t) \leqslant p(x_0, t). \tag{2.18}$$

Further, from

$$\sum_1^\infty P_n(x_0, \tau; x, t) \geqslant P_1(x_0, \tau; x, t)$$

we obtain

$$\liminf_{\Delta t \to 0} \frac{1}{\Delta t} \sum_1^\infty P_n(x_0, t; x, t + \Delta t) \geqslant p(x_0, t)\pi(x_0; x, t). \qquad (2.19)$$

Similarly, from

$$\sum_1^\infty [P_n(x_0, \tau; \infty, t) - P_n(x_0, \tau; x, t)]$$

$$\geqslant P_1(x_0, \tau; \infty, t) - P_1(x_0, \tau; x, t),$$

we find that

$$\liminf_{\Delta t \to 0} \frac{1}{\Delta t} \sum_1^\infty [P_n(x_0, t; \infty, t + \Delta t) - P_n(x_0, t; x, t + \Delta t)]$$

$$\geqslant p(x_0, t)\{1 - \pi(x_0; x, t)\}. \qquad (2.20)$$

From (2.18) and (2.20) we obtain

$$\limsup_{\Delta t \to 0} \frac{1}{\Delta t} \sum_1^\infty P_n(x_0, t; x, t + \Delta t)$$

$$= \limsup_{\Delta t \to 0} \frac{1}{\Delta t} \left\{ \sum_1^\infty P_n(x_0, t; \infty, t + \Delta t) \right.$$

$$\left. - \sum_1^\infty [P_n(x_0, t; \infty, t + \Delta t) - P_n(x_0, t; x, t + \Delta t)] \right\}$$

$$\leqslant \limsup_{\Delta t \to 0} \frac{1}{\Delta t} \sum_1^\infty P_n(x_0, t; \infty, t + \Delta t)$$

$$\qquad (2.21)$$

$$- \liminf_{\Delta t \to 0} \frac{1}{\Delta t} \sum_1^\infty [P_n(x_0, t; \infty, t + \Delta t) - P_n(x_0, t; x, t + \Delta t)]$$

$$\leqslant p(x_0, t) - p(x_0, t)\{1 - \pi(x_0; x, t)\}$$

$$= p(x_0, t)\pi(x_0; x, t).$$

From (2.19) and (2.21) it follows that

$$\lim_{\Delta t \to 0} \frac{1}{\Delta t} \sum_1^\infty P_n(x_0, t; x, t + \Delta t) = p(x_0, t)\pi(x_0; x, t). \qquad (2.22)$$

Therefore, as $\Delta t \to 0$,

$$\frac{\delta(x_0 ; x) - P(x_0, t ; x, t + \Delta t)}{\Delta t}$$

$$\to \delta(x_0 ; x)p(x_0, t) - p(x_0, t)\pi(x_0 ; x, t), \tag{2.23}$$

which is the equation (1.6). The proof of Theorem 2.2 is thus complete.

THEOREM 2.3. *There exists a common solution* $P(x_0, \tau ; x, t)$ *for the forward and backward equations, satisfying the initial condition* (1.3), *the Chapman–Kolmogorov equations,* $0 \leqslant P(x_0, \tau ; x, t) \leqslant 1$, *and*

$$P(x_0, \tau ; \infty, t) \leqslant 1. \tag{2.24}$$

Proof: Consider the function $P(x_0, \tau ; x, t)$ defined in Theorem 2.2. We have already seen that $P(x_0, \tau ; x, t)$ is a transition d.f. with the properties stated here. Since $0 \leqslant P(x_0, \tau ; x, t) \leqslant 1$, we have $0 \leqslant P(x_0, \tau ; \infty, t) \leqslant 1$. It remains to prove that $P(x_0, \tau ; x, t)$ satisfies the two systems of equations.

(a) From (2.8) and (2.9) we obtain

$$\frac{\partial}{\partial \tau} P_0(x_0, \tau ; x, t) = p(x_0, \tau)P_0(x_0, \tau ; x, t) \tag{2.25}$$

$$\frac{\partial}{\partial \tau} P_n(x_0, \tau ; x, t) = p(x_0, \tau)P_n(x_0, \tau ; x, t)$$

$$- p(x_0, \tau) \int_{-\infty}^{\infty} P_{n-1}(y, \tau ; x, t) \, d_y \pi(x_0, y, \tau) \qquad (n \geqslant 1). \tag{2.26}$$

Adding (2.25) and (2.26) for $n = 1, 2, \ldots$, we obtain

$$\frac{\partial}{\partial \tau} P(x_0, \tau ; x, t) = p(x_0, \tau)P(x_0, \tau ; x, t)$$

$$- p(x_0, \tau) \int_{-\infty}^{\infty} P(y, \tau ; x, t) \, d_y \pi(x_0 ; y, \tau); \tag{2.27}$$

the function $P(x_0, \tau ; x, t)$ thus is a solution of the backward equation.

(b) We now define a sequence of functions $\bar{P}_n(x_0, \tau ; x, t)$ $(n \geqslant 0)$, as follows. Let

$$\psi(x_0, \tau ; x, t) = \int_{-\infty}^{x} \exp\left[-\int_{\tau}^{t} p(y, s) \, ds\right] d_y \pi(x_0 ; y, \tau), \tag{2.28}$$

$$\bar{P}_0(x_0, \tau ; x, t) = \delta(x_0 ; x) \exp\left[-\int_{\tau}^{t} p(x_0, s) \, ds\right] \tag{2.29}$$

and

$$\bar{P}_n(x_0, \tau ; x, t) = \int_{\tau}^{t} d\sigma \int_{-\infty}^{\infty} p(y, \sigma)\psi(y, \sigma ; x, t) \, d_y \bar{P}_{n-1}(x_0, \tau ; y, \sigma) \qquad (n \geqslant 1). \tag{2.30}$$

We have

$$\frac{\partial}{\partial t}\bar{P}_0(x_0,\tau;x,t) = -p(x_0,t)\bar{P}_0(x_0,\tau;x,t) \tag{2.31}$$

$$\frac{\partial}{\partial t}\bar{P}_n(x_0,\tau;x,t) = \int_{-\infty}^{\infty} p(y,t)\pi(y;x,t)\,d_y\bar{P}_{n-1}(x_0,\tau;y,t)$$

$$+\int_{\tau}^{t} d\sigma \int_{-\infty}^{\infty} p(y,\sigma)\frac{\partial}{\partial t}\psi(y,\sigma;x,t)\,d_y\bar{P}_{n-1}(x_0,\tau;y,\sigma) \quad (n\geqslant 1). \tag{2.32}$$

The second integral on the right-hand side of (2.32) is

$$-\int_{\tau}^{t} d\sigma \int_{-\infty}^{\infty} p(y,\sigma)\,d_y\bar{P}_{n-1}(x_0,\tau;y,\sigma)\int_{-\infty}^{x} p(z,t)\,d_z\psi(y,\sigma;z,t)$$

$$= -\int_{\tau}^{t} d\sigma \int_{-\infty}^{x} p(z,t)\int_{-\infty}^{\infty} p(y,\sigma)\,d_z\psi(y,\sigma;z,t)\,d_y\bar{P}_{n-1}(x_0,\tau;y,\sigma) \tag{2.33}$$

$$= -\int_{-\infty}^{x} p(z,t)\,d_z\bar{P}_n(x_0,\tau;z,t).$$

From (2.31), (2.32), and (2.33) we find that the function

$$\bar{P}(x_0,\tau;x,t) = \sum_{n=0}^{\infty} \bar{P}_n(x_0,\tau;x,t) \tag{2.34}$$

satisfies the forward equation

$$\frac{\partial}{\partial t}\bar{P}(x_0,\tau;x,t) = -\int_{-\infty}^{x} p(y,t)\,d_y\bar{P}(x_0,\tau;y,t)$$

$$+\int_{-\infty}^{\infty} p(y,t)\pi(y;x,t)\,d_y\bar{P}(x_0,\tau;y,t). \tag{2.35}$$

Here we have anticipated that the integrals in (2.28)–(2.30) and the infinite series in (2.34) are convergent. However, we shall prove that the functions $\bar{P}_n(x_0,\tau;x,t)$ are identical with $P_n(x_0,\tau;x,t)$ and therefore $\bar{P}(x_0,\tau;x,t) \equiv P(x_0,\tau;x,t)$. Thus $P(x_0,\tau;x,t)$ is a common solution of the forward and the backward equations.

Clearly $\bar{P}_0(x_0,\tau;x,t) = P_0(x_0,\tau;x,t)$. Assume that $\bar{P}_n(x_0,\tau;x,t) = P_n(x_0,\tau;x,t)$ for $n=1,2,\ldots,n$; then from (2.30) we find that

$$\bar{P}_{n+1}(x_0,\tau;x,t) = \int_{\tau}^{t} d\sigma \int_{-\infty}^{\infty} p(y,\sigma)\psi(y,\sigma;x,t)\,d_yP_n(x_0,\tau;y,\sigma)$$

$$= \int_{\tau}^{t} d\sigma \int_{-\infty}^{\infty} p(y,\sigma)\psi(y,\sigma;x,t).$$

$$\int_\tau^\sigma p(x_0, \theta) \exp\left[-\int_\tau^\theta p(x_0, s)\, ds\right] d\theta \int_{-\infty}^\infty d_y P_{n-1}(z, \theta\,; y, \sigma)\, d_z\pi(x_0\,; z, \theta)$$

$$= \int_\tau^t p(x_0, \theta) \exp\left[-\int_\tau^\theta p(x_0, s)\, ds\right] d\theta \int_{-\infty}^\infty d_z\pi(x_0\,; z, \theta).$$

(2.36)

$$\int_\theta^t d\sigma \int_{-\infty}^\infty p(y, \sigma)\psi(y, \sigma\,; x, t)\, d_y \bar{P}_{n-1}(z, \theta\,; y, \sigma)$$

$$= \int_\tau^t p(x_0, \theta) \exp\left[-\int_\tau^\theta p(x_0, s)\, ds\right] d\theta \int_{-\infty}^\infty d_z\pi(x_0\,; z, \theta)\bar{P}_n(z, \theta\,; x, t)$$

$$= P_{n+1}(x_0, \tau\,; x, t).$$

By induction it follows that $\bar{P}_n(x_0, \tau\,; x, t) = P_n(x_0, \tau\,; x, t)$ for all n, as required. (In the above proof we have left out details regarding the justification of interchange of the order of integration.)

Investigation of the uniqueness of the solutions of the two systems of equations and the closely related question whether equality holds in (2.24) reveals the fact that the process has (in general) discontinuities more complicated than jumps [see Doob (1953)].

If the process is time homogeneous, then the functions $p(x, t)$ and $\pi(x\,; y, t)$ are independent of t; put

$$p(x, t) = p(x), \qquad \pi(x\,; y, t) = \pi(x\,; y). \tag{2.37}$$

Further, if $F(x_0, \tau\,; x, t) \equiv F(x_0\,; x, t - \tau)$, the forward and backward equations are given respectively by

$$\frac{\partial}{\partial t} F(x_0\,; x, t) = -\int_{-\infty}^x p(y)\, d_y F(x_0\,; y, t)$$

$$+ \int_{-\infty}^\infty p(y)\pi(y\,; x)\, d_y F(x_0\,; y, t)$$

(2.38)

and

$$\frac{\partial}{\partial t} F(x_0\,; x, t) = -p(x_0)F(x_0\,; x, t)$$

$$+ p(x_0) \int_{-\infty}^\infty d_y\pi(x_0\,; y)F(y\,; x, t).$$

(2.39)

For this case Feller (1940) has given a necessary and sufficient condition for equality to hold in (2.24).

3. THE COMPOUND POISSON PROCESS

This is a purely discontinuous process with

$$p(x, t) = \lambda, \qquad \pi(x\,; y, t) = B(y - x), \tag{3.1}$$

where λ is a constant $(0 < \lambda < \infty)$, and $B(x)$ is a distribution function $(-\infty < x < \infty)$. From (3.1) it is clear that the process is time homogeneous, as well as spatially homogeneous. Let us put

$$F(x_0, \tau; x, t) \equiv F(x - x_0, t - \tau). \tag{3.2}$$

The forward equation is given by

$$\frac{\partial}{\partial t} F(x, t) = -\lambda F(x, t) + \lambda \int_{-\infty}^{\infty} B(x - y) \, d_y F(y, t) \tag{3.3}$$

and the backward equation by

$$\frac{\partial}{\partial t} F(x, t) = -\lambda F(x, t) + \lambda \int_{-\infty}^{\infty} dB(y) F(x - y, t). \tag{3.4}$$

Since

$$\int_{-\infty}^{\infty} B(x - y) \, d_y F(y, t) = \Big[B(x - y) F(y, t) \Big]_{-\infty}^{\infty} - \int_{-\infty}^{\infty} d_y B(x - y) F(y, t)$$

$$= \int_{-\infty}^{\infty} dB(u) F(x - u, t), \tag{3.5}$$

we see that (3.3) reduces to (3.4). The two equations are thus identical for this process. To solve (3.4) we introduce the characteristic functions (c.f.)

$$\psi(\theta) = \int_{-\infty}^{\infty} e^{i\theta x} \, dB(x), \qquad \phi(\theta, t) = \int_{-\infty}^{\infty} e^{i\theta x} \, d_x F(x, t). \tag{3.6}$$

Then from (3.4) we obtain

$$\frac{\partial}{\partial t} \int_{-\infty}^{\infty} e^{i\theta x} \, d_x F(x, t) = -\lambda \psi(\theta) + \lambda \int_{-\infty}^{\infty} dB(y) \int_{-\infty}^{\infty} e^{i\theta x} d_x F(x - y, t)$$

$$= -\lambda \psi(\theta) + \lambda \int_{-\infty}^{\infty} e^{i\theta y} \, dB(y) \int_{-\infty}^{\infty} e^{i\theta u} \, d_u F(u, t)$$

$$= -\lambda \psi(\theta) + \lambda \psi(\theta) \phi(\theta, t),$$

or

$$\frac{\partial}{\partial t} \phi(\theta, t) = -\lambda [1 - \psi(\theta)] \phi. \tag{3.7}$$

The differential equation (3.7) has the solution

$$\phi(\theta, t) = A e^{-\lambda t [1 - \psi(\theta)]},$$

where

$$A = \phi(\theta, 0) = \int_{-\infty}^{\infty} e^{i\theta x} \, d_x F(x, 0) = 1.$$

Therefore,

$$\phi(\theta, t) = e^{-\lambda t[1 - \psi(\theta)]} = e^{-\lambda t} \sum_{0}^{\infty} \frac{(\lambda t)^n}{n!} [\psi(\theta)]^n. \tag{3.8}$$

Now let us define the functions $B_n(x)$ ($n \geqslant 0$) as follows:

$$B_0(x) = 0 \quad \text{if } x < 0, \qquad = 1 \quad \text{if } x \geqslant 0$$

$$B_n(x) = \int_{-\infty}^{\infty} B_{n-1}(x - y) \, dB(y) \qquad (n \geqslant 1). \tag{3.9}$$

It is seen that $B_1(x) = B(x)$; $B_n(x)$ is the n-fold convolution of $B(x)$ with itself, and its c.f. is given by

$$\int_{-\infty}^{\infty} e^{i\theta x} \, dB_n(x) = [\psi(\theta)]^n \qquad (n \geqslant 1). \tag{3.10}$$

From (3.8) and (3.10) we find that the transition d.f. of the process is given by

$$F(x, t) = \sum_{n=0}^{\infty} e^{-\lambda t} \frac{(\lambda t)^n}{n!} B_n(x) \tag{3.11}$$

and

$$F(x_0, \tau; x, t) = \sum_{n=0}^{\infty} e^{-\lambda(t-\tau)} \frac{[\lambda(t - \tau)]^n}{n!} B_n(x - x_0); \tag{3.12}$$

(3.12) is thus the unique solution of the forward (backward) equation.

From (2.8) and (2.9) we find that the functions

$$P_n(x_0, \tau; x, t) \equiv P_n(x - x_0, t - \tau)$$

are given by

$$P_0(x, t) = \begin{cases} 0 & \text{if } x < 0 \\ e^{-\lambda t} & \text{if } x \geqslant 0 \end{cases}$$

$$P_n(x, t) = \int_0^t \lambda e^{-\lambda \sigma} \, d\sigma \int_{-\infty}^{\infty} P_{n-1}(x - y, t - \sigma) \, dB(y) \qquad (n \geqslant 1). \tag{3.13}$$

Solving these equations successively for $n = 1, 2, \ldots$, we obtain

$$P_n(x, t) = e^{-\lambda t} \frac{(\lambda t)^n}{n!} B_n(x) \qquad (n \geqslant 0), \tag{3.14}$$

so that the solution obtained in Theorem 2.3 is

$$P(x, t) = \sum_{0}^{\infty} P_n(x, t) = \sum_{0}^{\infty} e^{-\lambda t} \frac{(\lambda t)^n}{n!} B_n(x) \tag{3.15}$$

which is identical with (3.11).

EXAMPLE 3.1.   Let $X(t)$ be the distance of a stone on a river bed at time t from its position at $t = 0$. The stone will lie on the river bed for a relatively long time; however, at some stage it will move down the river. The probability of a displacement occurring during $(t, t + \Delta t]$ is $\lambda \Delta t + o(\Delta t)$ independently of t (at least as a first approximation). Moreover, the magnitude of the displacement is a random variable having the d.f. $B(x)$ $(x \geqslant 0)$. This situation is described by (3.1), and therefore $X(t)$ is a compound Poisson process with the transition d.f.

$$\Pr\{X(t) \leqslant x \mid X(0) = 0\} = \begin{cases} \displaystyle\sum_0^\infty e^{-\lambda t}\frac{(\lambda t)^n}{n!}B_n(x) & (x \geqslant 0) \\ \\ 0 & (x < 0). \end{cases} \tag{3.16}$$

EXAMPLE 3.2.   The theory of collective risk, developed by Swedish actuaries, deals with the business of an insurance company, and is based on the following mathematical model: (a) During a time interval $(t, t + \Delta t]$, the probability of a claim occurring is $\Delta t + o(\Delta t)$, and the probability of more than one claim occurring is $o(\Delta t)$, these probabilities being independent of the claims which have occurred during $(0, t]$; (b) if a claim does occur, the amount claimed is a random variable with the d.f. $B(x)$ $(-\infty < x < \infty)$, negative claims occurring in the case of ordinary whole-life annuities.

It is clear that under these assumptions, the total amount $X(t)$ of all claims received by the company is a compound Poisson process whose transition d.f. is given by (3.11) (with $\lambda = 1$). Now suppose that (c) during an interval of length t, the company receives an amount μt from the totality of its policyholders; μt is called the gross risk premium. The function $Y(t) = u + \mu t - X(t)$ is called the risk reserve, with the initial value $Y(0) = u$. The presence of the term μt in $Y(t)$ indicates that in the process $Y(t)$, changes of state occur (although in a deterministic fashion) between jumps, these being the same as in $X(t)$ but with the directions reversed.

4. THE DENUMERABLE CASE

If the possible values of $X(t)$ are $\ldots, -1, 0, 1, 2, \ldots$, the process is said to be denumerable. In this case the functions

$$P_{jk}(\tau, t) = \Pr\{X(t) = k \mid X(\tau) = j\} \qquad (t \geqslant \tau \geqslant 0)$$
$$(j, k = \ldots, -1, 0, 1, 2, \ldots) \tag{4.1}$$

define the transition probabilities of the process; also let

$$P_{jk}(t, t) = \delta_{jk} = \begin{cases} 0 & \text{if } j \neq k \\ 1 & \text{if } j = k. \end{cases} \tag{4.2}$$

We have

$$P_{jk}(\tau, t) \geqslant 0, \qquad \sum_k P_{jk}(\tau, t) = 1; \tag{4.3}$$

the Chapman–Kolmogorov equations in this case are

$$P_{jk}(\tau, t) = \sum_k P_{jv}(\tau, s)P_{vk}(s, t) \qquad (\tau < s < t). \tag{4.4}$$

The denumerable Markov process $X(t)$ is said to be purely discontinuous if the following assumptions are satisfied.

(i) To every state j there corresponds a function $c_j(t)$ such that

$$\lim_{\Delta t \to 0} \frac{1 - P_{jj}(t, t + \Delta t)}{\Delta t} = c_j(t). \tag{4.5}$$

(ii) To every pair of states (j, k) with $j \neq k$, there corresponds a transition probability $\pi_{jk}(t)$ such that

$$\lim_{\Delta t \to 0} \frac{P_{jk}(t, t + \Delta t)}{\Delta t} = c_j(t)\pi_{jk}(t) \qquad (j \neq k). \tag{4.6}$$

The functions $c_j(t)$ and $\pi_{jk}(t)$ are continuous in t, and

$$c_j(t) \geqslant 0, \qquad \pi_{jj}(t) = 0, \qquad \sum_k \pi_{jk}(t) = 1. \tag{4.7}$$

It is clear that assumptions (i) and (ii) are equivalent to (1) and (2) of the general case; they lead to the *backward* equation

$$\frac{\partial}{\partial \tau} P_{jk}(\tau, t) = c_j(\tau)P_{jk}(\tau, t) - c_j(\tau) \sum_v \pi_{jv}(\tau) P_{vk}(\tau, t). \tag{4.8}$$

For the *forward* equation, however, we need a third assumption, namely:
(iii) For fixed k the limit in (4.6) is uniform with respect to j.
The forward equation is then

$$\frac{\partial}{\partial t} P_{jk}(\tau, t) = - c_k(t)P_{jk}(\tau, t) + \sum_v P_{jv}(\tau, t)c_v(t)\pi_{vk}(t). \tag{4.9}$$

The two systems of difference-differential equations (4.8) and (4.9) are the denumerable versions of the integro-differential equations discussed in Section 2, and were derived by Kolmogorov (1931). [See also Feller (1957).]

In the time-homogeneous case we shall use the simpler notation

$$P_{jk}(t) = \text{Pr}\,\{X(\tau + t) = k \,|\, X(\tau) = j\} \tag{4.10}$$

for the transition probabilities. Here $c_j(t)$ and $\pi_{jk}(t)$ are both independent of t, and the equations (4.8) and (4.9) reduce respectively to

$$P'_{jk}(t) = -c_j P_{jk}(t) + c_j \sum_v \pi_{jv} P_{vk}(t) \tag{4.11}$$

$$P'_{jk}(t) = -c_k P_{jk}(t) + \sum_v P_{jv}(t) c_v \pi_{vk}. \tag{4.12}$$

A comprehensive treatment of this case (with a different approach) has been given by Chung (1960).

The remarks made in Section 2 about the existence of solutions of equations (4.8) and (4.9) apply also to the denumerable case. However, in the special case where the number of states is finite, we shall prove that they have a common unique solution. In order to do this, let us suppose that the states are $1, 2, \ldots, N$ $(N < \infty)$ and consider the matrix

$$P(\tau, t) = [P_{jk}(\tau, t)] \qquad (j,k = 1, 2, \ldots, N). \tag{4.13}$$

The conditions (4.2)–(4.6) can be expressed in terms of this matrix as follows:

(i) $P(t, t) = I$, where $I = (\delta_{jk})$ is the unit matrix of order N.

(ii) $P(\tau, t) \geqslant 0$, $P(\tau, t)e = e$, where e is the N-dimensional column vector with the elements $(1, 1, \ldots, 1)$.

(iii) $P(\tau, t) = P(\tau, s)P(s, t)$ $(\tau < s < t)$.

(iv) $\dfrac{I - P(t, t + \Delta t)}{\Delta t} \to -A(t)$, where $A(t) = [a_{jk}(t)]$, and

$$a_{jj}(t) = -c_j(t), \qquad a_{jk}(t) = c_j(t)\pi_{jk}(t) \, (j \neq k) \qquad (j,k = 1, 2, \ldots, N). \tag{4.14}$$

We have

$$a_{jj}(t) \leqslant 0, \qquad a_{jk}(t) \geqslant 0 \tag{4.15}$$

and

$$\sum_{k=1}^{N} a_{jk}(t) = -c_j(t) + c_j(t) \sum_{k \neq j} \pi_{jk}(t) = 0. \tag{4.16}$$

The equations (4.8) and (4.9) can be written as

$$\frac{\partial}{\partial \tau} P(\tau, t) = -A(\tau)P(\tau, t) \tag{4.17}$$

$$\frac{\partial}{\partial t} P(\tau, t) = P(\tau, t)A(t). \tag{4.18}$$

We need the concept of the norm of a matrix; for a square matrix A of order N we define the norm $\|A\|$ as

$$\|A\| = \sum_{j,k=1}^{N} |a_{jk}|. \tag{4.19}$$

This norm has the following properties:
  (a) $\|A\| = 0$ if, and only if, A is a null matrix.
  (b) If c is a constant, then $\|cA\| = |c|\|A\|$.
  (c) If A and B are two matrices of order N, then

$$\|A + B\| \leqslant \|A\| + \|B\|, \qquad \|AB\| \leqslant \|A\|\|B\|. \qquad (4.20)$$

  (d) If the elements of A are continuous functions of s, then

$$\left\| \int_{c_1}^{c_2} A(s)\,ds \right\| \leqslant \int_{c_1}^{c_2} \|A(s)\,ds\| \qquad (c_1 < c_2). \qquad (4.21)$$

THEOREM 4.1. *Let us define a sequence* $\{P^{(n)}(\tau, t)\}$ *of matrices as follows:*

$$P^{(0)}(\tau, t) = I, \quad P^{(n)}(\tau, t) = \int_{\tau}^{t} P^{(n-1)}(\tau, s)A(s)\,ds \qquad (n \geqslant 1). \qquad (4.22)$$

Then if

$$P(\tau, t) = \sum_{n=0}^{\infty} P^{(n)}(\tau, t), \qquad (4.23)$$

$P(\tau, t)$ *is the common unique solution of the forward and backward equations of a purely discontinuous process with a finite number of states, and this solution satisfies the conditions* (i)–(iv).

Proof:[1] Integrating the equations (4.17) and (4.18) and using the condition $P(t, t) = I$, we obtain respectively

$$P(\tau, t) = I + \int_{\tau}^{t} A(s)P(s, t)\,ds \qquad (4.24)$$

$$P(\tau, t) = I + \int_{\tau}^{t} P(\tau, s)A(s)\,ds. \qquad (4.25)$$

Let $T \geqslant \tau$ be an arbitrary number, and

$$m = \max_{\tau \leqslant s \leqslant T} \|A(s)\|; \qquad (4.26)$$

$m < \infty$ since the $a_{jk}(t)$ are continuous functions of t. Let us ignore the trivial case where $m = 0$.
  (a) We shall first prove that each of the equations (4.24)–(4.25) has at most one solution. For, let P and Q be two solutions, and

$$m_1 = \max_{\tau \leqslant s \leqslant T} \|P - Q\|, \qquad 0 < m_1 < \infty;$$

then, considering the forward equation (4.25), we find that $P - Q$ must

[1] cf. Bellman (1960).

satisfy the equation

$$P - Q = \int_{\tau}^{t} (P - Q)A(s)\, ds. \tag{4.27}$$

We have

$$\|P - Q\| \leqslant \int_{\tau}^{t} \|P - Q\| \, \|A(s)\| \, ds$$

$$\leqslant m_1 \int_{\tau}^{t} \|A(s)\| \, ds \tag{4.28}$$

$$\leqslant m_1 m(t - \tau) \qquad (\tau \leqslant t \leqslant T).$$

Using (4.28) in (4.27) we obtain

$$\|P - Q\| \leqslant m_1 m \int_{\tau}^{t} (s - \tau) \|A(s)\| \, ds$$

$$\leqslant m_1 m^2 \int_{\tau}^{t} (s - \tau) \, ds$$

$$= m_1 \frac{m^2(t - \tau)^2}{2!} \qquad (\tau \leqslant t \leqslant T),$$

and proceeding in this manner, we find that

$$\|P - Q\| \leqslant m_1 \frac{m^n(t - \tau)^n}{n!} \to 0 \qquad \text{as } n \to \infty. \tag{4.29}$$

It follows that $\|P - Q\| = 0$, and therefore $P = Q$, which shows that the forward equation has not more than one solution. A similar result holds for the backward equation.

(b) Now consider the matrices defined by (4.22). We have

$$\|P^{(0)}(\tau, t)\| = 1,$$

$$\|P^{(1)}(\tau, t)\| \leqslant \int_{\tau}^{t} \|P^{(0)}(\tau, s)\| \, \|A(s)\| \, ds$$

$$\leqslant m(t - \tau) \qquad (\tau \leqslant t \leqslant T),$$

and proceeding as in (4.29) we find that

$$\|P^{(n)}(\tau, t)\| \leqslant \frac{m^n(t - \tau)^n}{n!} \qquad (n = 0, 1, 2; \ldots; \ \tau \leqslant t \leqslant T). \tag{4.30}$$

This shows that the series $\sum_{0}^{\infty} P^{(n)}(\tau, t)$ is uniformly convergent in $[\tau, T]$. Moreover, from (4.22) it follows that

$$P(\tau, t) = I + \int_{\tau}^{t} P(\tau, s)A(s)\, ds, \tag{4.31}$$

which shows that $P(\tau, t)$ defined by (4.23) satisfies the forward equation (4.25), and by (a) it is its unique solution.

Now, we have

$$P^{(0)}(\tau, t) = I, \quad P^{(1)}(\tau, t) = \int_{\tau}^{t} A(s)\, ds = \int_{\tau}^{t} A(s)P^{(0)}(s, t)\, ds,$$

$$P^{(2)}(\tau, t) = \int_{\tau}^{t} ds_1 \int_{\tau}^{s_1} A(s_2)\, ds_2\, A(s_1)$$

$$= \int_{\tau}^{t} ds_2 A(s_2) \int_{s_2}^{t} A(s_1)\, ds_1$$

$$= \int_{\tau}^{t} A(s_2)P^{(1)}(s_2, t)\, ds_2,$$

and quite generally

$$P^{(n)}(\tau, t) = \int_{\tau}^{t} A(s)P^{(n-1)}(s, t)\, ds \qquad (n \geqslant 1). \tag{4.32}$$

Adding (4.32) over $n = 1, 2, \ldots$, we obtain

$$P(\tau, t) = I + \int_{\tau}^{t} A(s)P(s, t)\, ds, \tag{4.33}$$

which shows that the function defined by (4.23) satisfies the backward equation, and again, by (a) is its unique solution.

(c) We shall now prove that the unique solution obtained above satisfies the conditions (i)–(iv). From (4.22) we obtain

$$P^{(0)}(t, t) = I, \qquad P^{(n)}(t, t) = 0 \qquad (n \geqslant 1), \tag{4.34}$$

so that $P(\tau, t) = I$, which is the condition (i). Also,

$$P^{(0)}(t, t + \Delta t) = I,$$

$$P^{(n)}(t, t + \Delta t) = \begin{cases} A(t)\Delta t + o(\Delta t) & (n = 1) \\ o(\Delta t) & (n > 1), \end{cases} \tag{4.35}$$

which lead to (iv). Next, we note that the $P^{(n)}(\tau, t)$ satisfy the relations

$$P^{(n)}(\tau, t) = \sum_{k=0}^{n} P^{(k)}(\tau, s)P^{(n-k)}(s, t) \qquad (\tau < s < t), \tag{4.36}$$

which can be established by induction. Adding (4.36) over $n = 0, 1, 2, \ldots$, we obtain (iii). Finally, from (4.35) we find that

$$P(\tau, \tau + h') = I + A(\tau)h' + o(h'), \tag{4.37}$$

so that $P(\tau, t) \geqslant 0$ for t in the neighborhood of τ. Suppose that there exists a finite δ which is the maximum value of h' such that $P(\tau, t) \geqslant 0$ for $\tau < t \leqslant$

$\tau + h'$. Then from (iii) we have

$$P(\tau, \tau + h) = P(\tau, \tau + h')P(\tau + h', \tau + h) \geqslant 0 \qquad (h' < h \leqslant 2h'). \ (4.38)$$

which contradicts the hypothesis about δ. Hence $P(\tau, t) \geqslant 0$ for all $t \geqslant \tau$. Moreover, since $P^{(0)}(\tau, t)e = e$, $P^{(n)}(\tau, t)e = 0$ $(n \geqslant 1)$, we have $P(\tau, t)e = e$. This proves (ii), and the proof of Theorem 4.1 is complete.

In the time-homogeneous case, the matrix $A(t)$ is independent of t, and the equations (4.17) and (4.18) reduce to

$$P'(t) = AP(t), \qquad P'(t) = P(t)A, \tag{4.39}$$

whose unique solution is given by

$$P(t) = e^{tA}. \tag{4.40}$$

This result also follows from (4.22) and (4.23).

5. THE POISSON PROCESS

Consider the process for which

$$P_{jj}(t, t + \Delta t) = 1 - \lambda(t)\Delta t + o(\Delta t) \tag{5.1}$$

$$P_{jk}(t, t + \Delta t) = \begin{cases} \lambda(t)\Delta t + o(\Delta t) & \text{if } k = j + 1 \\ o(\Delta t) & \text{if } k \neq j, \neq j + 1, \end{cases}$$

$(j, k = 0, 1, 2, \ldots)$, where $\lambda(t)$ is a continuous function of t. In this case the assumptions (i)–(iii) of Section 4 are valid, and

$$c_j(t) = \lambda(t), \qquad \pi_{jj+1} = 1, \qquad \pi_{jk} = 0 \qquad (\text{if } k \neq j + 1). \tag{5.2}$$

The forward equations of the process are given by

$$\frac{\partial}{\partial t}P_{j0}(\tau, t) = -\lambda(t)P_{j0}(\tau, t)$$

$$\frac{\partial}{\partial t}P_{jk}(\tau, t) = -\lambda(t)P_{jk}(\tau, t) + \lambda(t)P_{jk-1}(\tau, t) \qquad (k \geqslant 1), \tag{5.3}$$

and the backward equations by

$$\frac{\partial}{\partial \tau}P_{jk}(\tau, t) = \lambda(\tau)P_{jk}(\tau, t) - \lambda(\tau)P_{j+1,k}(\tau, t) \qquad (j \geqslant 0). \tag{5.4}$$

THEOREM 5.1. *The unique solution of the forward and backward equations of the process defined by* (5.1) *is given by*

$$P_{jk}(\tau, t) = \begin{cases} e^{-\Lambda(\tau,t)}[\Lambda(\tau, t)]^{k-j}/(k - j)! & (k \geqslant j) \\ 0 & (k < j), \end{cases} \tag{5.5}$$

where

$$\Lambda(\tau, t) = \int_{\tau}^{t} \lambda(s)\, ds \qquad (t > \tau \geqslant 0). \tag{5.6}$$

Proof: Let us first consider the forward equations, and define the probability generating function (p.g.f.)

$$G_j(z; \tau, t) = \sum_{k=0}^{\infty} P_{jk}(\tau, t) z^k \qquad (|z| < 1). \tag{5.7}$$

Multiplying the equations (5.3) successively by $1, z, z^2, \ldots$, and adding, we obtain

$$\frac{\partial}{\partial t} G_j(z; \tau, t) = -\lambda(t) G_j(z; \tau, t) + \lambda(t) z G_j(z; \tau, t),$$

or

$$\frac{\partial G}{\partial t} = -\lambda(t)(1 - z)G, \tag{5.8}$$

where $G \equiv G_j(z; \tau, t)$. The difference-differential equations (5.3) have thus been replaced by a single differential equation (5.8); to solve this, we multiply both sides of (5.8) by the factor

$$\exp\left[\Lambda(\tau, t)(1 - z)\right] = \exp\left[(1 - z) \int_{\tau}^{t} \lambda(s)\, ds\right].$$

We then obtain

$$\frac{\partial}{\partial t} \left\{ G e^{\Lambda(\tau,t)(1-z)} \right\} = 0,$$

which gives

$$G_j(z; \tau, t) = A e^{-\Lambda(\tau,t)(1-z)},$$

where A is determined from the condition that $G_j(z; t, t) = \sum_{k} \delta_{jk} z^k = z^j$. Thus $A = z^j$, and

$$G_j(z; \tau, t) = z^j e^{-\Lambda(\tau,t)(1-z)}. \tag{5.9}$$

Expanding (5.9) as a power series in z, we find that (5.5) gives the unique solution of the forward equations.

To solve the backward equations, we note from (5.2) that $P_{jk}(\tau, t) = 0$ for $j > k$. Therefore, putting $j = k$ in (5.4) we obtain the equation

$$\frac{\partial}{\partial \tau} P_{kk}(\tau, t) = \lambda(\tau) P_{kk}(\tau, t) \tag{5.10}$$

for $P_{kk}(\tau, t)$; proceeding as in (5.8), we obtain

$$P_{kk}(\tau, t) = e^{-\Lambda(\tau,t)}. \tag{5.11}$$

Substituting (5.11) in (5.4) with $j = k - 1$ we obtain

$$\frac{\partial}{\partial \tau} P_{k-1,k}(\tau, t) = \lambda(\tau) P_{k-1,k}(\tau, t) - \lambda(\tau) e^{-\Lambda(\tau,t)}, \tag{5.12}$$

whence we find that

$$P_{k-1,k}(\tau, t) = e^{-\Lambda(\tau,t)} \Lambda(\tau, t). \tag{5.13}$$

Proceeding in this manner we arrive at the solution (5.5). We have thus proved that (5.5) is the common unique solution of the two systems of equations.

Clearly, $P_{jk}(\tau, t) \geqslant 0$, and

$$\sum_{k=0}^{\infty} P_{jk}(\tau, t) = \lim_{z \to 1-0} G_j(z; \tau, t) = 1. \tag{5.14}$$

The process specified by (5.1) is called the (nonhomogeneous) Poisson process. When $\lambda(t) = \lambda$ (a constant), we obtain the homogeneous Poisson process, for which the transition probabilities are given by

$$P_{jk}(t) = \begin{cases} e^{-\lambda t}(\lambda t)^{k-j}/(k-j)! & (k \geqslant j) \\ 0 & (k < j). \end{cases} \tag{5.15}$$

The mean and variance of this process (assuming $j = 0$) are given by

$$E\{X(t)\} = \lambda t, \qquad \mathrm{Var}\,\{X(t)\} = \lambda t. \tag{5.16}$$

In the remainder of this section we deal only with this time-homogeneous process.

THEOREM 5.2.   *Let $X(t)$ be a time-homogeneous Poisson process, with $X(0) = j$. Consider the random variable*

$$T_j = \inf \{t \,|\, X(t) = j + 1\}; \tag{5.17}$$

T_j *is the time of occurrence of the first jump after the jth. Then*
   (a) T_j, T_{j+1}, ... *are mutually independent, having the negative exponential distribution*

$$\lambda e^{-\lambda t}\, dt \qquad (0 < t < \infty) \tag{5.18}$$

(in particular, each T_j is finite with probability one), and
   (b) *if $\tau_n = T_j + T_{j+1} + \cdots + T_{n-1}$, then $\tau_n \to \infty$ with probability one.*

   Proof: Let

$$\Pr \{T_j > t\} = Q(t) \qquad (Q(0) = 1). \tag{5.19}$$

From the assumptions (5.1) we find that

$$Q(t + \Delta t) = Q(t)P_{jj}(\Delta t)$$
$$= Q(t)(1 - \lambda \Delta t) + o(\Delta t),$$
(5.20)

which gives

$$\frac{Q(t + \Delta t) - Q(t)}{\Delta t} = -\lambda Q(t) + \frac{o(\Delta t)}{\Delta t},$$

or, in the limit as $\Delta t \to 0$,

$$Q'(t) = -\lambda Q(t),$$
(5.21)

which gives $Q(t) = e^{-\lambda t}$ $(t \geqslant 0)$. Hence

$$\Pr\{T_j \leqslant t\} = 1 - e^{-\lambda t} \qquad (t \geqslant 0)$$
(5.22)

gives the d.f. of the random variable T_j, the corresponding frequency function being given by (5.18). Since the process $X(t)$ is Markovian, $T_j, T_{j+1}, \ldots$ are mutually independent. From (5.22) we have $\Pr\{T_j < \infty\} = 1$. We have thus proved (a).

To prove (b), let us note that the characteristic function (c.f.) of T_j is given by

$$\int_0^\infty e^{i\theta t} \lambda e^{-\lambda t}\, dt = \left(1 - \frac{i\theta}{\lambda}\right)^{-1};$$
(5.23)

since $T_j, T_{j+1}, \ldots$ are mutually independent and identically distributed, the c.f. of τ_n is given by

$$\phi_n(\theta) = \left(1 - \frac{i\theta}{\lambda}\right)^{j-n} \qquad (n > j).$$
(5.24)

We have

$$|\phi_n(\theta)| = \left(1 + \frac{\theta^2}{\lambda^2}\right)^{(j-n)/2} \to 0 \qquad \text{as } n \to \infty,$$
(5.25)

and therefore $\tau_n \to \infty$ with probability one, as required.

Let us remark here that the result (5.18) also follows from the fact that $P_{jj}(t) = e^{-\lambda t}$ [see (5.15)]. However, it is instructive to derive it from the basic assumptions, as we have done. Further, the result (b) of Theorem 5.2 implies that the discontinuities of the process are all jumps, there being only a finite number of jumps in any finite interval $(0, t]$.

In applications it is customary to speak of an event E occurring in time, subject to the assumptions that during $(t, t + \Delta t]$, (i) the probability that E occurs once is $\lambda \Delta t + o(\Delta t)$, and (ii) the probability that E occurs more than once is $o(\Delta t)$, independently of the number of occurrences in $(0, t]$. If $X(t)$ is the number of occurrences of E during $(0, t]$, it is clear from these assumptions that $X(t)$ is precisely the process discussed here, with transition probabilities given by (5.15). We thus have an event E occurring in a Poisson process; Theorem 5.2 implies that in any finite interval, E occurs only a finite number of times, the time intervals between successive occurrences being mutually independent random variables with the distribution (5.18). This dual relationship between the Poisson distribution (5.15) and the negative exponential distribution (5.18) has important applications. Finally, we remark that E is also called a *purely random* event; this term is explained by the following theorem:

THEOREM 5.3. *The probability distribution of the time T_1 at which E occurs in $(0, T]$, given that it has occurred exactly once in that interval, is given by*

$$\Pr\{t < T_1 < t + dt \quad (0 < t \leqslant T) | X(T) = 1\} = \frac{dt}{T} \qquad (0 < t < T). \quad (5.26)$$

Proof: The required conditional distribution is given by

$$\frac{\Pr\{t < T_1 < t + dt; X(T) = 1\}}{\Pr\{X(T) = 1\}}$$

$$= \frac{\Pr\{t < T_1 < t + dt\} \cdot \Pr\{X(T) = 1 | T_1 = t\}}{e^{-\lambda T}(\lambda T)} \qquad (5.27)$$

$$= \frac{\lambda e^{-\lambda t} \, dt \cdot e^{-\lambda(T-t)}}{e^{-\lambda T}(\lambda T)} = \frac{dt}{T},$$

as required. Here we have used the result (5.18) and the fact that $X(t)$ is a Markov process.

6. THE BIRTH AND DEATH PROCESS

An important special case of the denumerable Markov process is the birth and death process, in which during a time interval $(t, t + \Delta t]$, a change of state from j to either $j + 1$ (a birth) or to $j - 1$ (a death) occurs with probability $\lambda_j \Delta t + o(\Delta t)$ or $\mu_j \Delta t + o(\Delta t)$, respectively, the probability of any other change of state being $o(\Delta t)$. Here the λ_j and μ_j are nonnegative constants; the process is therefore time homogeneous, and we have

$$P_{jj}(\Delta t) = 1 - (\lambda_j + \mu_j)\Delta t + o(\Delta t)$$

$$P_{jk}(\Delta t) = \begin{cases} \lambda_j \Delta t + o(\Delta t) & \text{if } k = j + 1 \\ \mu_j \Delta t + o(\Delta t) & \text{if } k = j - 1 \\ o(\Delta t) & \text{if } k \neq j, \, \neq j + 1, \, \neq j - 1 \ (j, k = 0, 1, 2, \ldots). \end{cases} \quad (6.1)$$

In the notation of Section 4, we have

$$c_j(t) = (\lambda_j + \mu_j), \quad \pi_{jk} = \begin{cases} \dfrac{\lambda_j}{\lambda_j + \mu_j} & \text{if } k = j + 1 \\[2ex] \dfrac{\mu_j}{\lambda_j + \mu_j} & \text{if } k = j - 1. \end{cases} \tag{6.2}$$

The forward equations of the process are found to be

$$P'_{jk}(t) = -(\lambda_k + \mu_k)P_{jk}(t) + \lambda_{k-1}P_{jk-1}(t) + \mu_{k+1}P_{jk+1}(t) \tag{6.3}$$

and the backward equations are

$$P'_{jk}(t) = -(\lambda_j + \mu_j)P_{jk}(t) + \mu_j P_{j-1,k}(t) + \lambda_j P_{j+1,k}(t)$$
$$(j, k \geqslant 0, \mu_0 = 0, \lambda_{-1} = 0). \tag{6.4}$$

Birth and death processes were introduced by Feller (1939), and have since been used to describe stochastic models for population growth (see Section 7), queues, epidemiology [see, for instance Bailey (1957), and Prabhu (1965)], and several other situations. Theoretical investigations have been carried out by Lederman and Reuter (1954), Karlin and Mc-Gregor [(1957a), (1957b)], and others.

In this section we shall study the special case of the *pure birth process*, where $\mu_j = 0$ ($j \geqslant 0$). The equations (6.3) and (6.4) then simplify to

$$P'_{jk}(t) = -\lambda_k P_{jk}(t) + \lambda_{k-1}P_{jk-1}(t) \qquad (k \geqslant 0) \tag{6.5}$$

and

$$P'_{jk}(t) = -\lambda_j P_{jk}(t) + \lambda_j P_{j+1,k}(t) \qquad (j \geqslant 0). \tag{6.6}$$

Here $\lambda_j \geqslant 0$ ($j \geqslant 1$); if $\lambda_0 = 0$, then the state 0 is an absorbing state, since if $X(t) = 0$ at some point t, then no births occur during $(t, t + \Delta t]$ and the process terminates. We shall, however, assume that $\lambda_0 \geqslant 0$. We then have the following theorems:

THEOREM 6.1. *The forward equations of the pure birth process with the λ_j all distinct, have the unique solution given by*

$$P_{jk}(t) = \begin{cases} 0 & (k < j) \\[2ex] \displaystyle\sum_{v=j}^{k} A_{jk}^{(v)} e^{-\lambda_v t} & (k \geqslant j), \end{cases} \tag{6.7}$$

where

$$A_{jk}^{(v)} = \frac{\lambda_j \lambda_{j+1} \cdots \lambda_{k-1}}{(\lambda_j - \lambda_v)(\lambda_{j+1} - \lambda_v) \cdots (\lambda_{v-1} - \lambda_v)(\lambda_{v+1} - \lambda_v) \cdots (\lambda_k - \lambda_v)} \tag{6.8}$$

For the solution (6.7) we have $\Sigma P_{jk}(t) = 1$ *if, and only if, the series*

$$\frac{1}{\lambda_j} + \frac{1}{\lambda_{j+1}} + \cdots = \infty. \tag{6.9}$$

Proof: Let us introduce the Laplace transform (L.T.)

$$P_{jk}^*(\theta) = \int_0^\infty e^{-\theta t} P_{jk}(t)\, dt \qquad (\theta > 0). \tag{6.10}$$

We have

$$\int_0^\infty e^{-\theta t} P'_{jk}(t)\, dt = \left[e^{-\theta t} P_{jk}(t) \right]_0^\infty + \theta \int_0^\infty e^{-\theta t} P_{jk}(t)\, dt$$
$$= -\delta_{jk} + \theta P_{jk}^*(\theta). \tag{6.11}$$

Taking transforms of both sides of the forward equations (6.5) and simplifying, we obtain

$$(\theta + \lambda_k) P_{jk}^*(\theta) = \delta_{jk} + \lambda_{k-1} P_{jk-1}^*(\theta) \qquad (k \geq 0). \tag{6.12}$$

Solving successively for $k = 0, 1, \ldots$, we find from (6.12) that $P_{jk}^*(\theta) = 0$ for $k < j$, and

$$P_{jk}^*(\theta) = \frac{\lambda_j \lambda_{j+1} \cdots \lambda_{k-1}}{(\theta + \lambda_j)(\theta + \lambda_{j+1}) \cdots (\theta + \lambda_k)}. \qquad (k \geq j). \tag{6.13}$$

Expressing the right-hand side of (6.13) in partial fractions, we obtain

$$P_{jk}^*(\theta) = \sum_{v=j}^k \frac{A_{jk}^{(v)}}{\theta + \lambda_v}, \tag{6.14}$$

where

$$A_{jk}^{(v)} = \lim_{\theta \to -\lambda_v} (\theta + \lambda_v) P_{jk}^*(\theta), \tag{6.15}$$

which leads to (6.8). Since the inverse transform of $(\theta + \lambda_v)^{-1}$ is known to be $e^{-\lambda_v t}$ ($t \geq 0$), (6.14) gives the required result (6.7).

To prove the second part of the theorem, let us add the equations (6.5) over $k = 0, 1, \ldots, k$; then we obtain for $k \geq j$,

$$S'_{jk}(t) = -\lambda_k P_{jk}(t), \tag{6.16}$$

where

$$S_{jk}(t) = P_{jj}(t) + P_{jj+1}(t) + \cdots + P_{jk}(t). \tag{6.17}$$

Now let us define the L.T.

$$S_{jk}^*(\theta) = \int_0^\infty e^{-\theta t} S_{jk}(t)\, dt. \tag{6.18}$$

From (6.16) we then obtain, since $S_{jk}(0) = 1$,

$$\theta S_{jk}^*(\theta) = 1 - \lambda_k P_{jk}^*(\theta). \qquad (6.19)$$

From (6.13) we find that

$$\lim_{k \to \infty} \lambda_k P_{jk}^*(\theta) = \begin{cases} 0 & \text{if } \sum \dfrac{1}{\lambda_v} = \infty. \\[2ex] \prod_j^\infty \left(1 + \dfrac{\theta}{\lambda_v}\right)^{-1} & \text{if } \sum \dfrac{1}{\lambda_v} < \infty. \end{cases} \qquad (6.20)$$

Hence it follows that $\lim_{k \to \infty} \theta S_{jk}^*(\theta) = 1$ or <1 according as the series (6.9) diverges or not. In the first case we must have $\lim_{k \to \infty} S_{jk}(t) = 1$ and in the second case $\lim_{k \to \infty} S_{jk}(t) < 1$ for all finite t, where

$$\lim_{k \to \infty} S_{jk}(t) = \sum_k P_{jk}(t). \qquad (6.21)$$

The proof of Theorem 6.1 is therefore complete.

The result (6.7) is due to Feller (1940), and the criterion (6.9) is due to Feller (1940) and Lundberg (1940). The following theorem is also due to Feller (1957).

THEOREM 6.2.   *The solution (6.7) of the forward equations of the pure birth process also satisfies the backward equations. Let us denote this solution as $F_{jk}(t)$, and let $P_{jk}(t)$ be an arbitrary nonnegative solution of the backward equations. Then*

$$P_{jk}(t) \geqslant F_{jk}(t). \qquad (6.22)$$

Proof: Proceeding as in (6.5) we obtain from (6.6)

$$(\theta + \lambda_j) P_{jk}^*(\theta) = \delta_{jk} + \lambda_j P_{j+1,k}^*(\theta) \qquad (j \geqslant 0). \qquad (6.23)$$

Let $P_{jk}^*(\theta) = 0 = F_{jk}^*(\theta)$ for $j > k$. Then solving for $j = k, k - 1, \ldots$ we obtain for $j \leqslant k$,

$$P_{jk}^*(\theta) = \frac{\lambda_{k-1}\lambda_{k-2} \cdots \lambda_j}{(\theta + \lambda_k)(\theta + \lambda_{k-1}) \ldots (\theta + \lambda_j)} = F_{jk}^*(\theta); \qquad (6.24)$$

from (6.13). Therefore $P_{jk}^*(\theta) = F_{jk}(\theta)$ is a solution of the backward equations.

Now integrating the equations (6.6) we obtain

$$P_{jk}(t) = \delta_{jk} e^{-\lambda_j t} + \lambda_j \int_0^t P_{j+1,k}(t - s) e^{-\lambda_j s}\, ds. \qquad (6.25)$$

For $j > k$ we have $P_{jk}(t) \geqslant 0$, while $F_{jk}(t) = 0$, so that (6.21) is satisfied for $j > k$. Putting $j = k$ in (6.25) we obtain

$$P_{kk}(t) \geqslant e^{-\lambda_k t} = F_{kk}(t), \tag{6.26}$$

and using (6.26) in (6.25) with $j = k - 1$, we obtain

$$P_{k-1,k}(t) \geqslant \lambda_{k-1} \int_0^t F_{kk}(t-s)e^{-\lambda_{k-1}(s)} ds$$
$$= F_{k-1,k}(t), \tag{6.27}$$

since $F_{jk}(t)$ satisfies (6.25). Proceeding in this manner we obtain (6.22) for all j, and the theorem is proved.

COROLLARY 6.3.   *If the series (6.9) diverges, the forward and the backward equations have the unique solution given by (6.7).*

Proof: Adding (6.22) over $k = 0, 1, 2, \ldots$, we obtain

$$\sum_{k=0}^{\infty} P_{jk}(t) \geqslant \sum_{k=0}^{\infty} F_{jk}(t). \tag{6.28}$$

If now the series (6.9) diverges, then $\sum_k F_{jk}(t) = 1$ by Theorem 6.1, and equation (6.28) gives $\sum P_{jk}(t) \geqslant 1$. In this case we must have $\sum_k P_{jk}(t) = 1$, which is possible if, and only if, equality holds in (6.22) for every k and finite t.

Further light is thrown on the problem of uniqueness of solutions of the two equations by the following theorem:

THEOREM 6.3.   *For the pure birth process $X(t)$ with $X(0) = j$, let T_j be the random variable defined by*

$$T_j = \inf \{t | X(t) = j + 1\}. \tag{6.29}$$

Then (a) $T_j, T_{j+1}, \ldots$ are mutually independent, T_j having the distribution

$$\lambda_j e^{-\lambda_j t} dt \qquad (0 < t < \infty); \tag{6.30}$$

and (b) if $\tau_n = T_j + T_{j+1} + \cdots + T_{n-1}$, then $\tau_n \to \infty$ with probability one if the series (6.9) diverges, and $\tau_n \to \tau < \infty$ with probability one if (6.9) converges.

Proof: The result (a) is analogous to (a) of Theorem 5.2, and can be proved similarly. In this case the T_j have negative exponential distributions with different parameters. To prove (b) we note that the c.f. of τ_n is given by

$$\phi_n(\theta) = \prod_{v=j}^{n-1} \left(1 - \frac{i\theta}{\lambda_v}\right)^{-1}. \tag{6.31}$$

We have

$$
\phi_n(\theta) \to
\begin{cases}
0 & \text{if } \sum \dfrac{1}{\lambda_v} = \infty \\[4ex]
\displaystyle\prod_{v=j}^{\infty}\left(1 - \dfrac{i\theta}{\lambda_v}\right)^{-1} & \text{if } \sum \dfrac{1}{\lambda} < \infty.
\end{cases}
\tag{6.32}
$$

From (6.32) it follows that with probability one $\tau_n \to \infty$ or $\tau_n \to \tau$ according as the series (6.9) diverges or not, where τ is a random variable with the c.f.

$$
\prod_{v=j}^{\infty}\left(1 - \frac{i\theta}{\lambda_v}\right)^{-1}.
\tag{6.33}
$$

The interpretation of the above result (b) is that if the series (6.9) diverges, then the discontinuities of the process are all jumps, there being only a finite number of jumps in any finite interval; the situation in this case is exactly as in the Poisson process. However, if (6.9) converges, then there is a (random) point of accumulation of jumps; if this occurs at τ (say), then the Markov property of the process indicates that the process starts anew from τ, and has a second point of accumulation of jumps, and so on. Thus we have discontinuities which are worse than jumps.

7. STOCHASTIC MODELS FOR POPULATION GROWTH

A stochastic model for population growth was described in Chapter 2, Section 7, where the underlying process was the so-called branching process. The problem of extinction in such a model was investigated by Francis Galton and H. W. Watson in 1874, and this seems to be the earliest stochastic treatment of population growth. More recent investigations of stochastic models are based on Feller's (1939) birth and death process defined in Section 6. We shall now describe some of these models; for a more complete treatment and an account of the earlier deterministic models, see Kendall (1949). We remark here that the populations described in this section may be human populations, bacterial colonies [see Bartlett (1960)], or cosmic ray showers [see Arley (1948)]. However, in describing human populations, we take into account only the female component of the population, and, moreover, in the models described below we ignore the age distribution of the population.

The Yule–Furry Process: Consider a population in which (a) there is no interaction among individuals, and (b) during a time interval of length Δt, each individual has a probability $\lambda \Delta t + o(\Delta t)$ of creating a new one. Let $X(t)$ be the number of individuals in the population (briefly, the population size) at time t; then our assumptions imply that $X(t)$ is a pure birth process with $\lambda_j = j\lambda \, (j \geqslant 1)$. Since the series

$$\sum_{j}^{\infty} \frac{1}{\lambda_v} = \frac{1}{\lambda}\left(\frac{1}{j} + \frac{1}{j+1} + \cdots\right) = \infty, \tag{7.1}$$

it follows from Corollary 6.1 that the forward and backward equations of the process have a unique solution. Putting $\lambda_j = j\lambda$ in (6.8) we find that

$$A_{jk}^{(v)} = \frac{j(j+1)\cdots(k-1)}{(j-v)(j+1-v)\cdots(-1)(1)(2)\cdots(k-v)}$$

$$= \binom{k-1}{k-j}\binom{k-j}{v-j}(-1)^{v-j} \qquad (j \leqslant v \leqslant k), \tag{7.2}$$

so that (6.7) gives

$$P_{jk}(t) = \binom{k-1}{k-j}\sum_{v=j}^{k}\binom{k-j}{v-j}(-1)^{v-j}(e^{-\lambda t})^v$$

$$= \binom{-j}{k-j}(-1)^{k-j}e^{-j\lambda t}(1 - e^{-\lambda t})^{k-j} \qquad (k \geqslant j) \tag{7.3}$$

and $P_{jk}(t) = 0$ for $k < j$. Therefore, (7.3) gives the transition probabilities of $X(t)$. Clearly, the (conditional) distribution (7.3) is a negative binomial; its generating function is found to be

$$G(z, t) = \sum_{k=1}^{\infty} P_{jk}(t)z^k = \left(\frac{pz}{1 - qz}\right)^j, \tag{7.4}$$

where $p = e^{-\lambda t}$ and $q = 1 - e^{-\lambda t}$. This result can also be obtained from the forward equations

$$P'_{jk}(t) = -\lambda k P_{jk}(t) + \lambda(k-1)P_{jk-1}(t) \qquad (k \geqslant 1) \tag{7.5}$$

in a manner similar to that used for (7.7) below (see Problem 17). The mean and variance of $X(t)$ are found to be

$$E\{X(t)\} = je^{\lambda t}, \qquad \text{Var}\,\{X(t)\} = je^{\lambda t}(e^{\lambda t} - 1). \tag{7.6}$$

The Feller–Arley Process: Consider the population model described in the previous section; but now let us introduce a third assumption, namely, (c) during an interval of length Δt, an individual has a probability $\mu\Delta t + o(\Delta t)$ of dying. We then obtain a birth and death process, in which $\lambda_j = j\lambda$ and $\mu_j = j\mu \, (j \geqslant 0)$. Let $P_n(t)$ be the probability distribution of $X(t)$ with a given initial condition; then the forward equations of the process are found to be

$$P'_n(t) = -n(\lambda + \mu)P_n(t) + \lambda(n-1)P_{n-1}(t) + \mu(n+1)P_{n+1}(t) \, (n \geqslant 0), \tag{7.7}$$

where $P_n(t) = 0$ for $n < 0$. To solve (7.7), let

$$G(z, t) = \sum_0^\infty P_n(t)z^n, \qquad G(z, 0) = z^j, \tag{7.8}$$

where $X(0) = j(\geqslant 1)$ is the initial population size; we have

$$\frac{\partial G}{\partial t} = \sum_1^\infty nP_n(t)z^{n-1}. \tag{7.9}$$

From (7.7) we then obtain

$$\frac{\partial G}{\partial t} = -(\lambda + \mu)z\frac{\partial G}{\partial z} + \lambda z^2\frac{\partial G}{\partial z} + \mu\frac{\partial G}{\partial z},$$

or

$$\frac{\partial G}{\partial t} - (z - 1)(\lambda z - \mu)\frac{\partial G}{\partial z} = 0. \tag{7.10}$$

To solve the partial differential equation (7.10), we consider the equations

$$\frac{dt}{1} = \frac{dz}{-(z - 1)(\lambda z - \mu)} = \frac{dG}{0}. \tag{7.11}$$

From $dG = 0$ we obtain

$$G = c_1 \text{ (constant)}, \tag{7.12}$$

and from

$$dt = \frac{dz}{-(z - 1)(\lambda z - \mu)}$$

we obtain

$$(\mu - \lambda)t = \log\frac{z - 1}{\lambda z - \mu} + \text{const.}, \qquad \text{or } \frac{\lambda z - \mu}{z - 1}e^{(\mu - \lambda)t} = c_2, \tag{7.13}$$

where c_2 is a constant. Eliminating one of these constants c_1, c_2 we obtain

$$G = \phi\left(\frac{\lambda z - \mu}{z - 1}e^{(\mu - \lambda)t}\right), \tag{7.14}$$

where the function ϕ is to be determined by the initial condition

$$\phi\left(\frac{\lambda z - \mu}{z - 1}\right) = G(z, 0) = z^j,$$

which gives

$$\phi(u) = \left(\frac{\mu - u}{\lambda - u}\right)^j. \tag{7.15}$$

From (7.14) and (7.15) we finally obtain

$$G(z, t) = \left\{ \frac{\mu(e^{(\lambda - \mu)t} - 1) + z(\lambda - \mu e^{(\lambda - \mu)t})}{(\lambda e^{(\lambda - \mu)t} - \mu) - \lambda z(e^{(\lambda - \mu)t} - 1)} \right\}^j, \tag{7.16}$$

leading to the solution of the forward equations (7.7). It can be verified that the solution of the backward equation also has the same solution (Problem 19). Now let us define the functions $\xi = \xi(t)$ and $\eta = \eta(t)$ as follows:

$$\frac{\xi}{\mu} = \frac{\eta}{\lambda} = \frac{e^{(\lambda - \mu)t} - 1}{\lambda e^{(\lambda - \mu)t} - \mu}. \tag{7.17}$$

Then (7.16) can be written as

$$G(z, t) = \left(\frac{\xi + (1 - \xi - \eta)z}{1 - \eta z} \right)^j. \tag{7.18}$$

When $j = 1$, (7.18) gives

$$P_0(t) = \xi, \quad P_n(t) = (1 - \xi)(1 - \eta)\eta^{n-1} \quad (n \geqslant 1), \tag{7.19}$$

which shows that the population size has a geometric distribution with a modified initial term. From (7.19) we find that the mean and variance of the population are given by

$$E\{X(t)\} = e^{(\lambda - \mu)t}$$
$$\text{Var}\{X(t)\} = \frac{\lambda + \mu}{\lambda - \mu} e^{(\lambda - \mu)t} \{e^{(\lambda - \mu)t} - 1\}. \tag{7.20}$$

In (7.19) and (7.20) we have assumed that $\lambda \neq \mu$. If $\lambda = \mu$, we substitute $\lambda - \mu = x$ in these results and make $x \to 0$; thus we find that

$$P_0(t) = \frac{\lambda t}{1 + \lambda t}, \quad P_n(t) = \frac{(\lambda t)^{n-1}}{(1 + \lambda t)^{n+1}} \quad (n \geqslant 1), \tag{7.21}$$

and

$$E\{X(t)\} = 1, \quad \text{Var}\{X(t)\} = 2\lambda t. \tag{7.22}$$

Of particular interest is the probability $P_0(t)$ that the population becomes extinct at or before time t. We have

$$\lim_{t \to \infty} P_0(t) = \begin{cases} 1 & \text{if } \lambda \leqslant \mu \\ \left(\dfrac{\mu}{\lambda} \right)^j & \text{if } \lambda > \mu; \end{cases} \tag{7.23}$$

thus ultimate extinction is a certain event unless the ratio $= \lambda/\mu =$ birth rate/death rate exceeds one. Further, since

$$\lim_{t \to \infty} P_n(t) = 0 \qquad (n \geqslant 1, \lambda > \mu), \tag{7.24}$$

we find that if $\lambda/\mu > 1$, the population either becomes extinct or grows indefinitely large, a result which is analogous to the one in the branching process model.

The Kendall Process: The last two models dealt with closed populations, in which there was no possibility of emigration or immigration. It is clear that introducing an emigration factor would only increase the value of the constant μ. To take into account immigration we introduce the new assumption that (d) during an interval of length Δt there is a probability $v\Delta t + o(\Delta t)$ of a new individual being added to the population from the outside world. We have then a birth and death process for which $\lambda_n = n\lambda + v$ and $\mu_n = n\mu$ $(n \geqslant 0)$, the forward equations being

$$\begin{aligned} P_n'(t) = &-(n\lambda + v)P_n(t) + [\lambda(n-1) + v]P_{n-1}(t) \\ &+ \mu(n+1)P_{n+1}(t) \qquad (n \geqslant 0). \end{aligned} \tag{7.25}$$

Proceeding as before we obtain the differential equation

$$\frac{\partial G}{\partial t} - (\lambda z - \mu)(z - 1)\frac{\partial G}{\partial z} = v(z - 1)G \tag{7.26}$$

for the generating function defined by (7.8). To solve (7.26) we have to consider the equations

$$\frac{dt}{1} = \frac{dz}{-(\lambda z - \mu)(z - 1)} = \frac{dG}{v(z - 1)G}. \tag{7.27}$$

From the first two of the terms in (7.27) we obtain (7.13); from

$$\frac{dz}{-(\lambda z - \mu)(z - 1)} = \frac{dG}{v(z - 1)G}$$

we obtain

$$G(z, t)(\lambda z - \mu)^{v/\lambda} = c_1. \tag{7.28}$$

From (7.13) and (7.28) we find after some simplification that

$$G(z, t) = \left(\frac{p}{1 - qz}\right)^{v/\lambda}, \tag{7.29}$$

where the initial population size is $X(0) = 0$,

$$p = \begin{cases} (\lambda - \mu)/(\lambda e^{(\lambda - \mu)t} - \mu) & (\lambda \neq \mu) \\ (1 + \lambda t)^{-1} & (\lambda = \mu), \end{cases} \tag{7.30}$$

and $q = 1 - p$. From (7.29) we see that $X(t)$ has a negative binomial distribution. As $t \to \infty$, (7.30) shows that $p \to 0$, $q \to 1$ if $\lambda \geqslant \mu$, while $p \to 1 - \lambda/\mu$, $q \to \lambda/\mu$ if $\lambda < \mu$. Therefore, if $\lambda \geqslant \mu$, no limiting distribution exists for $X(t)$ as $t \to \infty$ (that is, $X(t) \to \infty$ with probability one). If $\lambda < \mu$ we find from (7.29) that

$$\lim_{t \to \infty} G(z, t) = \left(1 - \frac{\lambda}{\mu}\right)^{\nu/\lambda} \left(1 - \frac{\lambda}{\mu} z\right)^{-\nu/\lambda}. \tag{7.31}$$

In particular, (7.31) gives

$$\lim_{t \to \infty} P_0(t) = \left(1 - \frac{\lambda}{\mu}\right)^{\nu/\lambda} < 1, \tag{7.32}$$

which shows that there is a positive probability that the population avoids ultimate extinction.

8. COMPLEMENTS AND PROBLEMS

Section 2

1. Let

$$L_n(x_0, \tau; t) = \int_\tau^t d\sigma \int_{-\infty}^\infty p(y, \sigma) \, d_y \bar{P}_n(x_0, \tau; y, \sigma) \qquad (n \geqslant 0). \tag{8.1}$$

Show that the necessary and sufficient condition that $P(x_0, \tau; \infty, t) = 1$ for all t is that

$$\lim_{n \to \infty} L_n(x_0, \tau; t) = 0 \tag{8.2}$$

[Feller (1940)]. In particular, if $p(x, t) \leqslant K$ (a constant), then

$$L_n(x_0, \tau; t) \leqslant K \int_\tau^t d\sigma \bar{P}_n(x_0, \tau; \infty, \sigma), \tag{8.3}$$

and since $\Sigma \, \bar{P}_n(x_0, \tau; \infty, t)$ is a convergent series, this gives $L_n(x_0, \tau; t) \to 0$ as $n \to \infty$.

2. Integrating the backward equation and using the condition (1.3), show that

$$F(x_0, \tau; x, t) = \exp\left[-\int_\tau^t p(x_0, s) \, ds\right] \left\{ \delta(x_0; x) \right. \tag{8.4}$$

$$\left. + \int_\tau^t p(x_0, \sigma) \exp\left[\int_\sigma^t p(x_0, s) \, ds\right] d\sigma \int_{-\infty}^\infty d_y \pi(x_0; y, \sigma) F(y, \tau; x, t). \right.$$

Hence show that if $F(x_0, \tau; x, t)$ is an arbitrary nonnegative solution of the backward equation, and $P(x_0, \tau; x, t)$ is the function defined in

Theorem 2.2, then

$$F(x_0, \tau; x, t) \geqslant P(x_0, \tau; x, t) \tag{8.5}$$

[Feller (1940)]. If $P(x_0, \tau; \infty, t) = 1$, then (8.5) shows that $P(x_0, \tau; x, t)$ is the unique solution of the backward equation.

3. *The Generalized Poisson Process:* If $p(x, t) = \lambda$ (a constant) and $\pi(x; y, t) = \pi(x; y)$ is independent of t, show that

$$P(x_0; x, t) = \sum_0^\infty e^{-\lambda t} \frac{(\lambda t)^n}{n!} \pi^{(n)}(x_0; x), \tag{8.6}$$

where the functions $\pi^{(n)}(x_0; x)$ are defined as follows:

$$\pi^{(0)}(x_0; x) = \delta(x_0; x)$$
$$\pi^{(n)}(x_0; x) = \int_{-\infty}^\infty \pi^{(n-1)}(y; x)\, d_y \pi(x_0; y) \qquad (n \geqslant 1). \tag{8.7}$$

Show further that (8.6) gives the (common) unique solution of the forward and backward equations. In particular, if $\pi(x; y) = B(y - x)$, where $B(x)$ is a d.f. $(-\infty < x < \infty)$, then (8.6) reduces to the d.f. (3.11) of a compound Poisson distribution.

Section 3

4. Let

$$\int_{-\infty}^\infty |x|\, dB(x) < \infty, \qquad \alpha = \int_{-\infty}^\infty x\, dB(x). \tag{8.8}$$

Show that the mean of the process $X(t)$ is $\lambda\alpha$.

5. Show that $X(t)$ can be represented as

$$X(t) = X_1 + X_2 + \cdots + X_{N(t)}, \tag{8.9}$$

where $N(t)$ is a homogeneous Poisson process with parameter λ, and $X_1, X_2, \ldots$ are random variables which are mutually independent, independent of $N(t)$, and have the d.f. $B(x)$.

6. The *ruin problem* of collective risk theory is concerned with the first passage time

$$T(u) = \inf\{t\,|\,u + \mu t - X(t) \leqslant 0\}; \tag{8.10}$$

$T(u)$ is the time at which the risk reserve first becomes nonpositive, and the company is ruined. [For a recent paper on the subject, see Prabhu (1961).]

Section 4

7. The exponential series for a square matrix A is

$$e^{tA} = 1 + tA + \frac{t^2}{2!}A^2 + \frac{t^3}{3!}A^3 + \cdots. \tag{8.11}$$

Since

$$\left\| \frac{t^n A^n}{n!} \right\| \leqslant \frac{|t|^n}{n!} \| A \|^n,$$

the series $\Sigma \| t^n A^n / n! \|$ converges, and therefore the series in (8.11) converges uniformly in $(0 \leqslant t \leqslant T)$. Show directly that the equations (4.39) have the unique solution $P(t) = e^{tA}$.

8. Show that under certain conditions we can express the solution (4.40) in the form

$$P(t) = \sum_{\nu=1}^{N} A^{(\nu)} e^{\lambda_\nu t}, \tag{8.12}$$

so that

$$P_{jk}(t) = \sum_{\nu=1}^{N} a_{jk}^{(\nu)} e^{\lambda_\nu t}. \tag{8.13}$$

Section 5

9. *Generalization of Theorem 5.3:* Show that the conditional distribution of the times at which an event E occurs in $(0, t]$ in a time-homogeneous Poisson process, given that it has occurred exactly n times in that interval, is the same as the distribution of a random sample of n values from a uniform distribution over the range $(0, t)$, arranged in the ascending order of magnitude.

10. *The Compound Poisson Distribution:* Let us consider a time-homogeneous process in which

$$P_{jj}(\Delta t) = 1 - \lambda \Delta t + o(\Delta t)$$

$$\tag{8.14}$$

$$P_{jk}(\Delta t) = \lambda a_{k-j} \Delta t + o(\Delta t),$$

where $a_j = 0$ for $j \leqslant 0$, and $a_1 + a_2 + \cdots = 1$. Let $a_j^{(0)} = \delta_{0j}$, and $\{a_j^{(n)}\}$ be the n-fold convolution of $\{a_j\}$ with itself, defined analogously to (3.9). Show that the transition probabilities of the process are given by

$$P_{jk}(t) = e^{-\lambda t} \sum_{0}^{\infty} \frac{(\lambda t)^n}{n!} a_{k-j}^{(n)}. \tag{8.15}$$

In particular, if $\{a_j\}$ is the logarithmic distribution given by

$$a_j = \frac{1}{\lambda} \frac{p^j}{j} \quad (j \geqslant 1), \qquad \lambda = \log(1-p)^{-1}, \tag{8.16}$$

then

$$P_{jk}(t) = \begin{cases} \binom{-t}{k-j} (1-p)^t (-p)^{k-j} & (k \geqslant j) \\ 0 & (k < j). \end{cases} \tag{8.17}$$

Section 6

11. Let $X(t)$ be a pure birth process with $X(0) = j$, and consider the random variable

$$\tau_k = \inf\{t \,|\, X(t) = k\}. \tag{8.18}$$

Inverting the transform (6.31), show that τ_k has the distribution $f_{jk}(t)\,dt$, where

$$f_{jk}(t) = \sum_{v=j}^{k-1} (\lambda_k - \lambda_v) A_{jk}^{(v)} e^{-\lambda_v t} \qquad (k \geqslant j, 0 < t < \infty). \tag{8.19}$$

We have

$$P_{jk}(t) = \int_0^t f_{jk}(s) e^{-\lambda_k(t-s)}\, ds, \tag{8.20}$$

a result which leads to (6.7).

12. *The Contagion Process:* This is a pure birth process with $\lambda_j = \lambda + j\alpha$ $(j \geqslant 0)$. Show that the transition probabilities of $X(t)$ are given by

$$P_{jk}(t) = e^{-(\lambda + j\alpha)t} \binom{-j - (\lambda/\alpha)}{k - j} (e^{-\alpha t} - 1)^{k-j} \qquad (k \geqslant j). \tag{8.21}$$

13. *The Polya Process:* This is nonhomogeneous process with

$$c_j(t) = \frac{1 + \alpha j}{1 + \alpha t}, \qquad \pi_{jk} = \begin{cases} 1 & \text{if } k = j + 1 \\ 0 & \text{if } k \neq j + 1. \end{cases} \tag{8.22}$$

If $X(\tau) = 0$, show that the p.g.f. of $X(t)$ is given by

$$G(z; \tau, t) = \left(\frac{p}{1 - qz}\right)^{1/\alpha}, \tag{8.23}$$

where $p \equiv p(\tau, t) = (1 + \alpha\tau)/(1 + \alpha t)$, and $q = 1 - p$. When $\alpha \to 0$, $G(z; \tau, t)$ tends to the p.g.f. of the homogeneous Poisson distribution.

14. *The Binomial Process:* In (6.1) if $\lambda_j = \lambda(N - j)$, $\mu_j = j\mu \,(0 \leqslant j \leqslant N)$, and $X(0) = 0$, show that the distribution of $X(t)$ is the binomial

$$\binom{N}{k} p^k q^{N-k} \qquad (0 \leqslant k \leqslant N), \tag{8.24}$$

where $p = \lambda[1 - e^{-(\lambda+\mu)t}]/(\lambda + \mu)$, and $q = 1 - p$.

15. *The Simple Queue:* Suppose that customers arrive in a queuing system in a Poisson process with parameter λ, and are served by a single clerk. The service times of the customers are random variables with the negative exponential distribution $\mu e^{-\mu t}\, dt$ $(0 < t < \infty)$, and these are assumed to be mutually independent, and also independent of the arrival process. Let $Q(t)$ be the number of customers present in the system at time; then $Q(t)$ is a birth and death process with $\lambda_j = \lambda$ and $\mu_j = j\mu$. For an investigation of this process using generating functions, see Bailey (1954).

16. *The Pure Death Process:* If $\lambda_j = 0$ $(j \geqslant 0)$ in (6.1), the resulting process is called a pure death process. Show, in particular, that if $\mu_j = j\mu$, the transition probabilities are given by

$$P_{jk}(t) = \begin{cases} \binom{j}{k} e^{-k\mu t}(1 - e^{-\mu t})^{j-k} & (k \leqslant j) \\ 0 & (k > j). \end{cases} \tag{8.25}$$

Show that the time for extinction has the distribution

$$e^{-\mu t}(1 - e^{-\mu t})^{j-1}\, j\mu\, dt \qquad (0 < t < \infty). \tag{8.26}$$

Section 7

17. Show that the p.g.f. $G(z, t)$ of the Yule–Furry process satisfies the differential equation

$$\frac{\partial G}{\partial t} - \lambda z(z - 1)\frac{\partial G}{\partial z} = 0, \tag{8.27}$$

and verify that (7.4) gives the solution of (8.27).

18. Let $\mu(t) = E\{X(t)\}$ and $\mu_2'(t) = E\{X(t)\}^2$ be the first two moments of the Yule–Furry process. From (7.5) obtain the differential equations

$$\frac{d\mu}{dt} = \lambda\mu(t) \tag{8.28}$$

$$\frac{d}{dt}\mu_2'(t) = 2\lambda\mu_2'(t) + \lambda\mu(t),$$

and hence obtain (7.6).

19. Show that the backward equations of the Feller–Arley process are

$$P_{jk}'(t) = -(\lambda + \mu)jP_{jk}(t) + j\mu P_{j-1,k}(t) + j\lambda P_{j+1,k}(t) \qquad (j \geqslant 0), \tag{8.29}$$

and that these lead to the p.g.f. (7.18).

20. Show that for the Feller–Arley process, the equations corresponding to (8.28) are

$$\frac{d\mu}{dt} = (\lambda - \mu)\mu(t) \tag{8.30}$$

$$\frac{d}{dt}\mu_2'(t) = 2(\lambda - \mu)\mu_2'(t) + (\lambda + \mu)\mu(t),$$

and hence obtain the results (7.20).

21. If $\lambda = 0$, the Kendall process reduces to the Poisson, with the p.g.f.

$$G(z, t) = \exp[-v/\mu(1 - e^{-\mu t})(1 - z)]. \tag{8.31}$$

22. *Time-Dependent Rates:* Consider a birth and death process with $\lambda_j = j\lambda(t)$ and $\mu_j = j\mu(t)$, where $\lambda(t)$, $\mu(t)$ depend on time. Show that the p.g.f. is given by (7.18), where now ξ and η are given by

$$\xi = \frac{1 - e^{-\rho}}{W}, \qquad \eta = 1 - \frac{1}{W} \tag{8.32}$$

where

$$\rho(t) = \int_0^t [\mu(s) - \lambda(s)] \, ds \tag{8.33}$$

and

$$W = e^{-\rho}\left\{1 + \int_0^t e^{\rho(s)}\mu(s) \, ds\right\}. \tag{8.34}$$

The probability of ultimate extinction is given by

$$\left\{\frac{\displaystyle\int_0^\infty e^{\rho(s)}\mu(s) \, ds}{1 + \displaystyle\int_0^\infty e^{\rho(s)}\mu(s) \, ds}\right\}^j \tag{8.35}$$

if the integral in (8.35) is convergent, and one otherwise [Kendall (1948)].

23. *Branching Process in Continuous Time:* Suppose that during a time interval $(t, t + \Delta t]$ any individual in a population gives way to a new distribution of individuals with a p.g.f.

$$z + g(z)\Delta t + o(\Delta t). \tag{8.36}$$

Show that the p.g.f. $G(z, t) = \sum_0^\infty P_{1k}z^k$ of the population size at time t satisfies the relation

$$G(z, t + s) = G(G(z, s), t). \tag{8.37}$$

Using (8.37), show that $G(z, t)$ satisfies the two differential equations

$$\frac{\partial G}{\partial t} = g(z)\frac{\partial G}{\partial z}, \qquad \frac{\partial G}{\partial t} = g(G(z, t)). \tag{8.38}$$

The solution of the second equation in (8.38) can be written in the form

$$t = \int_z^{G(z,t)} \frac{du}{g(u)}. \tag{8.39}$$

In the case of the Feller–Arley process, we have $g(z) = (1 - z)(\mu - \lambda z)$; show that (8.39) leads to (7.19) [Bartlett (1955)].

9. REFERENCES

Arley, Niels. ON THE THEORY OF STOCHASTIC PROCESSES AND THEIR APPLICATION TO THE THEORY OF COSMIC RADIATION. Copenhagen: Grads Vorlag, 1948.

Bailey, N. T. J. A CONTINUOUS TIME TREATMENT OF A SIMPLE QUEUE USING GENERATING FUNCTIONS. *J. Roy. Stat. Soc.,* **B 16** (1954), pp. 288–291.

———. THE MATHEMATICAL THEORY OF EPIDEMICS. London: Charles Griffin, 1957.

Bartlett, M. S. AN INTRODUCTION TO STOCHASTIC PROCESSES. New York: Cambridge University Press, 1955.

———. STOCHASTIC POPULATION MODELS IN ECOLOGY AND EPIDEMIOLOGY. London: Methuen, 1960.

Bellman, R. E. INTRODUCTION TO MATRIX ANALYSIS. New York: McGraw-Hill, 1960.

Bharucha-Reid, A. T. ELEMENTS OF THE THEORY OF MARKOV PROCESSES AND THEIR APPLICATIONS. New York: McGraw-Hill, 1960.

Chung, K. L. MARKOV CHAINS WITH STATIONARY TRANSITION PROBABILITIES. Berlin: Springer, 1960.

Doeblin, W. SUR CERTAINS MOUVEMENTS ALÉATOIRES DISCONTINUS. *Skand. Aktuar.,* **22** (1939), pp. 211–222.

Doob, J. L. TOPICS IN THE THEORY OF MARKOFF CHAINS. *Trans. Amer. Math. Soc.,* **52** (1942), pp. 37–64.

———. MARKOFF CHAINS-DENUMERABLE CASE. *Trans. Amer. Math. Soc.,* **58** (1945), pp. 455–473.

———. STOCHASTIC PROCESSES. New York: Wiley, 1953.

Feller, W. ZUR THEORIE DER STOCHASTISCHEN PROZESSE. *Math. Ann.,* **113** (1936), pp. 113–160.

———. DIE GRUNDLAGEN DER VOLTERRASCHEN THEORIE DES KAMPFES UMS DASEIN IN WAHRSCHEINLICHKEITSTHEORETISCHER BEHANDLUNG. *Acta Biotheoretica,* **5** (1939), pp. 11–40.

———. ON THE INTEGRO-DIFFERENTIAL EQUATIONS OF PURELY DISCONTINUOUS MARKOFF PROCESSES. *Trans. Amer. Math. Soc.,* **48** (1940), pp. 488–515. *Errata ibid* (1945) **58**, p. 474.

———. AN INTRODUCTION TO PROBABILITY THEORY AND ITS APPLICATIONS. New York: Wiley, 1957.

Karlin, S., and McGregor, J. L. THE DIFFERENTIAL EQUATIONS OF BIRTH AND DEATH PROCESSES AND THE STIELTJES MOMENT PROBLEM. *Trans. Amer. Math. Soc.,* **85** (1957a), pp. 489–546.

———. THE CLASSIFICATION OF BIRTH AND DEATH PROCESSES. *Trans. Amer. Math. Soc.,* **86** (1957b), pp. 366–400.

Kendall, D. G. ON THE GENERALIZED BIRTH AND DEATH PROCESS. *Ann. Math. Statist.,* **19** (1948), pp. 1–15.

Kendall, D. G. STOCHASTIC PROCESSES AND POPULATION GROWTH. *J. Roy. Stat. Soc.*, **B 11** (1949), pp. 230–264.

Kolmogorov, A. ÜBER DIE ANALYTISCHEN METHODEN IN DER WAHRSCHEINLICHKEITS-RECHNUNG. *Math. Ann.*, **104** (1931), pp. 415–458.

Ledermann, W., and Reuter, G. E. H. SPECTRAL THEORY FOR THE DIFFERENTIAL EQUATIONS OF SIMPLE BIRTH AND DEATH PROCESSES. *Phil. Trans. Roy. Soc., London* A **246** (1954), pp. 321–369.

Lundberg, O. ON RANDOM PROCESSES AND THEIR APPLICATION TO SICKNESS AND ACCIDENT STATISTICS. Stockholm: Uppsala, 1940.

Moyal, J. E. DISCONTINUOUS MARKOFF PROCESSES. *Acta Mathematica*, **98** (1957), pp. 221–264.

Prabhu, N. U. ON THE RUIN PROBLEM OF COLLECTIVE RISK THEORY. *Ann. Math. Statist.*, **23** (1961), pp. 757–764.

———. QUEUES AND INVENTORIES. New York: Wiley, 1965.

5

Renewal Theory

1. INTRODUCTION

Let $\{X_n, n = 1, 2, \ldots\}$ be a sequence of mutually independent random variables which assume nonnegative values. Let the distribution function (d.f.) of X_1 be $K(x)$ and the d.f. of X_n $(n = 2, 3, \ldots)$, $F(x)$ $(0 \leqslant x < \infty)$. We shall ignore the trivial case where $\Pr\{X_n = 0\} = 1$. If the possible values of X_n are nd $(n = 0, 1, 2, \ldots)$, where $d > 0$ (d fixed), we say that the process $\{X_n\}$ is discrete; otherwise, it is continuous. Let us denote

$$\int_0^\infty x \, dF(x) = \mu, \tag{1.1}$$

where μ is the mean of the X_n if the integral is convergent, and otherwise $\mu = \infty$.

Let $S_0 \equiv 0$, $S_n = X_1 + X_2 + \cdots + X_n$ $(n \geqslant 1)$ be the partial sums of the sequence $\{X_n\}$, and

$$F_n(x) = \Pr\{S_n \leqslant x\} \qquad (0 \leqslant x < \infty, n = 0, 1, \ldots) \tag{1.2}$$

the d.f. of S_n. We have then $F_0(x) \equiv 1$ for $x \geqslant 0$, and

$$F_1(x) = K(x) \tag{1.3}$$

$$F_{n+1}(x) = \int_0^x F_n(x - y) \, dF(y) \qquad (n = 1, 2, \ldots). \tag{1.4}$$

For $t > 0$ we define the random variable

$$N(t) = \max\{n \mid S_n \leqslant t\}. \tag{1.5}$$

Clearly, $N(t) + 1$ is the first passage time of the process $\{S_n\}$ beyond the barrier at t, and is thus a special case of the first passage time studied in Wald's sequential analysis (see Chapter 2, Section 8). It therefore follows from Theorem 8.5, Chapter 2, that $N(t)$ assumes only finite values, and has finite moments of all orders; in particular, $U(t) = E\{N(t)\} < \infty$. However, in the present case these results can be proved more easily. We first consider two important special cases.

Physical Interpretation. Consider a population of individuals (electric bulbs, industrial machinery, etc.) such that when any individual dies (fails) he is replaced by a new individual, and the individuals live and die independently of each other. Let the lifetime of an individual be a random variable having the d.f. $F(x)$. Suppose that at time $t = 0$, the population consists of an individual of age x_0; then the residual life time X_1 of this individual has the d.f. given by

$$K(x) = \frac{F(x + x_0) - F(x_0)}{1 - F(x_0)}. \tag{1.6}$$

If the initial individual is a new one, we have $x_0 = 0$, and therefore $K(x) = F(x)$; otherwise, $K(x) \neq F(x)$. It is sometimes convenient to think of the age of the initial individual as a random variable X_0 with a given d.f., say $\Phi(x_0)$. Then the d.f. of X_1 is given by

$$K(x) = \int_0^\infty \frac{F(x + x_0) - F(x_0)}{1 - F(x_0)} \, d\Phi(x_0). \tag{1.7}$$

It is clear that the first replacement (renewal) occurs at $t = X_1$, where X_1 has the d.f. (1.6) or (1.7); if this individual dies at age X_2, then the next replacement occurs at $t = X_1 + X_2$, and the process continues in this way. Here the lifetimes $X_2, X_3, \ldots$ of the successive replacements have the d.f. $F(x)$ by our assumption. We thus see that the process $\{X_n\}$ may be called a *renewal process*. The random variable $N(t)$ defined by (1.5) is the number of renewals during the interval $(0, t]$ (including any made at t, but excluding the initial individual). The case where $\Pr\{X_n = 0\} = 1$ corresponds to the situation where the individuals die instantaneously with probability one, and will be ignored here. The mean lifetime is given by μ where μ is defined by (1.1).

EXAMPLE 1.1 (THE BINOMIAL PROCESS). Let

$$\Pr\{X_k = 0\} = q, \qquad \Pr\{X_k = 1\} = p \qquad (p > 0, q = 1 - p, k = 1, 2, \ldots).$$
$$\tag{1.8}$$

For this process it is clear that renewals occur at $t = 0, 1, 2, \ldots$. Let N_j be the number of renewals in $(j - 1, j] \, (j = 1, 2, \ldots)$; then $N(t) = N_1 + N_2$

$+ \cdots + N_T$, where $T = [t]$ is the largest integer contained in t. The distribution of N_j is given by

$$\Pr \{N_j = n\} = pq^{n-1} \qquad (n \geqslant 1), \tag{1.9}$$

and its moment generating function (m.g.f.) by

$$E\{e^{\theta N_j}\} = \sum_{n=1}^{\infty} e^{n\theta} pq^{n-1} = (pe^{\theta}) \sum_{1}^{\infty} (qe^{\theta})^{n-1}$$
$$= \frac{pe^{\theta}}{1 - qe^{\theta}} \qquad [\mathrm{Re}(\theta) < \log q^{-1}]. \tag{1.10}$$

From (1.10) we find that

$$E\{N_j\} = \frac{1}{p}, \qquad \mathrm{Var}\,\{N_j\} = \frac{q}{p^2}. \tag{1.11}$$

Since $N_1, N_2, \ldots, N_T$ are identically distributed, the distribution of $N(t)$ is the T-fold convolution of (1.9) with itself. Therefore, the m.g.f. of $N(t)$ is given by

$$E\{e^{\theta N(t)}\} = \left(\frac{pe^{\theta}}{1 - qe^{\theta}} \right)^T, \tag{1.12}$$

which shows that $N(t)$ has a negative binomial distribution. From (1.11) we find that

$$U(t) = E\{N(t)\} = \sum_{1}^{T} E(N_j) = \frac{T}{p}, \tag{1.13}$$

$$\mathrm{Var}\,\{N(t)\} = \sum_{1}^{T} \mathrm{Var}\,\{N_j\} = \frac{Tq}{p^2}. \tag{1.14}$$

EXAMPLE 1.2 (THE MARKOVIAN CASE). Let

$$K(x) = F(x) = 1 - e^{-\lambda x} \qquad (0 \leqslant x < \infty). \tag{1.15}$$

On account of the well-known property of the negative exponential distribution (see Chapter 4, Section 5), we find here that renewals occur in a Poisson process, so that

$$\Pr \{N(t) = n\} = e^{-\lambda t} \frac{(\lambda t)^n}{n!} \qquad (n = 0, 1, \ldots) \tag{1.16}$$

and

$$U(t) = E\{N(t)\} = \lambda t; \qquad \mathrm{Var}\,\{N(t)\} = \lambda t. \tag{1.17}$$

2. THE RANDOM VARIABLE $N(t)$; THE RENEWAL FUNCTION

THEOREM   2.1.   *$N(t)$ is a "proper" random variable, with finite moments of all orders, that is,*

$$\text{(i) } \Pr\{N(t) < \infty\} = 1 \tag{2.1}$$

$$\text{(ii) } E\{N(t)\}^k < \infty \qquad (k = 1, 2, \ldots). \tag{2.2}$$

Proof: Since we have assumed that $\Pr\{X_k = 0\} < 1$, there exists an $\alpha > 0$ such $\Pr\{X_k \geqslant \alpha\} > 0$. Without loss of generality we may take $\alpha = 1$; then $\Pr\{X_k \geqslant 1\} = p > 0$. Now define a modified renewal process $\{\bar{X}_k\}$ by setting for $k = 1, 2, \ldots,$

$$\bar{X}_k = \begin{cases} 0 & \text{if } X_k < 1 \\ 1 & \text{if } X_k \geqslant 1. \end{cases} \tag{2.3}$$

Let $\bar{S}_n = \bar{X}_1 + \bar{X}_2 + \cdots + \bar{X}_n$, $\bar{N}(t) = \max\{n | \bar{S}_n \leqslant t\}$. It is clear that $\{\bar{X}_n\}$ is the binomial process considered in example 1.1. Since $\bar{S}_n \leqslant S_n$, we have $N(t) \leqslant \bar{N}(t)$; it follows that $N(t)$ is a proper random variable, since $\bar{N}(t)$ has this property. Moreover, we have proved that the m.g.f. $E\{e^{\theta_0 \bar{N}(t)}\}$ exists for some $\theta_0 > 0$; therefore, $E\{e^{\theta_0 N(t)}\} \leqslant E\{e^{\theta_0 \bar{N}(t)}\} < \infty$. Since $n^k < e^{\theta_0 n}$ for sufficiently large values of n, it follows that $E\{N(t)\}^k < \infty$ for all k.

THEOREM   2.2.   *The distribution of $N(t)$ is given by*

$$P_n(t) = \Pr\{N(t) = n\} = F_n(t) - F_{n+1}(t) \qquad (n = 0, 1, \ldots), \tag{2.4}$$

and its mean by

$$U(t) = E\{N(t)\} = \sum_{1}^{\infty} F_n(t). \tag{2.5}$$

Proof: We have

$$\Pr\{N(t) \geqslant n\} = \Pr\{S_n \leqslant t\} = F_n(t), \tag{2.6}$$

so that

$$\begin{aligned} P_n(t) &= \Pr\{N(t) \geqslant n\} - \Pr\{N(t) \geqslant n+1\} \\ &= F_n(t) - F_{n+1}(t), \end{aligned} \tag{2.7}$$

which proves (2.4). Further, we have

$$\begin{aligned} U(t) &= \sum_{0}^{\infty} n P_n(t) = \sum_{n=1}^{\infty} P_n(t) \sum_{k=1}^{n} (1) \\ &= \sum_{k=1}^{\infty} \sum_{n=k}^{\infty} P_n(t) = \sum_{1}^{\infty} F_k(t) \qquad \text{[from (2.6)]}, \end{aligned} \tag{2.8}$$

which is the result (2.5).

EXAMPLE 2.1.   Let $K(x) = F(x)$ and $dF(x) = e^{-\lambda x}\lambda^p x^{p-1} \dfrac{dx}{(p-1)!}$
$(0 < x < \infty)$. Then we have

$$dF_n(x) = e^{-\lambda x}\lambda^{np} x^{np-1}\, \frac{dx}{(np-1)!} \qquad (2.9)$$

and

$$F_n(x) = \int_0^x e^{-\lambda y}\lambda^{np}\, \frac{y^{np-1}}{(np-1)!}\, dy$$

$$= 1 - e^{-\lambda x}\sum_0^{np-1}\frac{(\lambda x)^r}{r!} \qquad (n \geqslant 1). \qquad (2.10)$$

Hence we find that

$$P_n(t) = F_n(t) - F_{n+1}(t)$$

$$= e^{-\lambda t}\sum_{np}^{np+p-1}\frac{(\lambda x)^r}{r!} - e^{-\lambda t}\sum_0^{np-1}\frac{(\lambda x)^r}{r!} \qquad (2.11)$$

$$= e^{-\lambda t}\sum_{np}^{np+p-1}\frac{(\lambda x)^r}{r!} \qquad (n = 0, 1, \dots).$$

When $p = 1$, this reduces to the Markovian case discussed in example 1.2; here (2.11) gives

$$P_n(t) = e^{-\lambda t}\frac{(\lambda t)^n}{n!} \qquad (n = 0, 1, \dots), \qquad (2.12)$$

in agreement with (1.16).

The Renewal Function; Renewal Density.   The function $U(t) = E\{N(t)\}$ gives the mean number of renewals occurring in the interval $(0, t]$. From Theorem 2.1 we see that $U(t) < \infty$ for all t; $U(t)$ is called the *renewal function*. If $K(t)$ and $F(t)$ are both absolutely continuous, with $K'(t) = k(t)$, and $F'(t) = f(t)$, it follows from (2.5) that $U'(t) = u(t)$ exists, where

$$u(t) = \sum_1^{\infty} f_n(t), \qquad f_n(t) = F_n'(t); \qquad (2.13)$$

$u(t)$ is called the renewal density. If we "confuse" expectation with probability, then $u(t)\, dt$ can be interpreted as the probability that a renewal occurs during $(t, t + dt]$. Now, if a renewal occurs during $(t, t + dt]$, then the dying individual is either the initial one itself, or the one which entered the population at some prior time, say $t - \tau$ $(0 < \tau \leqslant t)$; these considerations lead to the relation

$$u(t) = k(t) + \int_0^t u(t - \tau)f(\tau)\, d\tau. \qquad (2.14)$$

This is called the integral equation of renewal theory, and is the starting point in earlier discussions of the theory. Below we establish this equation rigorously (without assuming the existence of the density) and discuss the question of uniqueness of its solution. The proof of the following theorem is due to Doob (1948); an earlier proof by Feller (1941) made use of transforms. For simplicity let us assume that $K(t) = F(t)$.

THEOREM 2.3 (THE INTEGRAL EQUATION OF RENEWAL THEORY). *The renewal function $U(t)$ satisfies the integral equation*

$$U(t) = K(t) + \int_0^t U(t - \tau)\, dF(\tau); \qquad (2.15)$$

moreover, $U(t)$ is the unique solution of (2.15) which is bounded for all finite t.

Proof: From (2.5) we have

$$U(t) = F_1(t) + \sum_1^\infty F_{n+1}(t)$$

$$= K(t) + \sum_1^\infty \int_0^t F_n(t - \tau)\, dF(\tau)$$

$$= K(t) + \int_0^t \sum_1^\infty F_n(t - \tau)\, dF(\tau) \qquad (2.16)$$

$$= K(t) + \int_0^t U(t - \tau)\, dF(\tau);$$

since $U(t) < \infty$, it follows that $U(t) = \sum_1^\infty F_n(t)$ satisfies the integral equation (2.15). Conversely, let $V(t)$ be a solution of (2.15) which is bounded for all finite t; then

$$V(t) = K(t) + \int_0^t V(t - \tau)\, dF(\tau)$$

$$= F_1(t) + \int_0^t dF(\tau) \left\{ K(t - \tau) + \int_0^{t-\tau} V(t - \tau - s)\, dF(s) \right\}$$

$$= F_1(t) + F_2(t) + \int_0^t dF(\tau) \int_\tau^t V(t - \theta)\, dF(\theta - \tau)$$

$$= F_1(t) + F_2(t) + \int_0^t V(t - \theta) \int_0^\theta dF(\theta - \tau)\, dF(\tau)$$

$$= F_1(t) + F_2(t) + \int_0^t V(t - \theta)\, dF_2(\theta),$$

and proceeding in this manner, we find that

$$V(t) = F_1(t) + F_2(t) + \cdots + F_n(t) + \int_0^t V(t - \tau)\, dF_n(\tau) \qquad (n \geqslant 1). \quad (2.17)$$

Now, since the series $\sum_1^\infty F_n(t)$ converges, $F_n(t) \to 0$ as $n \to \infty$, and therefore

$$\int_0^t V(t - \tau)\, dF_n(\tau) \leqslant \underset{\tau \leqslant t}{\text{L.U.B.}} \, |V(\tau)| F_n(t) \to 0 \qquad (2.18)$$

as $n \to \infty$, and (2.17) gives $V(t) = \sum_1^\infty F_n(t) = U(t)$. This proves the uniqueness of $U(t)$ as a solution of (2.15).

Transforms. Let us denote by

$$K^*(\theta) = \int_0^\infty e^{-\theta x}\, dK(x), \qquad F^*(\theta) = \int_0^\infty e^{-\theta x}\, dF(x),$$

$$U^*(\theta) = \int_0^\infty e^{-\theta t}\, dU(t) \qquad (2.19)$$

the Laplace–Stieltjes transforms of $K(x)$, $F(x)$ and $U(t)$ respectively. Then from (2.15) we obtain

$$U^*(\theta) = K^*(\theta) + U^*(\theta)F^*(\theta),$$

which gives

$$U^*(\theta) = \frac{K^*(\theta)}{1 - F^*(\theta)} \qquad [\text{Re}(\theta) > 0], \qquad (2.20)$$

since

$$|F^*(\theta)| \leqslant \int_0^\infty e^{-\sigma x}\, dF(x) < 1 \qquad \text{if } \sigma = \text{Re}(\theta) > 0.$$

The solution of the integral equation (2.15) can then be obtained by inverting the transform (2.20) [see Feller (1941)].

EXAMPLE 2.2. In example 1.2 we have

$$K^*(\theta) = F^*(\theta) = \int_0^\infty e^{-\theta x - \lambda x}\lambda\, dx = \lambda(\lambda + \theta)^{-1}, \qquad (2.21)$$

so that from (2.20),

$$U^*(\theta) = \frac{\lambda(\lambda + \theta)^{-1}}{1 - \lambda(\lambda + \theta)^{-1}} = \frac{\lambda}{\theta}. \qquad (2.22)$$

Since

$$\lambda/\theta = \int_0^\infty e^{-\theta t}\lambda\, dt,$$

it follows from Theorem 2.3 that for the unique solution of (2.15) in this case we have $dU(t) = \lambda dt$, which gives $U(t) = \lambda t$, since $U(0) = 0$. This result agrees with (1.17).

THEOREM 2.4.   *Let $K(x) = F(x)$ and assume that $\mu = E(X_n) < \infty$, and $\sigma^2 = \text{Var}(X_n) < \infty$. Then if $t \to \infty$, $N(t)$ has an asymptotically normal distribution with mean t/μ and variance $t\sigma^2/\mu^3$. Thus*

$$\lim_{t \to \infty} \Pr\left\{ \frac{N(t) - t/\mu}{\sqrt{t\sigma^2/\mu^3}} < x \right\} = \frac{1}{\sqrt{2\pi}} \int_{-\infty}^{x} e^{-\frac{1}{2}u^2} \, du. \qquad (2.23)$$

Proof: This theorem was established for the discrete case by Feller (1949); the continuous time version is due to Takács (1956). The proof rests on the relation

$$\Pr\{N(t) < n\} = \Pr\{S_n > t\}. \qquad (2.24)$$

Let $n \to \infty$, $t \to \infty$ in such way that

$$\frac{t - n\mu}{\sigma\sqrt{n}} = -x \qquad (x \text{ fixed}). \qquad (2.25)$$

Since $X_1, X_2, \ldots$ are mutually independent and identically distributed random variables, the central limit theorem gives

$$\Pr\{S_n > t\} = \Pr\{S_n > n\mu - x\sigma\sqrt{n}\}$$

$$= \Pr\left\{ \frac{S_n - n\mu}{\sigma\sqrt{n}} > -x \right\} \qquad (2.26)$$

$$\to \frac{1}{\sqrt{2\pi}} \int_{-x}^{\infty} e^{-\frac{1}{2}u^2} \, du = \frac{1}{\sqrt{2\pi}} \int_{-\infty}^{x} e^{-\frac{1}{2}u^2} \, du,$$

as $n \to \infty$. Now,

$$\Pr\{N(t) < n\} = \Pr\left\{ \frac{N(t) - t/\mu}{\sqrt{t\sigma^2/\mu^3}} < \frac{n - t/\mu}{\sqrt{t\sigma^2/\mu^3}} \right\}, \qquad (2.27)$$

where, using (2.25), we can write

$$\frac{n - t/\mu}{\sqrt{t\sigma^2/\mu^3}} = x\sqrt{\frac{n\mu}{t}} = x\left(1 + \frac{x\sigma\sqrt{n}}{t}\right)^{\frac{1}{2}}. \qquad (2.28)$$

Again, we can write (2.25) as

$$\mu n - x\sigma\sqrt{n} - t = 0,$$

which is a quadratic equation in $\sqrt{n}$; this gives

$$\sqrt{n} = \frac{x\sigma + \sqrt{(x\sigma)^2 + 4t\mu}}{2\mu}, \qquad (2.29)$$

which shows that $\sqrt{n}/t \to 0$ as $t \to \infty$. From (2.27)–(2.29) we obtain

$$\Pr\{N(t) < n\} \to \Pr\left\{\frac{N(t) - t/\mu}{\sqrt{t\sigma^2/\mu^3}} < x\right\}, \qquad (2.30)$$

and the result (2.23) follows from (2.24), (2.26), and (2.30).

Let us note that since convergence of distribution functions does not always imply convergence of moments, Theorem 2.4 does not imply that

$$E\{N(t)\} \sim \frac{t}{\mu}, \qquad \operatorname{Var}\{N(t)\} \sim \frac{t\sigma^2}{\mu^3}. \qquad (2.31)$$

Nevertheless, these results are true [see Complement 4].

3. RENEWAL THEOREMS

In the Markovian case we saw that $U(t) = \lambda t$, so that $U(t)/t = \mu^{-1}$, where $\mu = E(X_n)$, is the mean lifetime. In the general case we shall prove that this relation holds asymptotically as $t \to \infty$. This result, due to Feller (1941), is one of a class of limit theorems concerning the renewal function $U(t)$. The following proof is due to Smith (1958). For convenience we shall assume that $K(x) = F(x)$.

THEOREM 3.1 (THE ELEMENTARY RENEWAL THEOREM). *We have*

$$\frac{U(t)}{t} \to \frac{1}{\mu} \qquad \text{as } t \to \infty, \qquad (3.1)$$

where $\mu = E(X_n) \leqslant \infty$, *the limit being interpreted as* 0 *when* $\mu = \infty$.

Proof: Let us first consider the case $\mu < \infty$, and write $N \equiv N(t) + 1$ and $S_N = t + Y(t)$, where $Y(t)$ is the residual lifetime of the individual alive at time t. Since N is the first passage time of the process $\{S_n\}$ beyond the barrier at t, Wald's equation [Theorem 8.6, Chapter 2] gives $E[t + Y(t)] = E(S_N) = \mu E(N) = \mu[U(t) + 1]$, so that

$$\frac{U(t)}{t} + \frac{1}{t} = \frac{E\{Y(t)\}}{\mu t} + \frac{1}{\mu}. \qquad (3.2)$$

Since the random variable $Y(t)$ assumes only nonnegative values, we have $E\{Y(t)\} \geqslant 0$, so that

$$\frac{U(t)}{t} + \frac{1}{t} \geqslant \frac{1}{\mu},$$

which gives

$$\liminf_{t\to\infty} \frac{U(t)}{t} \geqslant \frac{1}{\mu}. \qquad (3.3)$$

We now define a new renewal process $\{\bar{X}_n\}$ by putting

$$\bar{X}_n = \begin{cases} X_n & \text{if } X_n \leqslant A \\ 0 & \text{if } X_n > A \end{cases} \qquad (n = 1, 2, \ldots; A > 0). \qquad (3.4)$$

Let $\bar{S}_n = \bar{X}_1 + \bar{X}_2 + \cdots + \bar{X}_n$, $\bar{N}(t) = \max\{n|\bar{S}_n \leqslant t\}$, $\bar{U}(t) = E\{\bar{N}(t)\}$, and $\bar{Y}(t)$ the residual life at time t in this process. Clearly, $\bar{Y}(t) < A$, so that applying (3.2) to this process we obtain

$$\frac{\bar{U}(t)}{t} + \frac{1}{t} \leqslant \frac{A}{\mu_A t} + \frac{1}{\mu_A},$$

where $\mu_A = E(\bar{X}_n) \leqslant \mu < \infty$; hence

$$\limsup_{t \to \infty} \frac{\bar{U}(t)}{t} \leqslant \frac{1}{\mu_A}. \qquad (3.5)$$

However, we have $\bar{S}_n \leqslant S_n$, so that $N(t) \leqslant \bar{N}(t)$. Therefore, $U(t) \leqslant \bar{U}(t)$, and

$$\limsup_{t \to \infty} \frac{U(t)}{t} \leqslant \limsup_{t \to \infty} \frac{\bar{U}(t)}{t} \leqslant \frac{1}{\mu_A}. \qquad (3.6)$$

When $A \to \infty$,

$$\mu_A = \int_0^A x \, dF(x) \to \int_0^\infty x \, dF(x) = \mu,$$

so that (3.6) gives

$$\limsup_{t \to \infty} \frac{U(t)}{t} \leqslant \frac{1}{\mu}. \qquad (3.7)$$

From (3.3) and (3.7) the result (3.1) now follows.

If $\mu = \infty$, we again consider the modified process defined by (3.4); since $\mu_A \to \infty$ as $A \to \infty$ in this case, (3.6) gives $U(t)/t \to 0$ as $t \to \infty$.

More generally, we are concerned with the function $V(t, h) = E\{N(t, h)\}$, where $N(t, h)$ is the number of renewals which occur during the interval $(t, t + h]$. Clearly, $N(t, h) = N(t + h) - N(t)$, so that $V(t, h) = U(t + h) - U(t)$; from Theorems 2.1 and 2.2 we find that

$$V(t, h) = \sum_{n=1}^\infty \Pr\{t < S_n \leqslant t + h\} < \infty \qquad (3.8)$$

for all $t, h > 0$. For a continuous renewal process, Blackwell (1948) proved that $V(t, h) \to h/\mu$ as $t \to \infty$ for any fixed h; this result generalized an earlier result in the discrete case due to Kolmogorov (1936) and Erdös,

Feller, and Pollard (1949), which states that $u_n \to d/\mu$ as $n \to \infty$, where

$$u_n = \sum_{k=0}^{\infty} \Pr \{S_k = nd\} \qquad (n = 0, 1, \ldots). \tag{3.9}$$

The result for the continuous case was first obtained by Doob (1948) under a restriction. Blackwell's proof of this theorem is based on probabilistic arguments, but is somewhat difficult; we give below a simple proof due to Feller (1961), which does not distinguish between the discrete and the continuous cases.

A more general result due to Smith (1954) is the following:

$$\int_0^t Q(t - \tau) \, dU(\tau) \to \frac{1}{\mu} \int_0^{\infty} Q(s) \, ds, \tag{3.10}$$

where $Q(t)$ is a nonnegative, nonincreasing function of $t \geqslant 0$, which is integrable over $[0, \infty)$. This may be called the *key renewal theorem*, since a number of important results can be deduced from it. In particular, let $Q(t) = h^{-1}$ for $0 < t \leqslant h$, and $= 0$ otherwise; then

$$U(t) - U(t - h) = \int_{t-h}^t dU(\tau) \to \frac{1}{\mu} \int_0^h ds = \frac{h}{\mu},$$

which is Blackwell's theorem. In the reverse direction, (3.10) also follows from Blackwell's theorem; the proof given here follows Takács [see discussion in Smith (1958)].

We first prove a result due to Blackwell (1948).

THEOREM 3.2. *$U(t + h) - U(t)$ is a bounded function of t; in fact*

$$U(t + h) - U(t) \leqslant 1 + U(h). \tag{3.11}$$

Proof: Let us write $N \equiv N(t) + 1$ and consider $Y(t) = S_N - t$, the residual lifetime at time t. We have

$$\Pr \{N(t, h) \geqslant n\} = \int_0^h d_y \Pr \{Y(t) \leqslant y\} \Pr \{N(t, h) \geqslant n \,|\, Y(t) = y\}$$

$$= \int_0^h d_y \Pr \{Y(t) \leqslant y\} \Pr \{N(t, h) \geqslant n \,|\, N(t, y) = 1\} \tag{3.12}$$

$$= \int_0^h d_y \Pr \{Y(t) \leqslant y\} \Pr \{N(h - y) \geqslant n - 1\} \qquad (n \geqslant 1).$$

Hence

$$U(t + h) - U(t) = \sum_{n=1}^{\infty} \Pr \{N(t, h) \geqslant n\}$$

$$= \int_0^h dy \, \Pr \{Y(t) \leqslant y\} \sum_{n=1}^{\infty} \Pr \{N(h - y) \geqslant n - 1\}$$

$$= \int_0^h dy \, \Pr \{Y(t) \leqslant y\}[1 + E\{N(h - y)\}]$$ (3.13)

$$= \int_0^h dy \, \Pr \{Y(t) \leqslant y\}[1 + U(h - y)].$$

Now, since $U(t)$ is an increasing function of t, we have $U(h - y) \leqslant U(h)$ for $0 \leqslant y \leqslant h$. Therefore, (3.13) gives

$$U(t + h) - U(t) \leqslant [1 + U(h)] \Pr \{Y(t) \leqslant h\}$$
$$\leqslant 1 + U(h),$$ (3.14)

as required.

Feller's proof of Blackwell's result uses the following lemma, which we state without proof [see, for instance, Choquet and Deny (1960)].

LEMMA 3.1. *If $z(x)$ is a bounded solution of the equation*

$$z(x) = \int_0^{\infty} z(x - y) \, dF(y),$$ (3.15)

then $z(x) = constant$ in the continuous case, and $z(nd) = constant$ in the discrete case.

THEOREM 3.3. *In the case of a continuous renewal process, we have*

$$U(t + h) - U(t) \to \frac{h}{\mu} \quad as \ t \to \infty,$$ (3.16)

and in the discrete case

$$u_n \to \frac{d}{\mu} \quad as \ n \to \infty,$$ (3.17)

where in both cases the limits are interpreted as 0 if $\mu = \infty$.

Proof: We shall give the proof in three stages.

(a) For any interval $\Delta = (a, b]$, where $0 < a < b < \infty$, we define the measure

$$\mu(\Delta) = \sum_{n=0}^{\infty} \Pr \{a < S_n \leqslant b\}.$$ (3.18)

From Theorem 3.2 we find that $\mu(\Delta) \leqslant 1 + U(b - a) < \infty$ for intervals of finite length. In the discrete case we can write

$$\mu(\Delta) = \sum_{a < nd \leqslant b} u_n, \tag{3.19}$$

where u_n is defined by (3.9). Let $g(x) \geqslant 0$ be a continuous function of x, and for $t \geqslant 0$, let

$$\phi(t) = \int_0^t g(t - \tau)\mu(d\tau). \tag{3.20}$$

Then proceeding as in Theorem 2.3, we see that $\phi(t)$ is the unique bounded solution of the integral equation

$$\phi(t) = g(t) + \int_0^t \phi(t - \tau)\,dF(\tau). \tag{3.21}$$

Suppose that $g(x)$ vanishes outside the interval $\Delta = [0, h]$, and let

$$\|g\| = \sup_{0 \leqslant x \leqslant h} |g(x)| \tag{3.22}$$

be the norm of $g(x)$; $\|g\| < \infty$, since $g(x)$ is a continuous function in Δ. From $0 \leqslant t \leqslant h$ we obtain from (3.20),

$$\phi(t) = \int_0^t g(t - \tau)\mu(d\tau),$$

whence

$$|\phi(t)| \leqslant \|g\| \int_0^t \mu(d\tau) \leqslant \|g\| \int_0^h \mu(d\tau)$$

$$\leqslant \|g\| \mu(\Delta). \tag{3.23}$$

For $t > h$ (3.20) gives

$$\phi(t) = \int_{t-h}^t g(t - \tau)\mu(d\tau),$$

whence

$$|\phi(t)| \leqslant \|g\| \int_{t-h}^t \mu(d\tau) \leqslant \|g\| \mu(\Delta), \tag{3.24}$$

where we have used (3.11). From (3.23) and (3.24) we find that the norm $\|\phi\| = \sup_{t \geqslant 0} |\phi(t)|$ satisfies the inequality

$$\|\phi\| \leqslant c\|g\|, \tag{3.25}$$

where $c = \mu(\Delta)$. Let us further suppose that $g(x)$ has a continuous derivative $g'(x)$; then from (3.20) we obtain

$$\phi'(t) = \int_0^t g'(t - \tau)\mu(d\tau).$$
(3.26)

Proceeding as before, we find that

$$\|\phi'\| \leqslant c\|g'\| < \infty.$$
(3.27)

(b) Now let us define a family of functions of x depending on a parameter t by setting

$$z_t(x) = \phi(t + x) \qquad (t \geqslant 0, \quad -t < x < \infty).$$
(3.28)

Then (3.27) gives

$$\|z_t'(x)\| \leqslant c\|g'\|,$$
(3.29)

which shows that the family $\{Z_t(x)\}$ is equicontinuous. Out of a denumerable subset we can therefore select a sequence $\{t_n\}$ such that $\{z_{t_n}(x)\} \to z(x)$ uniformly in every bounded interval. From (3.21) we find that $z(x)$ satisfies the integral equation

$$z(x) = \int_0^\infty z(x - \tau)\, dF(\tau).$$
(3.30)

By the lemma it follows that

$$z(x) = \text{constant in the continuous case}$$
(3.31)

$$z(nd) = \text{constant in the discrete case.}$$
(3.32)

(c) Integrating (3.21) over $(0, t]$, where $t > h$, we obtain

$$\int_0^h g(s)\, ds = \int_0^t \phi(s)\, ds - \int_0^t ds \int_{\tau=0}^s \phi(s - \tau)\, dF(\tau)$$

$$= \int_0^t \phi(t - s)\, ds - \int_{\tau=0}^t dF(\tau) \int_{s=0}^{t-\tau} \phi(s)\, ds$$

$$= \int_0^t \phi(t - s)\, ds - \left[F(\tau) \int_0^{t-\tau} \phi(s)\, ds \right]_0^t$$

$$- \int_0^t F(\tau)\phi(t - \tau)\, d\tau$$

which simplifies to

$$\int_0^t \phi(t - s)[1 - F(s)]\, ds = \int_0^h g(s)\, ds \qquad (t > h).$$
(3.33)

Now let $\{t_n\}$ be a sequence such that $t_n \to \infty$ and $\phi(t_n - s) \to \xi$ for some s (since the convergence has been proved to be uniform, this holds for all s).

Then (3.33) gives

$$\xi \int_0^\infty [1 - F(s)]\, ds = \int_0^h g(s)\, ds. \tag{3.34}$$

The integral on the left-hand side of (3.34) has the value μ if $\mu < \infty$, and diverges otherwise; therefore,

$$\xi = \begin{cases} \dfrac{1}{\mu}\displaystyle\int_0^h g(s)\, ds & \text{if } \mu < \infty \\[2ex] 0 & \text{if } \mu = \infty. \end{cases} \tag{3.35}$$

We have thus proved that

$$\lim_{t \to \infty} \int_{t-h}^t g(t - \tau)\mu(d\tau) = \frac{1}{\mu} \int_0^h g(s)\, ds$$

or

$$\lim_{t \to \infty} \int_0^h g(s)\mu(t - ds) = \frac{1}{\mu} \int_0^h g(s)\, ds, \tag{3.36}$$

(the limit being interpreted as zero if $\mu = \infty$) for any function $g(x)$ which is continuous and has a continuous derivative. Since such functions are dense among continuous functions, (3.36) holds for every continuous function $g(x)$. It follows that as $t \to \infty$, the measure μ defined on the interval $(t - h, t]$ converges to the measure whose density function is μ^{-1}. Thus

$$U(t) - U(t - h) = \int_0^h \mu(t - ds) \to \int_0^h \frac{ds}{\mu} = \frac{h}{\mu}, \tag{3.37}$$

and we have proved the result for the continuous case. In the discrete case, the measure μ in the interval $(nd - d, nd]$ is given by u_n and (3.37) gives $u_n \to d/\mu$, as desired. The proof is therefore complete.

THEOREM 3.4 (THE KEY RENEWAL THEOREM). *Let $Q(t)$ be a non-negative, nonincreasing function of $t \geqslant 0$, such that*

$$\int_0^\infty Q(t)\, dt < \infty. \tag{3.38}$$

Then

$$\int_0^t Q(t - \tau)\, dU(\tau) \to \frac{1}{\mu} \int_0^\infty Q(t)\, dt \qquad \text{as } t \to \infty, \tag{3.39}$$

the limit being interpreted as zero if $\mu = \infty$.

Proof: Let us write

$$\int_0^t Q(t - \tau)\, dU(\tau) = I_1 + I_2, \tag{3.40}$$

where

$$I_1 = \int_0^{t/2} Q(t - \tau)\, dU(\tau), \qquad I_2 = \int_{t/2}^t Q(t - \tau)\, dU(\tau). \tag{3.41}$$

Since $Q(t)$ is nonincreasing and nonnegative, we have

$$I_1 \leqslant Q\!\left(\frac{t}{2}\right)\!\int_0^{t/2} dU(\tau) = Q\!\left(\frac{t}{2}\right)\! U\!\left(\frac{t}{2}\right)$$

$$\tag{3.42}$$

$$= \frac{\frac{t}{2} Q\!\left(\frac{t}{2}\right)\cdot U\!\left(\frac{t}{2}\right)}{\frac{t}{2}}.$$

Since $U(t/2)/(t/2) \to \mu^{-1}$ and $\tfrac{1}{2}tQ(t/2) \to 0$ as $t \to \infty$, it follows from (3.42) that

$$I_1 \to 0 \qquad \text{as } t \to \infty. \tag{3.43}$$

Now let

$$Q = \int_0^\infty Q(t)\, dt = \sum_{n=0}^\infty \int_{nh}^{nh+h} Q(t)\, dt\,; \tag{3.44}$$

since $Q(nh + h) \leqslant Q(t) \leqslant Q(nh)$ for $nh \leqslant t \leqslant nh + h$, (3.44) gives

$$h\sum_0^\infty Q(nh + h) \leqslant Q \leqslant h\sum_0^\infty Q(nh),$$

or

$$0 \leqslant Q - h\sum_1^\infty Q(nh) \leqslant hQ(0) < \varepsilon \tag{3.45}$$

if we choose $0 < h < \varepsilon/Q(0)$. If $[t/2h] = N$, then

$$I_2 = \int_{t/2}^t Q(t - \tau)\, dU(\tau) = \int_0^{t/2} Q(s)[-dU(t - s)]$$

$$= \sum_{n=0}^{N-1} \int_{nh}^{nh+h} Q(s)[-dU(t - s)],$$

whence

$$\sum_0^{N-1} Q(nh + h)[U(t - nh) - U(t - nh - h)] \leqslant I_2$$

$$\tag{3.46}$$

$$\leqslant \sum_0^{N-1} Q(nh)[U(t - nh) - U(t - nh - h)].$$

Now we can choose t so large that

$$\left| \frac{U(t - nh) - U(t - nh - h)}{h} - \frac{1}{\mu} \right| < \varepsilon \qquad (3.47)$$

and

$$h \sum_{N+1}^{\infty} Q(nh) < \varepsilon. \qquad (3.48)$$

From (3.45)–(3.48) we therefore find that

$$\left(\frac{1}{\mu} - \varepsilon \right) (Q - 2\varepsilon) < I_2 < \left(\frac{1}{\mu} + \varepsilon \right) (Q + \varepsilon). \qquad (3.49)$$

Since ε is arbitrary, this implies that

$$I_2 \to Q/\mu \qquad \text{as } t \to \infty. \qquad (3.50)$$

The result (3.39) then follows from (3.40), (3.43), and (3.50).

4. THE AGE OF THE POPULATION; RESIDUAL LIFE-TIME

4.1. The Age of the Population

Let $X(0)$ be the age of the initial individual. Then the age of the individual who is alive at time t (briefly, the age of the population) is given by

$$X(t) = \begin{cases} t + X(0) & \text{if } N(t) = 0 \\ t - S_{N(t)} & \text{if } N(t) > 0. \end{cases} \qquad (4.1)$$

It is easily seen that $X(t)$ is a time-homogeneous Markov process.

THEOREM 4.1.   *The transition distribution function of $X(t)$ is given by*

$$\Pr \{ X(t) \leqslant x \mid X(0) = x_0 \}$$

$$= \begin{cases} \int_{t-x}^{t} dU(\tau)[1 - F(t - \tau)] & (0 \leqslant x < t) \\[2mm] \dfrac{F(x_0 + t) - F(x_0)}{1 - F(x_0)} & (t \leqslant x < t + x_0) \qquad (4.2) \\[2mm] 1 & (x \geqslant t + x_0). \end{cases}$$

Proof: If a renewal occurs during $(0, t]$, then $0 \leqslant X(t) < t$; but if no renewal occurs, then $X(t) = t + X(0)$. The distribution function of $X(t)$

has therefore a discontinuity at $x = t + X(0)$. For $0 \leqslant x < t$ we therefore have

$$\Pr \{X(t) \leqslant x \,|\, X(0) = x_0\}$$

$$= \Pr \{t - S_N \leqslant x\} = \Pr \{S_N \geqslant t - x\}$$

$$= \sum_{n=1}^{\infty} \Pr \{t - x \leqslant S_n \leqslant t; S_{n+1} > t\}$$

$$= \sum_{n=1}^{\infty} \int_{t-x}^{t} d_\tau \Pr \{S_n \leqslant \tau\} \Pr \{S_{n+1} > t \,|\, S_n = \tau\} \tag{4.3a}$$

$$= \sum_{n=1}^{\infty} \int_{t-x}^{t} d_\tau \Pr \{S_n \leqslant \tau\} \Pr \{X_{n+1} > t - \tau\}$$

$$= \int_{t-x}^{t} \sum_{1}^{\infty} dF_n(\tau)[1 - F(t - \tau)] = \int_{t-x}^{t} dU(\tau)[1 - F(t - \tau)].$$

The same argument shows that for $t \leqslant x < t + x_0$,

$$\Pr \{X(t) \leqslant x \,|\, X(0) = x_0\} = \int_{0}^{t} dU(\tau)[1 - F(t - \tau)] \tag{4.3b}$$

$$= U(t) - \int_{0}^{t} U(t - \tau) \, dF(\tau) = K(t)$$

using the integral equation satisfied by $U(t)$. Finally, we have

$$\Pr \{X(t) = t + x_0 \,|\, X(0) = x_0\} = \Pr \{X_1 > t\}$$

$$= 1 - K(t). \tag{4.4}$$

From (1.6) we have $K(t) = [F(x_0 + t) - F(x_0)][1 - F(x_0)]^{-1}$; the theorem therefore follows from (4.3a), (4.3b), and (4.4).

The absolute (unconditional) distribution function of $X(t)$ is given by

$$\Pr \{X(t) \leqslant x\} = \int_{0}^{\infty} \Pr \{X(t) \leqslant x \,|\, X(0) = x_0\} \, d\Phi(x_0), \tag{4.5}$$

where $\Phi(x_0)$ is the distribution function of the initial age $X(0)$. The limiting distribution of $X(t)$ as $t \to \infty$ is of some interest. The existence of such a distribution as a Cesáro limit was proved by Doob (1948). The following theorem due to Smith (1954) proves its existence as an ordinary limit.

THEOREM 4.2. *We have*

$$\lim_{t \to \infty} \Pr \{X(t) \leqslant x \,|\, X(0) = x_0\}$$

$$= \begin{cases} \displaystyle\int_0^x \frac{1 - F(y)}{\mu} \, dy & \text{if } \mu < \infty \\[2ex] 0 & \text{if } \mu = \infty, \end{cases} \tag{4.6}$$

Proof: From (4.2) we see that we need only consider the distribution of $X(t)$ in the range $0 \leqslant x < t$; thus

$$\Pr \{X(t) \leqslant x \,|\, X(0) = x_0\} = \int_{t-x}^{t} dU(\tau)[1 - F(t - \tau)] \quad (0 \leqslant x < t). \tag{4.7}$$

Let us now define a function $Q(t)$ by setting

$$Q(t) = \begin{cases} 1 - F(t) & \text{if } 0 \leqslant t \leqslant x \\[1ex] 0 & \text{if } t > x. \end{cases} \tag{4.8}$$

Clearly, $Q(t)$ is a nonnegative and nonincreasing function of t, and, moreover,

$$\int_0^\infty Q(t) \, dt = \int_0^x [1 - F(t)] \, dt. \tag{4.9}$$

We can write (4.7) as

$$\Pr \{X(t) \leqslant x \,|\, X(0) = x_0\} = \int_0^\infty Q(t - \tau) \, dU(\tau). \tag{4.10}$$

From Theorem 3.4 we find that as $t \to \infty$,

$$\int_0^\infty Q(t - \tau) \, dU(\tau) \to \frac{1}{\mu} \int_0^x [1 - F(t)] \, dt, \tag{4.11}$$

the limit being interpreted as 0 when $\mu = \infty$. The theorem follows from (4.10) and (4.11).

Let us observe that the limiting distribution of $X(t)$ in the case $\mu < \infty$, is continuous, and has the frequency function

$$\frac{1 - F(x)}{\mu} \quad (0 < x < \infty). \tag{4.12}$$

4.2. The Stationary Process

The renewal process $\{X_n\}$ is called stationary if the distribution of $X(t)$ is independent of t. Clearly, for a stationary renewal process, the distribution of $N(t + s) - N(s) =$ number of renewals during $(s, s + t]$ depends only on t, and is therefore the same as that of $N(t)$. Hence, in particular, we have $U(t + s) - U(s) = U(t)$, or

$$U(t + s) = U(t) + U(s) \qquad (t, s \geqslant 0). \tag{4.13}$$

The only solution of (4.13) which is nonnegative and monotone is given by $U(t) = ct$, where $c \geqslant 0$. From the elementary renewal theorem we find that $c = \mu^{-1}$. Ignoring the trivial case where $U(t) \equiv 0$ for $t \geqslant 0$, we see that for a stationary renewal process $\mu < \infty$, and

$$U(t) = \frac{t}{\mu} \qquad (t \geqslant 0). \tag{4.14}$$

The stationary renewal process is thus an obvious generalization of the Markov renewal process, for which we have already seen that the relation (4.14) holds. The following theorem due to Doob (1948) investigates the conditions under which a stationary renewal process exists.

THEOREM 4.3. *A renewal process is stationary if, and only if, the mean lifetime $\mu < \infty$, and the initial age distribution $\Phi(x)$ is given by*

$$d\Phi(x) = \frac{1 - F(x)}{\mu} dx \qquad (0 < x < \infty). \tag{4.15}$$

Proof: Suppose that $\mu < \infty$ and the distribution of $X(0)$ is given by (4.15). Then we have

$$\Phi^*(\theta) = \int_0^\infty e^{-\theta x}\, d\Phi(x) = \int_0^\infty e^{-\theta x} \frac{1 - F(x)}{\mu} dx$$
$$= \frac{1 - F^*(\theta)}{\theta\mu} \quad [Re(\theta) > 0], \tag{4.16}$$

where $F^*(\theta)$ is the Laplace-Stieltjes transform of $F(x)$. The distribution of X_1 is given by

$$K(x) = \int_0^\infty \frac{F(x + x_0) - F(x_0)}{1 - F(x_0)} d\Phi(x_0) \qquad [\text{from (1.7)}]$$
$$= \int_0^\infty \frac{F(x + x_0) - F(x_0)}{\mu} dx_0$$
$$= \int_0^\infty \frac{1 - F(x_0)}{\mu} dx_0 - \int_0^\infty \frac{1 - F(x + x_0)}{\mu} dx \tag{4.17}$$
$$= \int_0^\infty \frac{1 - F(x_0)}{\mu} dx_0 - \int_x^\infty \frac{1 - F(x_0)}{\mu} dx_0$$
$$= \int_0^x \frac{1 - F(x_0)}{\mu} dx_0 = \Phi(x).$$

Therefore,

$$U^*(\theta) = \frac{K^*(\theta)}{1 - F^*(\theta)} = \frac{1 - F^*(\theta)}{\theta\mu[1 - F^*(\theta)]} = \frac{1}{\theta\mu}, \tag{4.18}$$

which gives readily $U(t) = t/\mu$. Substituting this in (4.2) and (4.5) and using (4.15), we find that for $0 \leqslant x < t$,

$$\Pr\{X(t) \leqslant x\} = \int_{t-x}^{t} \frac{d\tau}{\mu}[1 - F(t - \tau)] = \int_{0}^{x} \frac{1 - F(y)}{\mu} dy,$$

and for $x \geqslant t$,

$$\Pr\{X(t) \leqslant x\} = \int_{0}^{t} \frac{d\tau}{\mu}[1 - F(t - \tau)] + \int_{0}^{x-t} \frac{1 - F(x_0 + t)}{1 - F(x_0)} d\Phi(x_0)$$

$$= \int_{0}^{t} \frac{1 - F(y)}{\mu} dy + \int_{0}^{x-t} \frac{1 - F(x_0 + t)}{\mu} dx_0$$

$$= \int_{0}^{x} \frac{1 - F(y)}{\mu} dy.$$

We thus have

$$\Pr\{X(t) \leqslant x\} = \int_{0}^{x} \frac{1 - F(y)}{\mu} dy \qquad (0 \leqslant x < \infty), \tag{4.19}$$

which shows that the distribution of $X(t)$ is independent of t. The renewal process is therefore stationary.

Conversely, suppose that we have a stationary renewal process. Then we have seen that $\mu < \infty$ and $U(t) = t/\mu$; it remains to prove that the initial age distribution $\Phi(x)$ is given by (4.15). We have

$$\Pr\{X(t) \leqslant x\} = \int_{0}^{x} \frac{1 - F(y)}{\mu} dy \qquad (0 \leqslant x < t). \tag{4.20}$$

However, since the distribution of $X(t)$ is independent of t, (4.20) must hold for $0 \leqslant x < \infty$, and therefore

$$\Phi(x) = \Pr\{X(0) \leqslant x\} = \Pr\{X(t) \leqslant x\} = \int_{0}^{x} \frac{1 - F(y)}{\mu} dy \qquad (0 \leqslant x < \infty), \tag{4.21}$$

which is the required result.

4.3. The Residual Lifetime

The residual lifetime $Y(t)$ of the individual who is alive at time t is given by

$$Y(t) = S_{N+1} - t, \qquad N \equiv N(t). \tag{4.22}$$

We have already referred to $Y(t)$ in the proof of Theorem 3.1, where it was shown that

$$E\{Y(t)\} = \mu U(t) + \mu - t \qquad (4.23)$$

if $\mu < \infty$. This process $Y(t)$ is related to the age process $X(t)$ by the identity $X(t) + Y(t) = X_{N+1}$. The properties of $Y(t)$ can therefore be obtained from those of $X(t)$; the distribution of $Y(t)$ can, however, be obtained directly, as shown in the following theorem:

THEOREM 4.4.   *We have*

$$\Pr\{Y(t) \leqslant y\} = \int_t^{t+y} dU(\tau)[1 - F(t + y - \tau)], \qquad (4.24)$$

and

$$\lim_{t \to \infty} \Pr\{Y(t) \leqslant y\} = \begin{cases} \int_0^y \dfrac{1 - F(x)}{\mu} \, dx & \text{if } \mu < \infty \\[2mm] 0 & \text{if } \mu = \infty. \end{cases} \qquad (4.25)$$

Note that in (4.24), $U(t)$ *involves the initial value* $Y(0) = X_1$.

Proof: From (4.22) we find that

$$\Pr\{Y(t) \leqslant y\} = \Pr\{S_{N+1} \leqslant t + y\}$$

$$= \Pr\{t < X_1 \leqslant t + y\} + \sum_{n=1}^{\infty} \Pr\{S_n \leqslant t, \ t < S_{n+1} \leqslant t + y\}$$

$$= K(t + y) - K(t) \qquad (4.26)$$

$$+ \sum_{n=1}^{\infty} \int_0^t d_\tau \Pr\{S_n \leqslant \tau\} \Pr\{t < S_{n+1} \leqslant t + y \,|\, S_n = \tau\}$$

$$= K(t + y) - K(t) + \int_0^t dU(\tau)[F(t + y - \tau) - F(t - \tau)].$$

Now from Theorem (2.3) we have

$$U(t) = K(t) + \int_0^t U(t - \tau) \, dF(\tau)$$

$$= K(t) + [U(t - \tau)F(\tau)]_0^t - \int_0^t dU(t - \tau)F(\tau) \qquad (4.27)$$

$$= K(t) + \int_0^t dU(\tau)F(t - \tau).$$

Using (4.27), we can simplify (4.26) as

$$\Pr\{Y(t) \leqslant y\} = \left\{ K(t+y) + \int_0^{t+y} dU(\tau)F(t+y-\tau) \right\}$$

$$- \left\{ K(t) + \int_0^t dU(\tau)F(t-\tau) \right\} - \int_t^{t+y} dU(\tau)F(t+y-\tau)$$

$$= U(t+y) - U(t) - \int_t^{t+y} dU(\tau)F(t+y-\tau)$$

$$= \int_t^{t+y} dU(\tau)[1 - F(t+y-\tau)],$$

which is the result (4.24). To prove (4.25) we carry out an integration by parts in (4.24); after some simplification we find that

$$\Pr\{Y(t) \leqslant y\} = [U(t+y) - U(t)][1 - F(y)]$$

$$+ \int_0^y [U(t+y) - U(t+y-s)]\,dF(s). \tag{4.28}$$

Using Blackwell's theorem we therefore obtain

$$\lim_{t \to \infty} \Pr\{Y(t) \leqslant y\} = \frac{y}{\mu}[1 - F(y)] + \int_0^y \frac{s}{\mu}\,dF(s)$$

$$= \int_0^y \frac{1 - F(s)}{\mu}\,ds, \tag{4.29}$$

where the limit is interpreted as zero if $\mu = \infty$. We have thus proved (4.25).

If the renewal process is stationary, we have $U(t) = t/\mu$, $\mu < \infty$, and therefore (4.24) gives

$$\Pr\{Y(t) \leqslant y\} = \frac{1}{\mu}\int_t^{t+y} d\tau[1 - F(t+y-\tau)]$$

$$= \int_0^y \frac{1 - F(x)}{\mu}\,dx, \tag{4.30}$$

independently of t and the initial value $Y(0)$. Alternatively, this property of residual lifetime can be used to *define* a stationary process.

EXAMPLE 4.1. Let us consider a renewal process where the d.f. of lifetimes is given by $F(x) = 1 - e^{-\lambda x}$ ($0 \leqslant x < \infty$). If the process starts with an individual of age $X(0) = x_0$, then the residual lifetime of this initial individual has the d.f. given by

$$K(x) = \frac{F(x + x_0) - F(x_0)}{1 - F(x_0)} = \frac{e^{-\lambda x_0} - e^{-\lambda(x + x_0)}}{e^{-\lambda x_0}}$$

$$= 1 - e^{-\lambda x} \qquad (0 \leqslant x < \infty). \tag{4.31}$$

This d.f. is independent of x_0 and is in fact the same as that of the lifetime of a new individual. Thus this process has the same properties as the process studied in Example 1.2. We have $\Phi(x) = F(x)$, and therefore

$$\lambda \int_0^x [1 - F(y)]\, dy = \int_0^x \lambda e^{-\lambda y}\, dy = 1 - e^{-\lambda x} = \Phi(x), \tag{4.32}$$

so that by Theorem 4.2, this Markov renewal process is stationary. It follows that the distribution of the age $X(t)$ is given by

$$\Pr\{X(t) \leqslant x\} = \Pr\{X(0) \leqslant x\} = 1 - e^{-\lambda x}. \tag{4.33}$$

To verify this last result directly, we note that $U(t) = \lambda t$; the transition d.f. of $X(t)$ is therefore found to be

$$\Pr\{X(t) \leqslant x \,|\, X(0) = x_0\} = \begin{cases} 1 - e^{-\lambda x} & 0 \leqslant x < t \\ 1 - e^{-\lambda t} & t \leqslant x < t + x_0 \\ 1 & x \geqslant t + x_0; \end{cases} \tag{4.34}$$

since the distribution of x_0 is given by $d\Phi(x) = \lambda e^{-\lambda x}\, dx$, (4.33) follows easily from (4.34). The distribution of the residual lifetime is also found from (4.30) to be

$$\Pr\{Y(t) \leqslant y\} = 1 - e^{-\lambda y} \qquad (0 \leqslant y < \infty), \tag{4.35}$$

confirming once again the Markovian property of the process.

5. APPLICATION TO COUNTER MODELS

Consider a counter (registering mechanism) for detecting the presence of radioactive material. Impulses emitted by this material arrive at the counter, but because of inertia, the counter will not register some of these impulses. The time during which this inertia lasts is called dead time, and the remaining time is called free time. More specifically, suppose that an impulse arrives at time $t = 0$, and that the counter registers this impulse. This registration causes a dead time, and so the impulses arriving during this dead time will not be registered by the counter. The first impulse to arrive after the termination of this dead time will be registered by the counter, and this again causes a dead time, and so on. In the simpler case the impulses which arrive during a dead time do not cause any dead time, so that each dead time is caused only by a registered impulse. This is called a counter of type I. In a counter of type II, each arriving impulse causes a dead time, so that arrivals during a dead time prolong that dead time. For an extensive bibliography on the subject of counter models, see Smith (1958). Here we shall consider only counters of type I, and follow Pyke's (1958) very elegant treatment of this model.

Let the successive impulses arrive at the counter at the time instants $t_0 (= 0)$, t_1, t_2, ... Assume that the counter is free at time $t = 0$, so that the first impulse is registered. Let $X_n = t_n - t_{n-1}$ $(n \geqslant 1)$ be the intervals of time between the successive arrivals, and Y_0, Y_1, Y_2, ... the successive dead times. Our model is based on the following assumptions:

(a) The interarrival times X_1, X_2, X_3, ... are mutually independent and identically distributed random variables with the distribution function

$$F(x) = \Pr\{X_n \leqslant x\} \qquad (0 \leqslant x < \infty), \qquad (5.1)$$

where $F(0) = 0$.

(b) The dead times Y_0, Y_1, Y_2, ... are mutually independent random variables, which are independent of the X_n and have the distribution function

$$G(y) = \Pr\{Y_n \leqslant y\} \qquad (0 \leqslant y < \infty), \qquad (5.2)$$

where $G(0-) = 0$.

The above assumptions imply that $\{X_n\}$ and $\{Y_n\}$ are two independent renewal processes. Let us denote

$$\mu = \int_0^\infty x \, dF(x), \qquad v = \int_0^\infty y \, dG(y), \qquad (5.3)$$

where $\mu \leqslant \infty$, $v \leqslant \infty$. Let $S_n = X_1 + X_2 + \cdots + X_n$ $(n \geqslant 1)$, and

$$N(t) = \max \{n \mid S_n \leqslant t\}, \qquad U(t) = E\{N(t)\}. \qquad (5.4)$$

Clearly, $N(t) + 1$ is the number of impulses which arrive during the time interval $[0, t]$ (including the initial one).

We now define a sequence $\{n_j, j \geqslant 0\}$ of nonnegative integers as follows. Put $n_0 = 0$, and

$$n_1 = \min \{n \mid S_n > Y_0\},$$
$$n_2 = \min \{n \mid S_n > S_{n_1} + Y_1\},$$
$$n_3 = \min \{n \mid S_n > S_{n_2} + Y_2\}, \qquad (5.5)$$

$$\cdot \quad \cdot \quad \cdot \quad \cdot \quad \cdot \quad \cdot \quad \cdot \quad \cdot \quad \cdot \quad \cdot$$

$$n_j = \min \{n \mid S_n > S_{n_{j-1}} + Y_{j-1}\}.$$

Then the instants of successive registration of the impulses are t_0' $(= 0)$, t_1', t_2', ..., where $t_j' = t_{n_j}$ $(j = 0, 1, 2, \ldots)$. The intervals of time between the successive registrations are then given by

$$Z_j = t'_j - t'_{j-1} \qquad (j = 1, 2, \ldots); \qquad (5.6)$$

(see Figure 1). We have $Z_j = S_{n_j} - S_{n_{j-1}}$, and since $n_1 - n_0, n_2 - n_1, \ldots$ are identically distributed random variables, it follows that $\{Z_j\}$ is a renewal process. Put $T_n = Z_1 + Z_2 + \cdots + Z_n$, and

$$M(t) = \max \{n \,|\, T_n \leqslant t\}, \qquad V(t) = E\{M(t)\}. \qquad (5.7)$$

The number of impulses registered during $[0, t]$ is then given by $M(t) + 1$ (including the initial one). The ratio

$$B(t) = \frac{1 + U(t)}{1 + V(t)} \qquad (5.8)$$

is called the bias of the counter; it is intuitively clear that $B(t) > 1$. For a proper understanding of the working of the counter, it is obviously important to study the renewal process $\{Z_j\}$.

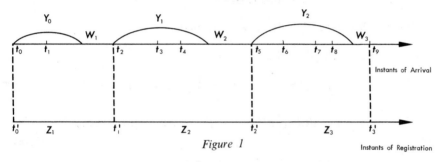

Figure 1

We also consider the random variables

$$W_j = Z_j - Y_{j-1} \qquad (j = 1, 2, \ldots); \qquad (5.9)$$

W_j is the free time following the jth registration. Clearly, $W_1, W_2, W_3, \ldots$ are identically distributed random variables; their distribution function is given by the following:

THEOREM 5.1. *We have*

$$K(x) = \Pr\{W_j \leqslant x\} = \int_{0-}^{\infty} \int_{t}^{x+t} [1 - F(x + t - \tau)] \, dG(t) \, dU(\tau),$$
$$(0 \leqslant x < \infty). \qquad (5.10)$$

Proof: Since the W_j are identically distributed, we need only consider $W_1 = t_{n_1} - Y_0$. For $Y_0 = t$ (fixed) it is clear that W_1 is the residual lifetime at time t of the renewal process $\{X_n\}$. Therefore,

$$\Pr\{W_1 \leqslant x \,|\, Y_0 = t\} = \int_{t}^{x+t} dU(\tau)[1 - F(x + t - \tau)] \qquad (5.11)$$

from (4.24). Hence we obtain

$$\Pr\{W_1 \leqslant x\} = \int_{0-}^{\infty} d_t \Pr\{Y_0 \leqslant t\} \Pr\{W_1 \leqslant x \,|\, Y_0 = t\}$$

$$= \int_{0-}^{\infty} dG(t) \int_{t}^{x+t} dU(\tau)[1 - F(x + t - \tau)],$$

(5.12)

which gives (5.10).

THEOREM 5.2. *We have*

(i) $H(z) = \Pr\{Z_j \leqslant z\} = \int_{0}^{z} G(t)[1 - F(z - t)] \, dU(t),$ (5.13)

(ii) $\Pr\{Z_j < \infty\} = H(\infty) = 1,$ (5.14)

(iii) $E(Z_j) = \begin{cases} \mu + \mu \int_{0}^{\infty} U(t) \, dG(t) & \text{if } \mu < \infty, \, \nu < \infty \\ \infty & \text{otherwise} \end{cases}$ (5.15)

Proof: We have $Z_j = W_j + Y_{j-1}$, so that

$$H(z) = \Pr\{W_j + Y_{j-1} \leqslant z\}$$

$$= \int_{0-}^{z} d_t \Pr\{Y_{j-1} \leqslant t\} \Pr\{W_j \leqslant z - t \,|\, Y_{j-1} = t\}$$

$$= \int_{0-}^{z} dG(t) \int_{t}^{z} dU(\tau)[1 - F(z - \tau)] \qquad [\text{from 5.11}]$$

$$= \left\{ G(t) \int_{t}^{z} dU(\tau)[1 - F(z - \tau)] \right\}_{0-}^{z}$$

(5.16)

$$\quad + \int_{0-}^{z} G(t) \, dU(t)[1 - F(z - t)]$$

$$= \int_{0}^{z} G(t)[1 - F(z - t)] \, dU(t),$$

which is the result (i). For $\theta > 0$ we find from (i) that

$$\int_{0}^{\infty} e^{-\theta z} H(z) \, dz = \int_{0}^{\infty} G(t) \, dU(t) \int_{t}^{\infty} e^{-\theta z}[1 - F(z - t)] \, dz$$

$$= \frac{1 - F^*(\theta)}{\theta} \int_{0}^{\infty} e^{-\theta t} G(t) \, dU(t),$$

where

$$F^*(\theta) = \int_{0}^{\infty} e^{-\theta x} \, dF(x) \qquad (\theta \geqslant 0)$$

is the Laplace–Stieltjes transform of $F(x)$. We have

$$U^*(\theta) = \int_0^\infty e^{-\theta t}\, dU(t) = \frac{F^*(\theta)}{1 - F^*(\theta)},$$

so that the Laplace–Stieltjes transform of $H(z)$ can be written as

$$H^*(\theta) = \int_0^\infty e^{-\theta z}\, dH(z) = \theta \int_0^\infty e^{-\theta z} H(z)\, dz$$

$$= F^*(\theta)\frac{\displaystyle\int_0^\infty e^{-\theta t} G(t)\, dU(t)}{\displaystyle\int_0^\infty e^{-\theta t}\, dU(t)}. \tag{5.17}$$

Hence, using an Abelian theorem, we obtain

$$H(\infty) = \lim_{\theta \to 0+} H^*(\theta) = \lim_{t \to \infty} G(t) = 1, \tag{5.18}$$

since $U(t) \to \infty$ as $t \to \infty$. We have thus proved (ii). Finally, let us observe that

$$\max(Y_0, X_1) \leqslant Z_1 \leqslant Y_0 + X_{n_1}, \tag{5.19}$$

so that $E(Z_1) < \infty$ if, and only if, $\mu < \infty$, $\nu < \infty$. Suppose that this condition is satisfied. From the definition of n_1 we obtain $E(n_1 \mid Y_0 = t) = 1 + U(t)$; since $Z_1 = S_{n_1}$ we find, using Wald's equation [Theorem 8.6, Chapter 2], that $E(Z_1 \mid Y_0 = t) = \mu E(n_1 \mid Y_0 = t) = \mu + \mu U(t)$. Therefore,

$$E(Z_1) = \int_{0-}^\infty dG(t)[\mu + \mu U(t)]$$

$$= \mu + \mu \int_0^\infty U(t)\, dG(t), \tag{5.20}$$

as required.

THEOREM 5.3. *If $\mu < \infty$, the asymptotic bias of the counter as $t \to \infty$ is given by*

$$\lim_{t \to \infty} B(t) = \begin{cases} \infty & \text{if } \nu = \infty \\ 1 + \displaystyle\int_0^\infty U(t)\, dG(t) & \text{if } \nu < \infty. \end{cases} \tag{5.21}$$

Proof: We have

$$\lim_{t \to \infty} B(t) = \lim_{t \to \infty} \frac{[1 + U(t)]/t}{[1 + V(t)]/t}$$

$$= \frac{1/\mu}{1/E(Z_j)}. \tag{5.22}$$

In view of (5.15), this gives the desired result.

THEOREM 5.4.   *Let $P_1(t)$ be the probability that the counter is free at time t, and $P_0(t) = 1 - P_1(t)$ the probability that it is not free (locked). Then*

$$P_0(t) = 1 - G(t) + \int_0^t [1 - G(t - \tau)] \, dV(\tau). \qquad (5.23)$$

Moreover, if $v < \infty$, then

$$\lim_{t \to \infty} P_0(t) = \begin{cases} \dfrac{v}{\mu} \left[1 + \int_0^\infty U(t) \, dG(t) \right]^{-1} & \text{if } \mu < \infty, \\[2mm] 0 & \text{if } \mu = \infty. \end{cases} \qquad (5.24)$$

Proof: We have

$$P_0(t) = \Pr \{Y_0 > t\} + \sum_{n=1}^\infty \Pr \{T_n \le t < T_n + Y_n\}$$

$$= 1 - G(t) + \sum_{n=1}^\infty \int_0^t d_\tau \Pr \{T_n \le \tau\} \Pr \{Y_n > t - \tau\} \qquad (5.25)$$

$$= 1 - G(t) + \int_0^t dV(\tau)[1 - G(t - \tau)],$$

since

$$V(t) = \sum_1^\infty \Pr \{T_n \le t\} < \infty.$$

Now consider the function $Q(t) = 1 - G(t) \ (t \ge 0)$; this is a nonnegative, nonincreasing function of t, and

$$\int_0^\infty Q(t) \, dt = \int_0^\infty [1 - G(t)] \, dt = \int_0^\infty t \, dG(t) = v. \qquad (5.26)$$

Therefore, if $v < \infty$, then by the key renewal theorem we find that

$$\int_0^t dV(\tau)[1 - G(t - \tau)] \to \frac{v}{E(Z_1)}, \qquad (5.27)$$

where the limit is interpreted as zero if $E(Z_1) = \infty$. This happens when $\mu = \infty$, and therefore (5.24) is proved.

EXAMPLE 5.1.   Let us now illustrate the above results by considering the model with a Poisson input and variable dead time. Thus here

$$dF(x) = \lambda e^{-\lambda x} \, dx \ (0 \le x < \infty), \qquad G(y) = \Pr \{Y_j \le y\}. \qquad (5.28)$$

We have $\Pr \{W_1 \le x \,|\, Y_0 = t\} = F(x)$ on account of the Markovian property of $\{X_n\}$, and therefore the distribution of free time is given by

$$K(x) = \Pr \{W_1 \le x\} = 1 - e^{-\lambda x} \quad (0 \le x < \infty). \qquad (5.29)$$

From (5.16) we find that

$$H(z) = \int_{0-}^{z} dG(t)[1 - e^{-\lambda(z-t)}], \tag{5.30}$$

so that

$$H^*(\theta) = \int_0^\infty e^{-\theta z}\, dH(z) = \int_0^\infty e^{-\theta z}\, dz \int_0^z \lambda e^{-\lambda(z-t)}\, dG(t)$$

$$= \int_{0-}^\infty dG(t) \int_t^\infty \lambda e^{-\theta z - \lambda(z-t)}\, dz = \frac{\lambda G^*(\theta)}{\theta + \lambda}, \tag{5.31}$$

where

$$G^*(\theta) = \int_{0-}^\infty e^{-\theta y}\, dG(y) \qquad (\theta > 0). \tag{5.32}$$

Now, let $H_n(z) = \Pr\{T_n \leqslant z\}$; clearly, $H_n(z)$ is the n-fold convolution of $H(z)$ with itself, so that

$$\int_0^\infty e^{-\theta z}\, dH_n(z) = \left(\frac{\lambda}{\theta + \lambda}\right)^n [G^*(\theta)]^n \qquad (n \geqslant 1). \tag{5.33}$$

Now,

$$\int_0^\infty e^{-\theta x}\lambda^n e^{-\lambda x}\frac{x^{n-1}}{(n-1)!}\, dx = \left(\frac{\lambda}{\theta + \lambda}\right)^n, \tag{5.34}$$

and, moreover, if $G_n(y)$ is the n-fold convolution of $G(y)$ with itself, then,

$$\int_0^\infty e^{-\theta y}\, dG_n(y) = [G^*(\theta)]^n. \tag{5.35}$$

From (5.33)–(5.35) we find that

$$H_n(z) = \int_0^z G_n(z-x)\lambda^n e^{-\lambda x}\frac{x^{n-1}}{(n-1)!}\, dx \qquad (n = 1, 2, \ldots). \tag{5.36}$$

The distribution of $M(t)$, the number of registrations during $(0, t]$, is given by

$$\Pr\{M(t) = n\} = H_n(t) - H_{n+1}(t) \qquad (n = 0, 1, \ldots), \tag{5.37}$$

and its mean by

$$V(t) = E\{M(t)\} = \sum_1^\infty H_n(t). \tag{5.38}$$

Since $U(t) = \lambda t$, we have

$$\int_0^\infty U(t)\, dG(t) = \lambda \int_0^\infty t\, dG(t) = \lambda v, \tag{5.39}$$

and $E(Z_1) = \lambda^{-1} + v$. The asymptotic bias is therefore given by

$$\lim_{t \to \infty} B(t) = 1 + \lambda v. \tag{5.40}$$

Finally,

$$\lim_{t \to \infty} P_0(t) = \frac{\lambda v}{1 + \lambda v}, \qquad \lim_{t \to \infty} P_1(t) = \frac{1}{1 + \lambda v}. \tag{5.41}$$

6. THE DISCRETE CASE; RECURRENT EVENTS

6.1. Formal Results

Let us now consider the case of a discrete renewal process $\{X_n, n = 1, 2, \ldots\}$, in which the distribution of X_1 is given by

$$\Pr\{X_1 = j\} = b_j \qquad (j = 0, 1, 2, \ldots), \tag{6.1}$$

and the distribution of X_n $(n \geqslant 2)$, by

$$\Pr\{X_n = j\} = a_j \qquad (j = 0, 1, \ldots; n \geqslant 2). \tag{6.2}$$

If there exists an integer $d > 1$ such that

$$b_j = 0, \qquad a_j = 0 \text{ whenever } j \neq vd \ (v = 0, 1, \ldots), \tag{6.3}$$

we say that the process is periodic; otherwise it is aperiodic. Let us denote the mean of X_n $(n \geqslant 2)$ by

$$\mu = E(X_n) = \sum_0^\infty j a_j, \tag{6.4}$$

where $\mu \leqslant \infty$. Now let us consider the partial sums $S_k = X_1 + X_2 + \cdots + X_k$ $(k \geqslant 1)$, and denote their distribution by

$$\Pr\{S_k = j\} = a_j^{(k)} \qquad (j = 0, 1, \ldots; \quad k = 1, 2, \ldots). \tag{6.5}$$

We have

$$
\begin{aligned}
a_j^{(1)} &= b_j, \\
a_j^{(k)} &= \sum_{v=0}^{j} a_{j-v}^{(k-1)} a_v \qquad (k \geqslant 2);
\end{aligned}
\tag{6.6}
$$

the probabilities $a_j^{(k)}$ can be obtained successively for $k = 1, 2, \ldots$ by using the relations (6.6). As the discrete analogue of $N(t)$, we shall consider the random variable N_n defined by

$$N_n = \max\{k \mid S_k \leqslant n\}. \tag{6.7}$$

It is easily seen that N_n is the number of renewals occurring in $[0, n]$.

From Theorem (2.2) we find that

$$P_{n,k} = \Pr\{N_n = k\} = \sum_{j=0}^{n} a_j^{(k)} - \sum_{j=0}^{n} a_j^{(k+1)}, \tag{6.8}$$

and

$$U_n = E\{N_n\} = \sum_{k=1}^{\infty} \sum_{j=0}^{n} a_j^{(k)} = \sum_{j=0}^{n} \sum_{k=1}^{\infty} a_j^{(k)} \tag{6.9}$$

$$= u_0 + u_1 + \cdots + u_n,$$

where

$$u_j = \sum_{k=1}^{\infty} a_j^{(k)} \tag{6.10}$$

= expected number of partial sums S_k which take the value j.

The renewal equation in this case reduces to

$$U_n = \sum_0^n b_j + \sum_{m=0}^n U_{n-m} a_m \qquad (n \geqslant 0),$$

whence we obtain

$$u_n = U_n - U_{n-1}$$

$$= b_n + \sum_0^n U_{n-m} a_m - \sum_0^{n-1} U_{n-1-m} a_m$$

$$= b_n + u_0 a_n + \sum_0^{n-1} (U_{n-m} - U_{n-1-m}) a_m$$

$$= b_n + u_0 a_n + \sum_0^{n-1} u_{n-m} a_m.$$

This can be written as

$$u_n = b_n + \sum_{m=0}^n u_{n-m} a_m \qquad (n \geqslant 0); \tag{6.11}$$

we shall call this the renewal equation of the discrete process. Now let us define the generating functions

$$B(z) = \sum_0^{\infty} b_j z^j, \qquad A(z) = \sum_0^{\infty} a_j z^j,$$

$$U(z) = \sum_0^{\infty} u_n z^n \qquad (|z| < 1). \tag{6.12}$$

Multiplying the equation (6.11) by z^n and adding over $n = 0, 1, 2. \ldots$, we obtain

$$U(z) = B(z) + U(z)A(z),$$

whence

$$U(z) = \frac{B(z)}{1 - A(z)}. \tag{6.13}$$

EXAMPLE 6.1.   Let the distribution of X_n be given by

$$\Pr\{X_n = 0\} = q, \qquad \Pr\{X_n = 1\} = p \qquad (n \geq 1), \tag{6.14}$$

where $0 < p < 1$, and $q = 1 - p$. We have

$$\Pr\{S_k = j\} = \binom{k}{j} p^j q^{k-j} \qquad (0 \leq j \leq k). \tag{6.15}$$

From (6.8) we find that

$$
\begin{aligned}
P_{nk} &= \Pr\{N_n = k\} \\
&= \sum_{j=0}^{n} \binom{k}{j} p^j q^{k-j} - \sum_{j=0}^{n} \binom{k+1}{j} p^j q^{k+1-j} \\
&= \sum_{j=0}^{n} \binom{k}{j} p^j q^{k-j} - \sum_{j=0}^{n} \left\{ \binom{k}{j} + \binom{k}{j-1} \right\} p^j q^{k+1-j} \\
&= \sum_{j=0}^{n} \binom{k}{j} p^{j+1} q^{k-j} - \sum_{j=1}^{n} \binom{k}{j-1} p^j q^{k+1-j} \\
&= \sum_{j=0}^{n} \binom{k}{j} p^{j+1} q^{k-j} - \sum_{j=0}^{n-1} \binom{k}{j} p^{j+1} q^{k-j} \\
&= \binom{k}{n} p^{n+1} q^{k-n} \\
&= \binom{-n-1}{k-n} (-q)^{k-n} p^{n+1} \qquad (k \geq n);
\end{aligned}
\tag{6.16}
$$

thus N_n has a negative binomial distribution. To obtain U_n, note that the generating function X_n is $q + pz$; therefore,

$$
\begin{aligned}
U(z) &= \frac{q + pz}{1 - q - pz} = \frac{q + pz}{p(1 - z)} \\
&= \frac{q}{p} + \frac{1}{p}(z + z^2 + \cdots),
\end{aligned}
\tag{6.17}
$$

which gives $u_0 = qp^{-1}$, $u_n = p^{-1}$ $(n \geqslant 1)$, and

$$U_n = \frac{q}{p} + \frac{n}{p} = \frac{n+1}{p} - 1. \tag{6.18}$$

These results may be compared with those derived in example (1.1).

6.2. Recurrent Events

Since discrete renewal theory was developed by Feller (1949, 1957) in the context of the theory of recurrent events, we shall derive further results in terms of recurrent events. A recurrent event[1] on the basic sample space is a family $\varepsilon = \{E_1, E_2, \ldots\}$ of events with the property

$$\Pr\{E_{n_1}, E_{n_2}, \ldots, E_{n_r}\} = \Pr\{E_{n_1}\} \Pr\{E_{n_2 - n_1}\} \cdots \Pr\{E_{n_r - n_{r-1}}\} \tag{6.19}$$

for every set of positive integers $n_1 < n_2 \cdots < n_r$ $(r \geqslant 1)$. Let

$$u_n = \Pr\{E_n\} \tag{6.20}$$

be the probability that ε occurs at time n; then (6.19) can be written as

$$\Pr\{E_{n_1}, E_{n_2}, \ldots, E_{n_r}\} = u_{n_1} u_{n_2 - n_1} \cdots u_{n_r - n_{r-1}}. \tag{6.21}$$

We shall also define

$$f_n = \Pr\{\varepsilon \text{ occurs for the first time at time } n\} \qquad (n \geqslant 1)$$

$$f_0 = 0. \tag{6.22}$$

We shall assume that ε has occurred at time $n = 0$, and put $u_0 = 1$. Then if ε occurs at time n, it might be either occurring for the first time at time n, or it might have occurred sometime earlier; in the latter case suppose that it occurred for the first time at m $(1 \leqslant m \leqslant n - 1)$. We thus obtain the recurrence relation

$$u_n = f_n + \sum_{m=1}^{n-1} u_{n-m} f_m \qquad (n \geqslant 1). \tag{6.23}$$

A comparison of (6.23) with (6.11) shows that we have here a special case of the discrete time renewal equation, where the distribution of the basic random variables $\{X_k\}$ is given by

$$\Pr\{X_k = n\} = f_n. \tag{6.24}$$

The X_k $(k \geqslant 2)$ are easily seen to be the intervals of time between the successive occurrences of ε, while X_1 is the time till the first occurrence of ε. The X_k are called the recurrence times of ε. The mean recurrence time

---

[1] This definition is due to Kingman (1963).

is $\mu = \sum_{1}^{\infty} n f_n$. Further,

$$f_n^{(r)} = \Pr\{S_r = n\}$$

$$= \Pr\{\text{the } r\text{th occurrence of } \varepsilon \text{ takes place at time } n\}, \tag{6.25}$$

and therefore

$$\sum_{r=1}^{\infty} f_n^{(r)} = \Pr\{\varepsilon \text{ occurs at time } n\} = u_n, \tag{6.26}$$

in agreement with (6.10). The random variable N_n is the number of occurrences of ε during $(0, n]$. We have

$$E(N_n) = u_1 + u_2 + \cdots + u_n \qquad (n \geqslant 1). \tag{6.27}$$

Let us define the generating functions

$$F(z) = \sum_{1}^{\infty} f_n z^n, \qquad U(z) = 1 + \sum_{1}^{\infty} u_n z^n \qquad (|z| < 1); \tag{6.28}$$

then from (6.23) we obtain the relation

$$U(z) - 1 = F(z) + F(z)[U(z) - 1],$$

or

$$U(z) = \frac{1}{1 - F(z)}. \tag{6.29}$$

It is important to distinguish between the two cases

$$\text{(a)} \ \sum f_n = 1; \qquad \text{(b)} \ \sum f_n < 1; \tag{6.30}$$

ε is called a persistent or a transient recurrent event according as (a) or (b) is true. From (6.29) it is seen that ε is persistent or transient according as

$$\sum u_n = \infty \qquad \text{or} \ \sum u_n < \infty. \tag{6.31}$$

Moreover, if there exists a $d > 1$ such that $f_n = 0$ whenever $n \neq \nu d$, and is the greatest integer with this property we say that ε is periodic, and has period d; otherwise, ε is aperiodic.

If ε is transient, it follows from (6.31) that $u_n \to 0$ as $n \to \infty$. If ε is persistent, then

$$u_n \to \frac{1}{\mu} \qquad \text{if } \varepsilon \text{ is aperiodic,}$$

$$\tag{6.32}$$

$$u_{nd} \to \frac{d}{\mu} \qquad \text{if } \varepsilon \text{ has period } d,$$

the limit in each case being interpreted as 0 if $\mu = \infty$. This result has already been proved in Section 3. This can also be stated as follows. If the power series $U(z)$ and $F(z)$ with positive coefficients are connected by the relation (6.29), and $F(1) = 1$, then

$$\lim_{n \to \infty} u_n = \lim_{z \to 1-0} (1 - z^m)U(z), \tag{6.33}$$

where m is the greatest common divisor of those indices n for which $f_n > 0$ ($m = 1$ in the aperiodic case; and $m = d$, the period, in the periodic case).

The following two theorems, due to Feller (1949), give the generating functions of the distribution of the random variable N_n, and its first two moments. For the asymptotic distribution of N_n, see remarks at the beginning of the proof of Theorem 2.4.

THEOREM 6.1. *Let* $P_n(z) = E(z^{N_n})$ *be the probability generating function of* N_n, $U_n = E(N_n)$, *and* $V_n = E(N_n^2)$; *then*

(a) $\displaystyle \sum_{n=1}^{n} P_n(z)t^n = \frac{1}{1-t} \cdot \frac{1 - F(t)}{1 - zF(t)},$ (6.34)

(b) $\displaystyle \sum_{n=1}^{\infty} U_n t^n = \frac{1}{1-t} \cdot \frac{F(t)}{1 - F(t)},$ (6.35)

(c) $\displaystyle \sum_{n=1}^{\infty} V_n t^n = \frac{1}{1-t} \cdot \frac{F(t) + [F(t)]^2}{[1 - F(t)]^2} (|t| < 1, |z| < 1).$ (6.36)

Proof: From (6.8) we have

$$P_{n,k} = \Pr\{N_k = n\} = \sum_{r=1}^{n} [f_r^{(k)} - f_r^{(k+1)}], \tag{6.37}$$

so that

$$\sum_{n=1}^{\infty} P_{n,k} t^n = \sum_{n=1}^{\infty} t^n \sum_{r=1}^{n} [f_r^{(k)} - f_r^{(k+1)}]$$

$$= \sum_{r=1}^{\infty} [f_r^{(k)} - f_r^{(k+1)}] \sum_{n=r}^{\infty} t^n$$

$$= \frac{1}{1-t} \left[\sum_{r=1}^{\infty} f_r^{(k)} t^r - \sum_{r=1}^{\infty} f_r^{(k+1)} t^r \right]$$

$$= \frac{1}{1-t} \{[F(t)]^k - [F(t)]^{k+1}\}$$

$$= \frac{1 - F(t)}{1 - t} [F(t)]^k,$$

and

$$\sum_{k=0}^{\infty} z^k \sum_{n=1}^{\infty} P_{n,k} t^n = \frac{1-F(t)}{1-t} \cdot \sum_{k=0}^{\infty} [zF(t)]^k$$

$$= \frac{1}{1-t} \cdot \frac{1-F(t)}{1-zF(t)}. \tag{6.38}$$

However, the double series in (6.38) can be written as

$$\sum_{n=1}^{\infty} t^n \sum_{k=0}^{\infty} P_{n,k} z^k = \sum_{n=1}^{\infty} t^n P_n(z);$$

we have thus proved (a). Differentiating (6.38) twice with respect to z, we obtain

$$\sum_{k=0}^{\infty} k z^{k-1} \sum_{n=1}^{\infty} P_{n,k} t^n = \frac{F(t)}{1-t} \cdot \frac{1-F(t)}{[1-zF(t)]^2} \tag{6.39}$$

$$\sum_{k=0}^{\infty} k(k-1) z^{k-1} \sum_{n=1}^{\infty} P_{n,k} t^n = \frac{2[F(t)]^2}{1-t} \cdot \frac{1-F(t)}{[1-zF(t)]^3}. \tag{6.40}$$

Letting $z \to 1$ and simplifying, we obtain the results (b) and (c).

THEOREM 6.2. *Let G be an aperiodic, persistent event whose recurrence time has finite mean μ and variance σ^2. Then*

(a) $\quad E(N_n) = \dfrac{n}{\mu} + \dfrac{\sigma^2 + \mu - \mu^2}{2\mu^2} + o(1)$ $\qquad\qquad$ (6.41)

(b) $\quad \mathrm{Var}\,(N_n) = \dfrac{n\sigma^2}{\mu^3} + o(n).$ $\qquad\qquad$ (6.42)

Proof: Let

$$q_n = \sum_{\nu=n+1}^{\infty} f_\nu, \quad r_n = \sum_{\nu=n+1}^{\infty} q_\nu \quad (n \geqslant 0), \tag{6.43}$$

$$Q(t) = \sum_{0}^{\infty} q_n t^n, \quad R(t) = \sum_{0}^{\infty} r_n t^n \quad (|t| < 1). \tag{6.44}$$

We have

$$Q(t) = \sum_{0}^{\infty} t^n \sum_{n+1}^{\infty} f_\nu = \sum_{1}^{\infty} f_\nu \sum_{0}^{\nu-1} t^n = \frac{1}{1-t} \sum_{1}^{\infty} f_\nu (1-t^\nu),$$

so that

$$Q(t) = \frac{1-F(t)}{1-t}. \tag{6.45}$$

Similarly,

$$R(t) = \frac{\mu - Q(t)}{1 - t}, \tag{6.46}$$

since

$$\sum_{0}^{\infty} q_{\nu} = \sum_{0}^{\infty} \sum_{\nu+1}^{\infty} f_{n} = \sum_{1}^{\infty} f_{n} \sum_{0}^{n-1} (1) = \sum_{1}^{\infty} n f_{n} = \mu < \infty.$$

From (6.45) and (6.46) we see that

$$\sum_{0}^{\infty} q_{n} = Q(1) = F'(1) = \mu < \infty \tag{6.47}$$

$$\sum_{0}^{\infty} r_{n} = R(1) = Q'(1) = \tfrac{1}{2}F''(1) < \infty \tag{6.48}$$

by our assumptions; therefore, for each fixed n, we have $q_{n} < \infty$, $r_{n} < \infty$. Using (6.45) we obtain from (6.35)

$$\begin{aligned}
\sum_{1}^{\infty} U_{n} t^{n} &= \frac{1}{(1 - t)[1 - F(t)]} - \frac{1}{1 - t} \\[2mm]
&= \frac{1}{(1 - t)^{2} Q(t)} - \frac{1}{1 - t} \\[2mm]
&= \frac{\mu - Q(t) + Q(t)}{\mu(1 - t)^{2} Q(t)} - \frac{1}{1 - t} \\[2mm]
&= \frac{R(t)}{\mu[1 - F(t)]} + \frac{1}{\mu(1 - t)^{2}} - \frac{1}{1 - t} \\[2mm]
&= \sum_{0}^{\infty} g_{n} t^{n} + \frac{1}{\mu} \sum_{0}^{\infty} (n + 1) t^{n} - \sum_{0}^{\infty} t^{n},
\end{aligned} \tag{6.49}$$

where

$$\sum_{0}^{\infty} g_{n} t^{n} = \frac{R(t)}{\mu[1 - F(t)]}. \tag{6.50}$$

We have

$$\begin{aligned}
\lim_{n \to \infty} g_{n} &= \lim_{t \to 1 - 0} \frac{(1 - t)R(t)}{\mu[1 - F(t)]} \\[2mm]
&= \lim_{t \to 1 - 0} \frac{1 - t}{1 - F(t)} \cdot \frac{R(t)}{\mu} \\[2mm]
&= \frac{R(1)}{\mu^{2}} = \frac{F''(1)}{2\mu^{2}} = \frac{\sum_{1}^{\infty} n(n - 1) f_{n}}{2\mu^{2}}.
\end{aligned} \tag{6.51}$$

From (6.49) and (6.50) we find that

$$E(N_n) = U_n = g_n + \frac{n+1}{\mu} - 1 = \frac{n}{\mu} + \frac{\sigma^2 - \mu^2 + \mu}{2\mu^2} + o(1), \quad (6.52)$$

which is the result (a).

Again, using (6.45) and (6.46), we find from (6.36) that

$$\sum_1^\infty V_n t^n = \frac{1 - (1-t)Q(t) + [1 - (1-t)Q(t)]^2}{(1-t)^3[Q(t)]^2}$$

$$= \frac{2 - 3(1-t)Q(t) + (1-t)^2[Q(t)]^2}{(1-t)^3[Q(t)]^2}$$

$$= 2\frac{\mu^2 - [Q(t)]^2 + [Q(t)]^2}{\mu^2(1-t)^3[Q(t)]^2} - \frac{3}{(1-t)^2Q(t)} + \frac{1}{1-t}$$

$$= \frac{1}{1-t} + \frac{2}{\mu^2(1-t)^3} + U(t)\sum_0^\infty h_n t^n,$$

(6.53)

where

$$\sum_0^\infty h_n t^n = \frac{1}{1-t} \cdot \left\{ 2\frac{R(t)[\mu + Q(t)]}{\mu^2 Q(t)} - 3 \right\}. \quad (6.54)$$

We have

$$\lim_{n\to\infty} h_n = \lim_{t\to 1-0} (1-t)\sum_0^\infty h_n t^n$$

$$= \lim_{t\to 1-0} \left\{ 2\frac{R(t)[\mu + Q(t)]}{\mu^2 Q(t)} - 3 \right\}$$

(6.55)

$$= \frac{4R(1)}{\mu^2} - 3 = \frac{2\sigma^2 - \mu^2 - 2\mu}{\mu^2} = h \text{ (say)}.$$

Therefore, for the coefficient of t^n in the series $U(t)\sum_0^\infty h_n t^n$ we have

$$\sum_{m=0}^n u_m h_{n-m} = \sum_0^n u_m[h + o(1)] = \frac{n}{\mu}h + o(n). \quad (6.56)$$

From (6.53)–(6.56) we obtain

$$E(N_n^2) = V_n = \frac{(n+1)(n+2)}{\mu^2} + n\frac{2\sigma^2 - \mu^2 - 2\mu}{\mu^3} + o(n)$$

(6.57)

$$= \frac{n^2}{\mu^2} + n\frac{2\sigma^2 - \mu^2 + \mu}{\mu^3} + o(n).$$

Finally, from (6.52) and (6.57) we find that

$$\operatorname{Var}(N_n) = V_n - U_n^2$$

$$= \frac{n^2}{\mu^2} + n\frac{2\sigma^2 - \mu^2 + \mu}{\mu^3} - \frac{n^2}{\mu^2} - n\frac{\sigma^2 - \mu^2 + \mu}{\mu^3} + o(n) \quad (6.58)$$

$$= \frac{n\sigma^2}{\mu^3} + o(n),$$

which is the result (b). The theorem is therefore completely proved.

7. SOME EXAMPLES OF RECURRENT EVENTS

7.1. Counter Model of Type I

Let us consider a counter model of type I described in Section 5, and define the events

$$E_n = \{n\text{th arriving impulse is registered}\} \quad (7.1)$$

$(n \geq 1)$. Clearly, the family $\{E_1, E_2, \ldots\}$ is a recurrent event, since with every registration the process starts anew. We have

$$f_n = \operatorname{Pr}\{\text{the first registered impulse is the }n\text{th}\}$$

$$= \operatorname{Pr}\{S_{n-1} \leq Y_0 < S_n\}$$

$$= \int_{0-}^{\infty} d_y \operatorname{Pr}\{Y_0 \leq y\} \operatorname{Pr}\{S_{n-1} \leq y < S_n\}$$

$$= \int_{0-}^{\infty} dG(y) \operatorname{Pr}\{N(y) = n - 1\} \quad (7.2)$$

$$= \int_{0-}^{\infty} dG(y)[F_{n-1}(y) - F_n(y)] \quad (n \geq 1).$$

From (7.2) we find that

$$\sum_1^n f_\nu = \int_{0-}^{\infty} dG(y)[1 - F_n(y)] = 1 - \int_{0-}^{\infty} F_n(y)\, dG(y). \quad (7.3)$$

Assuming that $F(0) < 1$, we have $U(y) = \sum_1^{\infty} F_n(y) < \infty$, so that $F_n(y) \to 0$ as $n \to \infty$. Therefore, (7.3) gives $\Sigma f_n = 1$. Thus ε is a persistent event. The mean recurrence time is given by

$$\lambda = \sum_{v=1}^{\infty} \left(\sum_{n=v}^{\infty} f_n \right) = \sum_{v=1}^{\infty} \int_{0-}^{\infty} dG(y)F_{v-1}(y)$$

$$= \int_{0-}^{\infty} dG(y)\left\{ 1 + \sum_{1}^{\infty} F_n(y) \right\} \tag{7.4}$$

$$= 1 + \int_{0}^{\infty} U(y)\,dG(y).$$

Since $U(t) = t/\mu + o(t)$ as $t \to \infty$, the integral in the last expression behaves like

$$\int_{0}^{\infty} \frac{t}{\mu}\,dG(t) = \frac{v}{\mu}, \tag{7.5}$$

so that, if $\mu < \infty$, $\lambda < \infty$ if, and only if, $v < \infty$. If $\mu = \infty$, a similar argument shows that $\lambda < \infty$ if $v < \infty$.

From the definition (5.5) of the sequence $\{n_j\}$ we see that $n_1, n_2 - n_1, \ldots,$ are the recurrence times of ε.

7.2. Counter Model of Type II, with Constant Dead Time

Let Y_0, Y_1, Y_2, ... be the dead times caused by the successive arrivals (see Figure 2), and

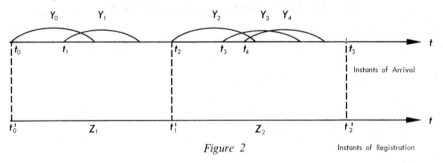

Figure 2 Instants of Registration

$$E_n = \{n\text{th arriving impulse is registered}\}$$

$$= \{Y_0 < S_n, S_1 + Y_1 < S_n, S_2 + Y_2 < S_n, \ldots, S_{n-1} + Y_{n-1} < S_n\}$$

$$(n \geqslant 1); \tag{7.6}$$

then $\varepsilon = \{E_1, E_2, \ldots\}$ is a recurrent event. We shall consider the special case where the dead times are a constant $= d$ (say); thus $Y_n = d$ with probability one. We have in this case

$$u_n = \Pr\{S_n > d, S_n - S_1 > d, S_n - S_2 > d, \ldots, S_n - S_{n-1} > d\}$$

$$= \Pr\{S_n > d, S_{n-1} > d, S_{n-2} > d, \ldots, S_1 > d\}, \tag{7.7}$$

since $S_n - S_r = X_{r+1} + X_{r+2} + \cdots + X_n$ and has the same distribution as S_{n-r}. However, since $S_1 > d$ implies $S_r > d$ $(r > 1)$, (7.7) reduces to

$$u_n = \Pr\{S_1 > d\} = 1 - F(d) = q \qquad \text{(say)} \ (n \geqslant 1). \qquad (7.8)$$

Since we have assumed that the initial impulse was registered, we put $u_0 = 1$. We have $\Sigma u_n = \infty$; therefore, ε is a persistent event. To obtain the probabilities f_n of first occurrence, we first find that

$$U(z) = 1 + \sum_1^\infty u_n z^n = 1 + q \sum_1^\infty z^n = \frac{1 - pz}{1 - z}, \qquad (7.9)$$

so that

$$F(z) = 1 - \frac{1}{U(z)} = 1 - \frac{1 - z}{1 - pz} = \frac{qz}{1 - pz}. \qquad (7.10)$$

From (7.10) we readily obtain

$$f_n = qp^{n-1} \qquad (n \geqslant 1), \qquad \lambda = \sum_1^\infty nf_n = q^{-1}. \qquad (7.11)$$

From (7.8) and (7.11) we see that $u_n = \lambda^{-1}$ $(n \geqslant 1)$, so that in this case we have an exact result. (In examples 7.1 and 7.2 we have once again followed Pyke's (1958) treatment).

7.3. A First Passage Problem

Let $\{X_n\}$ be a sequence of mutually independent and identically distributed random variables, and $S_n = X_1 + X_2 + \cdots + X_n$ $(n \geqslant 1)$ their partial sums. Let E_n be the event

$$E_n = \{S_1 \leqslant 0, S_2 \leqslant 0, \ldots, S_{n-1} \leqslant 0, S_n = 0\}; \qquad (7.12)$$

then it is seen that $\varepsilon = \{E_1, E_2, \ldots\}$ is a recurrent event. First passages of the type E_n will be studied in detail in the next chapter. Here we prove the following theorem.

THEOREM 7.1. *Except in the case where* $\Pr\{X_n = 0\} = 1$, ε *is a transient recurrent event.*

Proof: The probabilities of first occurrence of ε are given by

$$f_1 = \Pr\{S_1 = 0\}$$
$$f_2 = \Pr\{S_1 < 0, S_2 = 0\}$$
$$f_3 = \Pr\{S_1 < 0, S_2 < 0, S_3 = 0\} \qquad (7.13)$$
$$\cdot \ \cdot \ \cdot \ \cdot \ \cdot \ \cdot \ \cdot \ \cdot \ \cdot \ \cdot \ \cdot \ \cdot \ \cdot \ \cdot \ \cdot \ \cdot \ \cdot$$
$$f_n = \Pr\{S_1 < 0, S_2 < 0, \ldots, S_{n-1} < 0, S_n = 0\},$$

and therefore,

$$\sum_1^\infty f_n \leqslant \Pr\{S_1 = 0\} + \Pr\{S_1 < 0\} = 1 - \Pr\{S_1 > 0\}. \qquad (7.14)$$

From (7.14) we find that $\Sigma f_n = 1$ implies $\Pr\{X_1 > 0\} = 0$. However, if $\Pr\{X_1 > 0\} = 0$, then $f_1 = \Pr\{X_1 = 0\} \leqslant 1$, while

$$f_2 = \Pr\{X_1 < 0, X_1 + X_2 = 0\}$$
$$\leqslant \Pr\{X_1 < 0, X_2 > 0\} = 0, \qquad (7.15)$$

which gives $f_2 = 0$. Similarly $f_3 = f_4 = \cdots = 0$, so that $\Sigma f_n = f_1$. This shows that $f = 1$ if, and only if, $\Pr\{X_1 = 0\} = 1$, and the theorem is therefore proved.

7.4. Markov Chains

Let $\{X_n\}$ be a Markov chain with the states $j = 0, \pm 1, \pm 2, \ldots$, and for a fixed j, consider the events

$$E_n = \{X_n = j\} \qquad (n = 0, 1, 2, \ldots). \qquad (7.16)$$

From the definition of the chain we have, for $n_1 < n_2 < \cdots < n_r \ (r \geqslant 1)$,

$$\Pr\{E_{n_1}, E_{n_2}, \ldots, E_{n_r}\} = \Pr\{E_{n_1}\} \Pr\{E_{n_2-n_1}\} \cdots \Pr\{E_{n_r-n_{r-1}}\}, \qquad (7.17)$$

so that $\varepsilon = \{E_1, E_2, E_3, \ldots\}$ is a recurrent event. In the notation of this section, we have

$$f_n = f_{jj}^{(n)}, \qquad u_n = P_{jj}^{(n)} \quad (n \geqslant 1), \qquad u_0 = 1, \qquad (7.18)$$

and

$$\mu = \sum_1^\infty n f_{jj}^{(n)}. \qquad (7.19)$$

The recurrence time of ε is given by the random variable $T_{jj} = \min\{n \mid X_n = j\}$, where $X_0 = j$. The behavior of $P_{jj}^{(n)}$ as $n \to \infty$ then is a direct consequence of the results of this chapter. Further, the random variable N_n gives the number of returns of the system to the state j during $[0, n]$, and the properties of N_n described in this section hold also in this case.

8. COMPLEMENTS AND PROBLEMS

Section 1

1. The intensity function $\mu(x)$ for the lifetime of an individual is defined by

$$\mu(x)\,dx = \Pr\{x < X < x + dx \mid X > x\}. \qquad (8.1)$$

Show that if $\mu(x)$ is known, then the frequency distribution of the lifetime is given by

$$f(x)\, dx = \mu(x) \exp\left[-\int_0^x \mu(x)\, dx\right] \qquad (0 < x < \infty). \qquad (8.2)$$

In particular, for the negative exponential lifetime distribution of example 1.2, show that the intensity function is given by $\mu(x) = \lambda$.

Section 2

2. Show that

$$\sum_0^\infty z^n \int_0^\infty P_n(t) e^{-\theta t}\, dt = \frac{1 - F^*(\theta)}{\theta[1 - zF^*(\theta)]} \qquad [|z| < 1, \qquad Re(\theta) > 0], \qquad (8.3)$$

where we have assumed that $K(x) = F(x)$. Deduce from (8.3) that $U^*(\theta) = F^*(\theta)/[1 - F^*(\theta)]$ as in (2.20), and, further, that

$$\int_0^\infty V(t) e^{-\theta t}\, dt = \frac{F^*(\theta) + [F^*(\theta)]^2}{\theta[1 - F^*(\theta)]}, \qquad (8.4)$$

where $V(t) = E\{N(t)\}^2$.

3. Show that $V(t) = \sum_1^\infty (2n - 1) F_n(t)$, and that

$$V(t) = U(t) + 2\int_0^t U(t - \tau)\, dU(\tau). \qquad (8.5)$$

In general, the rth moment $E\{N(t)\}^r$ $(r > 1)$ can be expressed in terms of the renewal function [Smith (1958)].

4. Putting

$$Q(t) = 1 - \frac{1}{\mu}\int_0^t [1 - F(x)]\, dx \qquad (t \geqslant 0) \qquad (8.6)$$

in the key renewal theorem, show that for a continuous process with finite mean μ and variance σ^2,

$$U(t) = \frac{t}{\mu} + \frac{\sigma^2 - \mu^2}{2\mu^2} + o(1). \qquad (8.7)$$

Also, prove that

$$\text{Var}\,\{N(t)\} = \frac{\sigma^2}{\mu^3} t + o(t) \qquad (8.8)$$

[Smith (1954)].

5. When the conditions of Theorem 2.4 are not satisfied, then a number of other limiting distributions arise [see Feller (1949)].

6. Show that with probability one,

$$\frac{N(t)}{t} \to \frac{1}{\mu} \qquad \text{as } t \to \infty, \tag{8.9}$$

the limit being interpreted as zero if $\mu = \infty$ [Doob (1948)].

7. Show that there is a number K, depending on s, but neither on t, nor on the initial distribution, and such that

$$E[N(t + s) - N(t)]^2 \leqslant K \qquad (t > 0, s > 0). \tag{8.10}$$

[Doob (1948)].

Section 4

8. Show that the mean of the limiting distribution (4.12) is given by $(\sigma^2 + \mu^2)/2\mu$, where $\sigma^2 = \text{Var}(X_n) < \infty$, and its Laplace transform is given by $[1 - F^*(\theta)]/\theta\mu$ $(\mu < \infty)$.

9. If t is selected at random from an interval $(0, T)$, show that

$$\lim_{T \to \infty} \text{Pr}\,\{Y(t) \leqslant y\} = \int_0^y \frac{1 - F(x)}{\mu}\,dx. \tag{8.11}$$

10. Show that the limiting distribution of the number of renewals during $(t, t + s]$ is given by

$$\lim_{t \to \infty} \text{Pr}\,\{N(t + s) - N(t) = n\} = \text{Pr}\,\{N^*(s) = n\}, \tag{8.12}$$

where $N^*(s)$ is the number of renewals during $(0, s]$ in the stationary process.

11. *The Case of a Discrete Process.* Theorems 4.2 and 4.4 have been proved for a continuous process. Show that for a discrete process

$$\lim_{n \to \infty} \text{Pr}\,\{X(nd) \leqslant md\} = \lim_{n \to \infty} \text{Pr}\,\{Y(nd) \leqslant md\}$$

$$= \sum_{j=0}^{m-1} \frac{1 - F(jd)}{\mu}\,d. \tag{8.13}$$

12. If $\mu < \infty$, show that with probability one,

$$\frac{X(t)}{t} \to 0, \tag{8.14}$$

and, further, if the initial age has a finite mean, then

$$\frac{E\{X(t)\}}{t} \to 0 \tag{8.15}$$

[Doob (1948)].

13. If the X_n have a finite variance σ^2, then prove that with probability one,

$$\frac{1}{t}\int_0^t X(\tau)\, d\tau \to \frac{\sigma^2 + \mu^2}{2\mu} \tag{8.16}$$

[Doob (1948)].

Section 5

14. *Type I Counters with Constant Dead Time.* Suppose that the dead time is a constant ($= d$ say). Show that the transform of $V(t)$, the expected number of registrations during $(0, t]$, is given by

$$\int_0^\infty e^{-\theta t}\, dV(t) = \frac{\int_d^\infty e^{-\theta t}\, dU(t)}{1 + \int_0^d e^{-\theta t}\, dU(t)}, \tag{8.17}$$

and that the asymptotic bias of the counter is given by

$$\lim_{t\to\infty} B(t) = 1 + U(d) \qquad \text{if } \mu < \infty. \tag{8.18}$$

The probability that the counter is locked at time t is given by

$$P_0(t) = \begin{cases} 1 & \text{if } 0 \leqslant t \leqslant d \\ V(t) - V(t - d) & \text{if } t > d, \end{cases} \tag{8.19}$$

and hence we find that

$$\lim_{t\to\infty} P_0(t) = \frac{d}{\mu[1 + U(d)]}. \tag{8.20}$$

15. *Type I Counters with Negative Exponential Dead Time.* If the dead times have the distribution function $G(t) = 1 - e^{-\beta t}$, then show that

$$H^*(\theta) = \frac{F^*(\theta) - F^*(\beta + \theta)}{1 - F^*(\beta + \theta)}, \tag{8.21}$$

and

$$\lim_{t\to\infty} B(t) = [1 - F^*(\beta)]^{-1}. \tag{8.22}$$

16. *Type II Counters with Constant Dead Time.* In the notation of Section 7.2, show that

$$f_n = \Pr\{X_1 < d, X_2 < d, \ldots, X_{n-1} < d, X_n > d\}. \tag{8.23}$$

If Z_1, Z_2, ..., are the intervals between successive registrations, then use (8.23) to show that

$$H(z) = \Pr\{Z_n \leqslant z\} = \sum_1^\infty f_n \int_{0-}^z K_n(z - u)\,dL(u), \qquad (8.24)$$

where

$$K(u) = \frac{F(u)}{F(d)} \quad (u \leqslant d), \qquad L(u) = \frac{F(u) - F(d)}{1 - F(d)} \quad (u \geqslant d), \quad (8.25)$$

and $K_n(u)$ is the n-fold convolution of $K(u)$ with itself [Pyke (1958)].

17. Let $\{X_n\}$ and $\{Y_n\}$ be two renewal processes with the distribution functions $F(x)$ and $G(x)$ respectively, and such that $\{X_n + Y_n\}$ is also a renewal process. Let $U(t)$ be the renewal function of this last process. Let $S_0 \equiv 0$, and for $n \geqslant 1$, define

$$S_{2n} = X_1 + Y_1 + X_2 + Y_2 + \cdots + X_n + Y_n$$
$$S_{2n+1} = X_1 + Y_1 + X_2 + Y_2 + \cdots + X_{n+1}. \qquad (8.26)$$

Let us define the random variable $A(t)$ as follows:

$$A(t) = \begin{cases} 1 & \text{if } S_{2n} \leqslant t < S_{2n+1} \qquad \text{for some } n \geqslant 0 \\ 0 & \text{otherwise.} \end{cases} \qquad (8.27)$$

Show that for $t \geqslant 0$,

$$P_0(t) = \Pr\{A(t) = 1\}$$
$$= 1 - F(t) + \int_0^t [1 - F(t - \tau)]\,dU(\tau), \qquad (8.28)$$

and

$$\lim_{t \to \infty} P_0(t) = \frac{E(X_n)}{E(X_n) + E(Y_n)} \qquad (8.29)$$

whenever at least one term of the denominator is finite, the limit being interpreted as zero when $E(Y_n) = \infty$ and one when $E(X_n) = \infty$ [Pyke (1958)]. As a particular case we have Theorem 5.4.

Section 6

18. In a renewal system each item has a probability p of dying before the end of the first month of life and a probability $q = 1 - p$ of dying at the end of the second month. If the initial item was a new one, show that the expected number of replacements in the first $2n$ months is given by

$$\frac{2n}{1 + q} - \frac{q^2}{(1 + q)^2} + \frac{q^{2n+2}}{(1 + q)^2}. \qquad (8.30)$$

19. If the lifetime distribution is given by $a_n = pq^{n-1}$ $(n \geqslant 1)$, show that the expected number of replacements during $(0, n]$ is np. Interpret this result.

20. If ε is a persistent event whose recurrence time has finite mean μ and variance σ^2, show that

$$\sum_0^\infty \left(u_n - \frac{1}{\mu} \right) = \frac{\sigma^2 + \mu^2 - \mu}{2\mu^2} \tag{8.31}$$

[Feller (1949)].

21. At time n, let X_n be the time that has elapsed since the last occurrence of a recurrent event ε. Show that $\{X_n\}$ is a Markov chain whose transition probabilities are given by

$$P_{ij}^{(n)} = \Pr\{X_n = j \mid X_0 = i\}$$

$$= \begin{cases} u_{n-j} r_j & \text{if } 0 \leqslant j < n \\ \dfrac{r_{n+i}}{r_i} & \text{if } j = n + i \\ 0 & \text{otherwise.} \end{cases} \tag{8.32}$$

where $r_j = f_{j+1} + f_{j+2} + \cdots$ $(j \geqslant 0)$. Show that the stationary distribution of X_n exists if and only if $\mu < \infty$, in which case it is given by

$$v_j = \frac{r_j}{\mu} \qquad (j \geqslant 0). \tag{8.33}$$

22. *Delayed Recurrent Events.* If X_1, the first occurrence time of ε, has the distribution $\{b_n\}$, while the recurrence times X_k $(k \geqslant 2)$ have the distribution $\{f_n\}$, ε is called a delayed recurrent event. In this case $u_0 = 0$, and the equation (6.29) becomes

$$U(z) = \frac{B(z)}{1 - F(z)}. \tag{8.34}$$

If ε is persistent and aperiodic, prove that

$$u_n \to \frac{B(1)}{\mu} \tag{8.35}$$

[Feller (1957)]. Feller also discusses the more general equation (6.13).

Section 7

23. For application to the theory of runs in Bernoulli trials, see Feller (1957).

24. *Symmetric Random Walk.* Consider the (classical) symmetric random walk described in Chapter 2, Section 6, 6.1. Let ε be the event = {the particle returns to the origin}; clearly, ε is a recurrent event. The probabilities u_n and f_n are positive only when n is even, and we have

$$u_{2n} = \binom{2n}{n}\left(\frac{1}{2}\right)^{2n}.$$ (8.36)

Show that $U(z) = (1 - z^2)^{-\frac{1}{2}}$, and hence that

$$F(z) = 1 - (1 - z^2)^{\frac{1}{2}}.$$ (8.37)

It follows from (8.37) that ε is a persistent null event, with period 2. Expanding $F(z)$ as a power series in z, we find that

$$f_{2n} = \frac{1}{2n - 1}\binom{2n - 1}{n}\left(\frac{1}{2}\right)^{2n-1}.$$ (8.38)

The generating function of the probabilities $f_{2n}^{(r)}$ is $[F(z)]^r$, but it is not easy to obtain $f_{2n}^{(r)}$ explicitly from this. However, show that the recurrence times X_k have the same distribution as $1 + T_1$, where for $i \geqslant 1$, the random variable T_i is the first passage time from i to 0. Hence we obtain

$$f_{2n}^{(r)} = \Pr\{r + T_r = 2n\}$$
$$= \frac{r}{2n - r}\binom{2n - r}{n}\left(\frac{1}{2}\right)^{2n-r} \qquad (r \leqslant 2n),$$ (8.39)

using the results derived in Chapter 2, Section 6, 6.1. [For a geometric proof see Feller (1957).]

25. *The Number of Returns to the Origin.* For the symmetric random walk of problem 24, let N_{2n} be the number of returns to the origin during $(0, 2n]$. Use Theorem 6.1 to show that

$$\Pr\{N_{2n} = k\} = \binom{2n - k}{n}\left(\frac{1}{2}\right)^{2n-k} \qquad (k \leqslant n)$$
$$\sim \frac{1}{\sqrt{n\pi}}e^{-k^2/4n} \qquad (n \to \infty),$$ (8.40)

and

$$E(N_{2n}) = (2n + 1)\binom{2n}{n}\left(\frac{1}{2}\right)^{2n} - 1$$
$$\sim 2\left(\frac{n}{\pi}\right)^{\frac{1}{2}} \qquad (n \to \infty).$$ (8.41)

Since the recurrence times have an infinite mean, Theorem 2.4 does not apply here. Show, however, that for any $\alpha > 0$,

$$\lim_{n \to \infty} \Pr \{N_{2n} < \alpha\sqrt{2n}\} = \sqrt{\frac{2}{\pi}} \int_0^\alpha e^{-\frac{1}{2}t^2} \, dt \qquad (8.42)$$

[Feller (1957)].

26. *Markov Chains.* In a Markov chain, if the recurrence time of a persistent state j has finite mean μ and variance σ^2, show that

$$\lim_{n \to \infty} \left(\sum_{k=0}^n P_{jj}^{(k)} - \frac{n+1}{\mu} \right) = \frac{\sigma^2 + \mu^2 - \mu}{2\mu^2}. \qquad (8.43)$$

In a finite Markov chain, σ^2 is always finite and (8.45) can be used to evaluate σ^2 [Feller (1957)].

9. REFERENCES

Blackwell, D. A RENEWAL THEOREM. *Duke Math. J.,* **15** (1948), pp. 145–150.

Choquet, G., and Deny, J. SUR L'EQUATION DE CONVOLUTION $\mu = \mu*\sigma$. *C. R. Acad. Sci., Paris,* **250** (1960), pp. 799–801.

Doob, J. L. RENEWAL THEORY FROM THE POINT OF VIEW OF THE THEORY OF PROBABILITY. *Trans. Amer. Math. Soc.,* **63** (1948), pp. 422–438.

Erdös, P., Feller, W., and Pollard, H. A THEOREM ON POWER SERIES. *Bull. Amer. Math. Soc.,* **55** (1949), pp. 201–204.

Feller, W. ON THE INTEGRAL EQUATION OF RENEWAL THEORY. *Ann. Math. Statist.,* **12** (1941), pp. 243–267.

——. FLUCTUATION THEORY OF RECURRENT EVENTS. *Trans. Amer. Math. Soc.,* **67** (1949), pp. 98–119.

——. AN INTRODUCTION TO PROBABILITY THEORY AND ITS APPLICATIONS. New York: Wiley, 1957.

——. A SIMPLE PROOF FOR RENEWAL THEOREMS. *Comm. on Pure and App. Math.,* **14** (1961), pp. 285–293.

Kingman, J. F. C. A CONTINUOUS TIME ANALOGUE OF THE THEORY OF RECURRENT EVENTS. *Bull. Amer. Math. Soc.,* **69** (1963), pp. 268–272.

Kolmogorov, A. N. ANFANSGRÜNDE DER THEORIE DER MARKOFFSCHEN KETTEN MIT UNENDLICHEN IRELEN MÖGLICHEN ZUSTANDEN. *Rec. Math. Mat. Sbornik N. S.,* **1** (1936), pp. 607–610.

Pyke, Ronald. ON RENEWAL PROCESSES RELATED TO TYPE I AND TYPE II COUNTER MODELS. *Ann. Math. Statist.,* **29** (1958), pp. 737–754.

Smith, W. L. ASYMPTOTIC RENEWAL THEOREMS. *Proc. Roy. Soc. Edinb.* A **64** (1954), pp. 9–48.

——. RENEWAL THEORY AND ITS RAMIFICATIONS. *J. Roy. Stat. Soc.,* B **20** (1958), pp. 243–302.

Takács, L. ON A PROBABILITY PROBLEM ARISING IN THE THEORY OF COUNTERS. *Proc. Cam. Phil. Soc.,* **32** (1956), pp. 488–498.

6

Further Results from Renewal Theory

1. LADDER INDICES

Let $\{X_n, n \geq 1\}$ be a sequence of mutually independent and identically distributed random variables. Renewal theory developed in the last chapter was restricted to the case where the X_n assume only nonnegative values; in this chapter we extend some of the results so obtained to the general case where the X_n assume values in the range $(-\infty < x < \infty)$. In particular, we deal with the fluctuation theory of random variables, developed by Sparre Andersen [(1953 a), (1953 b), (1954)] using ingenious combinatorial methods, and simplified and extended by Spitzer [(1956), (1960 b)]. Our treatment here follows Feller (1959), who introduced further simplification, using the theory of recurrent events. More specifically, Feller's method is based on *ladder indices*, a concept which was introduced by Blackwell (1953) in the proof of the extension of his renewal theorem to the general case. In this section we give some results concerning ladder indices.

Let the distribution function of the X_n be denoted by

$$F(x) = \Pr\{X_n \leq x\} \qquad (-\infty < x < \infty). \qquad (1.1)$$

Let $S_0 \equiv 0$, and $S_n = X_1 + X_2 + \cdots + X_n \, (n \geqslant 1)$ be the partial sums of the X_n; their distribution function will be denoted by

$$F_n(x) = \Pr\{S_n \leqslant x\} \qquad (n \geqslant 1, \qquad -\infty < x < \infty). \qquad (1.2)$$

It is seen that the $F_n(x)$ satisfy the relations

$$F_1(x) = F(x), \qquad F_{n+1}(x) = \int_{-\infty}^{\infty} F_n(x - y)\, dF(y) \qquad (n \geqslant 1). \qquad (1.3)$$

We define a sequence $\{N_k, k = 0, 1, 2, \ldots\}$ of random variables, called the ladder indices of $\{S_n\}$, as follows:

$$N_0 \equiv 0$$

$$N_1 = \min\{n \,|\, S_n > 0\}$$

$$N_2 = \min\{n > N_1 \,|\, S_n - S_{N_1} > 0\} \qquad (1.4)$$

$$\cdot \quad \cdot \quad \cdot \quad \cdot \quad \cdot \quad \cdot \quad \cdot \quad \cdot \quad \cdot \quad \cdot \quad \cdot \quad \cdot$$

$$N_k = \min\{n > N_{k-1} \,|\, S_n - S_{N_{k-1}} > 0\} \qquad (k \geqslant 1).$$

We have

$$f_n = \Pr\{N_1 = n\}$$
$$= \Pr\{S_1 \leqslant 0, S_2 \leqslant 0, \ldots, S_{n-1} \leqslant 0, S_n > 0\} \qquad (n \geqslant 1). \qquad (1.5)$$

Moreover, since $S_n - S_{N_{k-1}} = X_{N_{k-1}+1} + \cdots + X_n$, it is distributed as $S_{n-N_{k-1}}$, independently of $S_{N_{k-1}}$; therefore, the random variables, $N_1, N_2 - N_1, N_3 - N_2, \ldots$ are mutually independent and have the same distribution. This statement is equivalent to the statement that if E_n is the event

$$E_n = \{n \text{ is a ladder index}\} \qquad (n \geqslant 1), \qquad (1.6)$$

then $\varepsilon = \{E_1, E_2, \ldots\}$ is a recurrent event. In the notation of Chapter 5, Section 6.2,

$$u_n = \Pr\{E_n\}$$
$$= \Pr\{S_r < S_n \qquad (r = 0, 1, \ldots, n-1)\} \qquad (1.7)$$

is the probability that n is a ladder index, while (1.5) gives the probability f_n that n is the first ladder index. We also set

$$u_0 = 1, \qquad f_0 = 0. \qquad (1.8)$$

To obtain the generating function of the f_n, we first establish the following result due to Feller (1959).

THEOREM 1.1. *Let*

$$f_n^{(r)} = \Pr\{n \text{ is the } r\text{th ladder index}\} \qquad (1 \leqslant r \leqslant n). \qquad (1.9)$$

Then

$$\sum_{r=1}^{n} \frac{1}{r} f_n^{(r)} = \frac{1}{n} \Pr\{S_n > 0\}. \tag{1.10}$$

Proof : We first prove that if $S_n > 0$, then there exist $r > 1$ cyclic permutations of $(X_1, X_2, \ldots, X_n)$ such that n is a ladder index for the corresponding sequence of partial sums; for each such cyclic permutation the sequence contains exactly r ladder indices.

Let us consider the cyclic permutation $(X_{a+1}, X_{a+2}, \ldots, X_a)$, and denote by $S_j^{(a)}$ its partial sums. We have

$$S_0^{(a)} = 0$$

$$S_j^{(a)} = \begin{cases} X_{a+1} + X_{a+2} + \cdots + X_{a+j} = S_{a+j} - S_a & (j = 1, 2, \ldots, n-a) \\ X_{a+1} + \cdots + X_n + X_1 + \cdots + X_{j-n+a} = S_n - S_a + S_{j-n+a} & \\ & (j = n-a, n-a+1, \ldots, n). \end{cases} \tag{1.11}$$

Let S_a be the first maximal term among $(S_0, S_1, \ldots, S_n)$, that is, $S_j < S_a$ $(j = 1, 2, \ldots, a-1)$, and $S_j \leqslant S_a$ $(j = a, a+1, \ldots, n)$. Then from (1.11) we obtain

$$S_j^{(a)} \leqslant 0 < S_n \qquad (j = 0, 1, \ldots, n-a)$$
$$S_j^{(a)} < S_n \qquad (j = n-a+1, \ldots, n); \tag{1.12}$$

thus $S_j^{(a)} < S_n = S_n^{(a)}$ for all j, and hence n is a ladder index for $(S_0^{(a)}, S_1^{(a)}, \ldots, S_n^{(a)})$. Accordingly, there is at least one cyclic permutation for which the sequence of partial sums has n as a ladder index, and without loss of generality we take this to be the initial one itself, that is, $S_j < S_n$ $(j = 0, 1, \ldots, n-1)$. It follows from (1.11) that $S_j^{(a)} < S_n^{(a)}$ if, and only if, $S_j < S_a$ $(j = 0, 1, \ldots, a-1)$, that is, if a is a ladder index for $(S_0, S_1, \ldots, S_n)$. In other words, n is a ladder index for $(S_0^{(a)}, S_1^{(a)}, \ldots, S_n^{(a)})$ if, and only if, a is a ladder index for $(S_0, S_1, \ldots, S_n)$. This proves our assertion.

To prove (1.10), let us call two permutations which differ only by a cyclic permutation equivalent. There are $n!f_n^{(r)}$ permutations which have n as the rth ladder index; the equivalence class of each contains n permutations, and exactly r among them have the same property. The number of equivalence classes is therefore

$$\Pr\{S_n > 0\} (n-1)! = \sum_{r=1}^{n} \frac{n!f_n^{(r)}}{r}, \tag{1.13}$$

which is the desired result.

THEOREM 1.2. *The probability generating function of N_1 is given by*

$$F(t) = \sum_{1}^{\infty} f_n t^n = 1 - \exp\left[-\sum_{1}^{\infty} \frac{t^n}{n} \Pr\{S_n > 0\}\right] \qquad |t| < 1. \tag{1.14}$$

Proof: From (1.10) we have

$$\sum_{n=1}^{\infty} \frac{t^n}{n} \Pr\{S_n > 0\} = \sum_{r=1}^{\infty} \frac{1}{r} \sum_{n=r}^{\infty} f_n^{(r)} t^n$$

$$= \sum_{r=1}^{\infty} \frac{1}{r} [F(t)]^r = \log[1 - F(t)]^{-1}, \tag{1.15}$$

which gives the required result. Here we have used the fact that $f_n^{(r)}$ is the r-fold convolution of $f_n^{(1)} = f_n$ with itself.

T HEOREM 1.3. *Let*

$$A = \sum_{1}^{\infty} \frac{1}{n} \Pr\{S_n \leqslant 0\}, \qquad B = \sum_{1}^{\infty} \frac{1}{n} \Pr\{S_n > 0\}. \tag{1.16}$$

Then

$$\text{(a)} \ \Pr\{N_1 < \infty\} = \begin{cases} 1 & \text{if } B = \infty \\ 1 - e^{-B} & \text{if } B < \infty, \end{cases} \tag{1.17}$$

and (b) *if* $B = \infty$, *then*

$$E(N_1) = \begin{cases} e^A & \text{if } A < \infty \\ \infty & \text{if } A = \infty. \end{cases} \tag{1.18}$$

Proof: The result (a) follows directly from (1.14). To obtain (b), we note that differentiation of the series $\Sigma t^n \Pr\{S_n > 0\}/n$ is not permissible at $t = 1$, since $B = \infty$. However, we can write

$$\frac{1 - F(t)}{1 - t} = (1 - t)^{-1} \exp\left[- \sum_{1}^{\infty} \frac{t^n}{n} \Pr\{S_n > 0\} \right]$$

$$= \exp\left[\sum_{1}^{\infty} \frac{t^n}{n} [1 - \Pr\{S_n > 0\}] \right] \tag{1.19}$$

$$= \exp\left[\sum_{1}^{\infty} \frac{t^n}{n} \Pr\{S_n \leqslant 0\} \right].$$

Hence

$$E(N_1) = F'(1) = \lim_{t \to 1-0} \frac{1 - F(t)}{1 - t} = e^A, \tag{1.20}$$

which gives (b).

The result (1.14) is due to Sparre Andersen (1954) [see also (1.21) and (1.36) below]. Further results can also be obtained by using the fact that ladder indices define a recurrent event. The following theorem is a systematic statement of these results:

THEOREM 1.4.   *We have*

(a) $1 + \sum_{1}^{\infty} t^n \Pr\{S_1 > 0, S_2 > 0, \ldots, S_n > 0\}$

$$= \exp\left[\sum_{1}^{\infty} \frac{t^n}{n} \Pr\{S_n > 0\}\right] \qquad (|t| < 1), \tag{1.21}$$

$$\text{(b)}\quad \sum_{0}^{\infty} u_n = \begin{cases} \infty & \text{if } B = \infty \\ e^B & \text{if } B < \infty, \end{cases} \tag{1.22}$$

and

$$\text{(c)}\quad u_n \to \begin{cases} e^{-A} & \text{if } A < \infty \\ 0 & \text{if } A = \infty \end{cases} \tag{1.23}$$

as $n \to \infty$.

Proof: The result (a) is a direct consequence of the relation

$$U(t) = \sum_{0}^{\infty} u_n t^n = [1 - F(t)]^{-1} = \exp\left[\sum_{1}^{\infty} \frac{t^n}{n} \Pr\{S_n > 0\}\right], \tag{1.24}$$

where the u_n are defined by (1.7), and the fact that we can write

$$u_n = \Pr\{S_1 > 0, S_2 > 0, \ldots, S_n > 0\} \qquad (n \geqslant 1). \tag{1.25}$$

The result (b) then follows from (a). To prove (c) we may use the fact that $u_n \to 1/E(N_1)$ if the recurrent event ε defined by the ladder indices is persistent nonnull, and $u_n \to 0$ otherwise. More directly, we find that

$$\lim_{n \to \infty} u_n = \lim_{t \to 1-0} (1 - t)U(t)$$

$$= \lim_{t \to 1-0} \exp\left[-\sum_{1}^{\infty} \frac{t^n}{n} \Pr\{S_n \leqslant 0\}\right] = e^{-A}, \tag{1.26}$$

which is the result (c).

The ladder indices defined above may be called *strong ladder indices*. If in definition (1.4), $>$ is replaced by $\geqslant$, we obtain *weak ladder indices*; for these, results corresponding to Theorems 1.1–1.4 can be established exactly in the same manner as above. Thus, in particular, if

$$g_n = \Pr\{S_1 < 0, S_2 < 0, \ldots, S_{n-1} < 0, S_n \geqslant 0\} \qquad (n \geqslant 1), \tag{1.27}$$

then

$$G(t) = \sum_{1}^{\infty} g_n t^n = 1 - \exp\left[-\sum_{1}^{\infty} \frac{t^n}{n} \Pr\{S_n \geqslant 0\}\right]. \tag{1.28}$$

By applying the above results to the random variables $-X_n$, we obtain what may be called their duals. In particular, let us consider the weak ladder indices of the partial sums $\{-S_n\}$, and let

$$v_0^* = 1, \qquad v_n^* = \Pr\{S_1 \leqslant 0, S_2 \leqslant 0, \ldots, S_n \leqslant 0\} \qquad (n \geqslant 1). \quad (1.29)$$

The following theorem (1.5) is then the dual of Theorem 1.4, and its proof is obvious.

THEOREM 1.5.   *We   have*

(a) $$V^*(t) = \sum_0^\infty v_n^* t^n = \exp\left[\sum_1^\infty \frac{t^n}{n} \Pr\{S_n \leqslant 0\}\right] \qquad (1.30)$$

(b) $$\sum_0^\infty v_n^* = E(N_1) \leqslant \infty, \qquad (1.31)$$

and as $n \to \infty$

(c) $$v_n^* \to \begin{cases} e^{-B} & \text{if } B < \infty \\ 0 & \text{if } B = \infty. \end{cases} \qquad (1.32)$$

So far we have not assumed the existence of a finite mean for the random variables X_n. The results obtained have all been stated in terms of the two series A and B. The following theorem due to Spitzer (1956) relates the convergence or divergence of these series to the sign of the mean when it exists.

THEOREM 1.6.   *Let* $E|X_n| < \infty$, *and* $\mu = E(X_n)$.
   (a) *If* $\mu > 0$, *then* $B = \infty$, $A < \infty$.   (1.33)

   (b) *If* $\mu < 0$, *then* $B < \infty$, $A = \infty$.   (1.34)

   (c) *If* $\mu = 0$, *and* $\Pr\{X_n = 0\} < 1$, *then* $B = \infty$, $A = \infty$.   (1.35)

Proof :   If $\mu \neq 0$, the strong law of large numbers gives

$$\Pr\left\{\frac{S_n}{n} \to \mu\right\} = 1. \qquad (1.36)$$

If $\mu > 0$, then (1.36) shows that

$$\Pr\{S_n > 0 \text{ i.o.}\} = 1.$$

But

$$0 = 1 - \Pr\{S_n > 0 \text{ i.o.}\} \geqslant \Pr\{S_1 \leqslant 0, S_2 \leqslant 0, \ldots\}$$

$$= 1 - \Pr\{S_n > 0 \text{ for some } n\} = 1 - \sum_1^\infty f_n, \qquad (1.37)$$

which gives $f = \sum_1^\infty f_n = 1$. From Theorem 1.3(a) it follows that $B = \infty$.

If $\mu < 0$, then from (1.36) we find that

$$\Pr\{S_n > 0 \text{ i.o.}\} = 0, \tag{1.38}$$

so that

$$
\begin{aligned}
1 &= 1 - \Pr\{S_n > 0 \text{ i.o.}\} \\
&= \Pr\{S_1 \leqslant 0, S_2 \leqslant 0, \ldots\} \\
&\quad + \sum_{k=1}^{\infty} \Pr\{S_k > 0, S_{k+1} \leqslant 0, S_{k+2} \leqslant 0, \ldots\}.
\end{aligned}
\tag{1.39}
$$

The last expression is equal to

$$
\begin{aligned}
\lim_{n\to\infty} \sum_{k=1}^{n} & \Pr\{S_k > 0\} \Pr\{S_{k+1} \leqslant 0, S_{k+2} \leqslant 0, \ldots \,|\, S_k > 0\} \\
&\leqslant \lim_{n\to\infty} \sum_{k=1}^{n} \Pr\{S_1 \leqslant 0, S_2 \leqslant 0, \ldots\}.
\end{aligned}
\tag{1.40}
$$

From (1.39) and (1.40) we therefore find that

$$1 \leqslant (1-f) + \lim_{n\to\infty} \sum_{k=1}^{n} (1-f). \tag{1.41}$$

This gives $f < 1$, and from Theorem 1.3(a) it follows that $B < \infty$.

If $\mu = 0$, the sequence of partial sums $\{S_n\}$ is recurrent, and

$$\Pr\{|S_n| < \varepsilon \text{ i.o.}\} = 1. \tag{1.42}$$

so that $\Pr\{S_n > 0 \text{ i.o.}\} = 1$ if $\Pr\{X_n = 0\} < 1$, and, as in (1.37), we obtain $f = 1$ and $B = \infty$.

We have thus proved that $B = \infty$ if $\mu \geqslant 0$ and $B < \infty$ if $\mu < 0$. Considering the weak ladder indices of the sequence $\{-S_n\}$, we find similarly that $A = \infty$ if $\mu \leqslant 0$, and $A < \infty$ if $\mu > 0$. The theorem is therefore completely proved.

2. THE RENEWAL PROCESS $\{Z_k\}$

Let $N_1, N_2, \ldots$ be the successive ladder indices of the sequence $\{S_n\}$, and set

$$
\begin{aligned}
Z_1 &= S_{N_1} \\
Z_k &= S_{N_k} - S_{N_{k-1}} \qquad (k = 2, 3, \ldots).
\end{aligned}
\tag{2.1}
$$

From the definition of the N_k we see that $\{Z_k\}$ is a sequence of mutually independent and identically distributed random variables, which assume only positive values. The following theorem due to Baxter (1958) gives the joint distribution of N_1 and Z_1.

THEOREM 2.1. *We have*

$$E(t^{N_1} e^{-\theta Z_1}) = 1 - \exp\left[-\sum_1^\infty \frac{t^n}{n} \int_{0+}^\infty e^{-\theta x}\, dF_n(x) \right] \qquad (|t| < 1, \quad \theta > 0).$$

$$(2.2)$$

Proof: For $n \geq 1$, and $x > 0$, let

$$f_n(x) = \Pr\{n \text{ is the first ladder index}, S_n \leq x\}$$
$$= \Pr\{S_1 \leq 0, S_2 \leq 0, \ldots, S_{n-1} \leq 0, 0 < S_n \leq x\}; \quad (2.3)$$

then

$$\Pr\{N_1 = n, Z_1 \leq x\} = f_n(x) \qquad (2.4)$$

and

$$E(t^{N_1} e^{-\theta Z_1}) = \sum_1^\infty t^n \int_{0+}^\infty e^{-\theta x}\, df_n(x) = f(\theta, t) \text{ (say)}. \qquad (2.5)$$

Let us also define

$$f_n^{(r)}(x) = \Pr\{n \text{ is the } r\text{th ladder index}, S_n \leq x\}$$

$$(1 \leq r \leq n, n \geq 1, x > 0). \qquad (2.6)$$

We have $f_n^{(1)}(x) = f_n(x)$, and, moreover, if

$$f_r(\theta, t) = \sum_1^\infty t^n \int_{0+}^\infty e^{-\theta x}\, df_n^{(r)}(x), \qquad (2.7)$$

then

$$f_r(\theta, t) = [f_1(\theta, t)]^r = [f(\theta, t)]^r \qquad (r \geq 1). \qquad (2.8)$$

Now, from Theorem 1.1 we have

$$\sum_1^n \frac{1}{r} f_n^{(r)}(x) = \frac{1}{n} \Pr\{0 < S_n \leq x\} \qquad (x > 0), \qquad (2.9)$$

whence

$$\sum_1^\infty \frac{t^n}{n} \int_{0+}^\infty e^{-\theta x}\, d_x \Pr\{0 < S_n \leq x\}$$

$$= \sum_{r=1}^\infty \frac{1}{r} \sum_{n=r}^\infty t^n \int_{0+}^\infty e^{-\theta x}\, df_n^{(r)}(x)$$

$$= \sum_{r=1}^\infty \frac{1}{r} [f(\theta, t)]^r \qquad [\text{from} (2.8)] \qquad (2.10)$$

$$= \log[1 - f(\theta, t)]^{-1},$$

which is the result (2.2).

THEOREM 2.2.   (a) *The Laplace–Stieltjes transform of the distribution of Z_1 is given by*

$$\psi(\theta) = E(e^{-\theta Z_1}) = 1 - \exp\left(-\sum_1^\infty \frac{1}{n}\int_{0+}^\infty e^{-\theta x}\, dF_n(x)\right) \qquad (\theta > 0). \quad (2.11)$$

(b) *We have*

$$\Pr\{Z_1 < \infty\} = \begin{cases} 1 & \text{if } B = \infty \\ 1 - e^{-B} & \text{if } B < \infty. \end{cases} \quad (2.12)$$

(c) *If the X_n do not have a mean, or if $E(X_n) = \infty$, then $E(Z_1) = \infty$. If $E|X_n| < \infty$, and $\mu = E(X_n) > 0$, then*

$$E(Z_1) = \mu e^A < \infty. \quad (2.13)$$

Proof: Since the transform $E(t^{N_1} e^{-\theta Z_1})$ defined by (2.2) is a power series in t with nonnegative coefficients, we can let $t \to 1 - 0$. This gives (a). Letting $\theta \to 0+$ in (2.11) obtain (b). If $E|X_n| < \infty$, we note from Theorem 1.6 that $B = \infty$ if, and only if, $\mu = E(X_n) \geqslant 0$; in this case Z_1 is a proper random variable on account of (b). If $\mu > 0$, then Wald's equation [Chapter 2 (Theorem 8.6)] gives

$$E(Z_1) = E(S_{N_1}) = \mu E(N_1) = \mu e^A < \infty, \quad (2.14)$$

where we have used (1.18). If the X_n do not have a finite mean, then since $Z_1 \geqslant \max(0, X_1)$, we find that

$$E(Z_1) \geqslant \int_0^\infty x\, dF(x) = \infty. \quad (2.15)$$

We have thus proved (c). [See also equation (3.6).]

Let $T_n = Z_1 + Z_2 + \cdots + Z_n\, (n \geqslant 1)$ be the partial sums of the renewal process $\{Z_k\}$; then the renewal function of this process is given by

$$V(t) = \sum_1^\infty \Pr\{T_n \leqslant t\}. \quad (2.16)$$

Since $\Pr\{Z_1 = 0\} = 0$, $V(t) < \infty$ for $t \geqslant 0$. The following theorem is essentially a restatement of this result in terms of the original sequence $\{S_n\}$.

THEOREM 2.3.   *Let*

$$u_n(x) = \Pr\{S_1 > 0, S_2 > 0, \ldots, S_{n-1} > 0, 0 < S_n \leqslant x\} \qquad (n \geqslant 1, x > 0);$$

then (2.17)

$$u(x) = \sum_1^\infty u_n(x) < \infty \quad (2.18)$$

for all finite $x > 0$.

Proof : If $B < \infty$, Theorem 1.4 gives $u(\infty) = \sum_1^\infty u_n = e^B - 1$; therefore, $u(x) < u(\infty) < \infty$ for $x > 0$. If $B = \infty$, then Z_1 is a proper random variable by Theorem 2.2 (b). We have

$$
\begin{aligned}
V(x) &= \sum_{k=1}^{\infty} \Pr\{S_{N_k} \leqslant x\} \\
&= \sum_{k=1}^{\infty} \sum_{n=k}^{\infty} Pr\{N_k = n, S_n \leqslant x\} \\
&= \sum_{n=1}^{\infty} \sum_{k=1}^{n} \Pr\{n \text{ is the } k\text{th ladder index, and } S_n \leqslant x\} \\
&= \sum_{n=1}^{\infty} \Pr\{n \text{ is a ladder index, and } S_n \leqslant x\} \qquad (2.19) \\
&= \sum_{n=1}^{\infty} \Pr\{S_r < S_n (r = 0, 1, \dots, n-1), S_n \leqslant x\} \\
&= \sum_1^{\infty} \Pr\{S_1 > 0, S_2 > 0, \dots, S_{n-1} > 0, 0 < S_n \leqslant x\} \\
&= \sum_1^{\infty} u_n(x) = u(x);
\end{aligned}
$$

since $V(x) < \infty$, this proves the required result in the case $B = \infty$.

COROLLARY 2.1.   *If $B = \infty$, then*

$$
1 + \int_{0+}^{\infty} e^{-\theta x}\, du(x) = \exp\left[\sum_1^{\infty} \frac{1}{n} \int_{0+}^{\infty} e^{-\theta x}\, dF_n(x) \right] \qquad (\theta > 0). \quad (2.20)
$$

Proof : From (2.19) we find that $u(x) = V(x)\, (x > 0)$ if $B = \infty$. Therefore,

$$
1 + \int_{0+}^{\infty} e^{-\theta x}\, du(x) = 1 + \int_{0+}^{\infty} e^{-\theta x}\, dV(x)
$$

$$
= 1 + \frac{\psi(\theta)}{1 - \psi(\theta)} = [1 - \psi(\theta)]^{-1}, \quad (2.21)
$$

and the result (2.21) then follows from (2.11).

Considering the weak ladder indices of the random variables $-X_n$, we obtain the following theorem corresponding to Theorem 2.3.

THEOREM 2.4.   *Let*

$$
v_n^*(x) = \Pr\{S_1 \leqslant 0, S_2 \leqslant 0, \dots, S_{n-1} \leqslant 0, -x < S_n \leqslant 0\}
$$

$$
(n \geqslant 1, x > 0), \quad (2.22)
$$

and

$$v^*(x) = \sum_1^\infty v_n^*(x).$$ (2.23)

Then $v^*(x) < \infty$ for $x > 0$. In particular, if $A < \infty$,

$$v^*(x) < e^A - 1 < \infty.$$ (2.24)

3. EXTENSION OF THE RENEWAL THEOREM

For the sequence $\{X_n\}$ of mutually independent and identically distributed random variables, let us define the function

$$U(t) = \sum_1^\infty \Pr\{S_n \le t\} \quad (-\infty < t < \infty).$$ (3.1)

In this section we extend the renewal theorem 3.3 of Chapter 5 to the general case where the X_n assume positive and negative values. The theorem was established for the discrete case by Chung and Wolfowitz (1952), while in the continuous case it was first established under a restriction by Chung and Pollard (1952), and later, by Blackwell (1953) without this restriction. Our proof here follows Blackwell both in the discrete and the continuous case.

Let $N(t) = \max\{n \,|\, S_n \le t\}$; then

$$\Pr\{N(t) \ge n\} = \Pr\{S_r \le t \text{ for some } r \ge n\}$$
$$\ge \Pr\{S_n \le t\},$$ (3.2)

so that

$$U(t) \le \sum_{n=1}^\infty \Pr\{N(t) \ge n\}.$$ (3.3)

Thus $U(t)$ is in general not equal to the mean of the random variable $N(t)$. Thus Theorem 2.1, Chapter 5, cannot be applied to the general case, and we cannot therefore conclude that $U(t) < \infty$. More generally,

$$U(t + h) - U(t) = \sum_1^\infty \Pr\{t < S_n \le t + h\} \le \infty.$$ (3.4)

However, the renewal theorem makes sense only if

$$U(t + h) - U(t) < \infty$$ (3.5)

for finite t, h. Unfortunately it is not easy to determine the conditions under which (3.5) holds. If $E|X_n| < \infty$, then it follows from the results of Chapter 2, Section 8, that a necessary condition for (3.5) is that $\mu = E(X_n) \neq 0$. A sufficient condition is that $\mu > 0$ (Theorem 3.1). Now, if

$$\int_{-\infty}^{0} |x|\, dF(x) < \infty, \qquad \int_{0}^{\infty} x\, dF(x) = \infty, \qquad (3.6)$$

we shall write $E(X_n) = \infty$ for convenience. Similarly, $E(X_n) = -\infty$ if

$$\int_{-\infty}^{0} |x|\, dF(x) = \infty, \qquad \int_{0}^{\infty} x\, dF(x) < \infty. \qquad (3.7)$$

It will be found that the renewal theorem in the general case holds if $0 < \mu = E(X_n) \leqslant \infty$. Blackwell's proof of the theorem makes use of an integral representation of $U(t + h) - U(t)$ in terms of the renewal function of the process $\{Z_k\}$ which we have studied in Section 2. In Theorem 3.1 we establish this preliminary result, which also shows that $\mu > 0$ is a sufficient condition for (3.5). Theorems 3.2 and 3.3 deal with the continuous and the discrete case respectively.

THEOREM 3.1.   *Let* $0 < \mu = E(X_n) \leqslant \infty$. *Then for* $t > 0$, $h > 0$ *we have*

$$U(t + h) - U(t) = V(t + h) - V(t)$$

$$+ \int_{0}^{\infty} dv^*(x)[V(t + x + h) - V(t + x)], \qquad (3.8)$$

and for $t < 0$, $h > 0$,

$$U(t + h) - U(t) = [v^*(-t) - v^*(-t - h)]$$

$$+ \int_{0}^{\infty} dv^*(x)[V(t + x + h) - V(t + x)]. \qquad (3.9)$$

In both cases we have

$$U(t + h) - U(t) \leqslant e^A[1 + V(h)] < \infty. \qquad (3.10)$$

Proof: Since $\mu > 0$, we have $B = \infty$, $A < \infty$ from Theorem 1.6. Therefore, N_1 is a proper random variable with the finite mean $E(N_1) = e^A$. Further, we have

$$v^*(x) < v^*(\infty) = e^A - 1. \qquad (3.11)$$

Now,

$$U(t + h) - U(t) = \sum_{n=1}^{\infty} \Pr\{t < S_n \leq t + h\}$$

$$= \sum_{k=0}^{\infty} \sum_{n=1}^{\infty} \Pr\{t < S_n \leq t + h, N_k \leq n < N_{k+1}\}$$

$$= \sum_{n=1}^{\infty} \Pr\{t < S_n \leq t + h, n < N_1\} + \sum_{k=1}^{\infty} \Pr\{t < S_{N_k} \leq t + h\}$$

$$+ \sum_{k=1}^{\infty} \sum_{n=1}^{\infty} \int_0^{\infty} d_\tau \Pr\{S_{N_k} \leq \tau\}.$$

$$\Pr\{t < S_n \leq t + h, N_k < n < N_{k+1} | S_{N_k} = \tau\}$$

$$= \sum_{n=1}^{\infty} \Pr\{S_1 \leq 0, S_2 \leq 0, \ldots, S_{n-1} \leq 0, t < S_n \leq t + h \leq 0\} \tag{3.12}$$

$$+ \sum_{k=1}^{\infty} \Pr\{t < T_k \leq t + h\} + \sum_{k=1}^{\infty} \sum_{n=1}^{\infty} \int_0^{\infty} d_\tau \Pr\{T_k \leq \tau\}.$$

$$\Pr\{t - \tau < S_{n-N_k} \leq t + h - \tau, 0 < n - N_k < N_{k+1} - N_k\}$$

$$= [v^*(-t) - v^*(-t - h)] + [V(t + h) - V(t)] + \int_0^{\infty} dV(\tau) \int_{\tau - t - h}^{\tau - t} dv^*(x),$$

since $N_{k+1} - N_k$ has the same distribution as N_1 and is independent of N_k. The last integral is

$$= \int_0^{\infty} dv^*(x) \int_{t+x}^{t+x+h} dV(\tau) = \int_0^{\infty} dv^*(x)[V(t + x + h) - V(t + x)], \tag{3.13}$$

the interchange of the order of integration being justified because

$$\int_0^{\infty} dv^*(x) \int_{t+x}^{t+x+h} dV(\tau) \leq \int_{0+}^{\infty} dv^*(x)[1 + V(h)] \tag{3.14}$$

$$= [1 + V(h)]v^*(\infty) < e^A[1 + V(h)] < \infty.$$

In (3.12) let us note that

$$v^*(-t) - v^*(-t - h) = 0$$

if $t > 0$, while

$$V(t + h) - V(t) = 0$$

if $t < 0$. Therefore, (3.12) and (3.13) yield (3.8) for $t > 0$ and (3.9) for $t < 0$.

Moreover, from (3.8) we obtain

$$U(t + h) - U(t) \leqslant [1 + V(h)] + \int_0^\infty dv^*(x)[1 + V(h)]$$

$$= [1 + V(h)][1 + v^*(\infty)] \tag{3.15}$$

$$= e^A[1 + V(h)]$$

which proves (3.10) for $t > 0$. For $t < 0$ we find from (3.9) that

$$U(t + h) - U(t) = [v^*(-t) - v^*(-t - h)]$$

$$+ \int_{-t-h}^\infty dv^*(x)V(t + x + h) - \int_{-t}^\infty dv^*(x)V(t + x)$$

$$= \int_{-t}^\infty dv^*(x)[V(t + x + h) - V(t + x)]$$

$$+ \int_{-t-h}^{-t} dv^*(x)[1 + V(t + x + h)] \tag{3.16}$$

$$\leqslant \int_{-t}^\infty dv^*(x)[1 + V(h)] + \int_{-t-h}^{-t} dv^*(x)[1 + V(h)]$$

$$= [1 + V(h)]\int_{-t-h}^\infty dv^*(x)$$

$$\leqslant [1 + V(h)]e^A.$$

We have thus proved the theorem completely.

THEOREM 3.2. *For a continuous renewal process* $\{X_n\}$ *with* $0 < \mu$ $= E(X_n) \leqslant \infty$, *we have*

$$\lim_{t \to \infty} [U(t + h) - U(t)] = \frac{h}{\mu} \qquad (h > 0), \tag{3.17}$$

$$\lim_{t \to -\infty} [U(t + h) - U(t)] = 0. \tag{3.18}$$

Proof: Since $\mu > 0$, Z_1 is a proper random variable, with mean $E(Z_1) = \mu e^A \leqslant \infty$. Since $V(t)$ is the renewal function of the process $\{Z_k\}$, we have

$$\lim_{t \to \infty} [V(t + h) - V(t)] = \frac{h}{E(Z_1)}. \tag{3.19}$$

Now let $0 < t_1 < t$, then we can write (3.8) as

$$U(t + h) - U(t) = I_1 + I_2, \tag{3.20}$$

where

$$I_1 = \int_0^{t_1} dv^*(x)[V(t + x + h) - V(t + x)] + [V(t + h) - V(t)]$$

and

$$I_2 = \int_{t_1}^{\infty} dv^*(x)[V(t + x + h) - V(t + x)].$$

In (3.20) let t first, and then $t_1 \to \infty$; then, using (3.19) we find that

$$
\begin{aligned}
I_1 &\to \frac{h}{E(Z_1)}\left[1 + \int_0^{t_1} dv^*(x)\right] \\
&\to \frac{h}{E(Z_1)}\left[1 + \int_0^{\infty} dv^*(x)\right] = \frac{he^A}{E(Z_1)} = \frac{h}{\mu},
\end{aligned}
\tag{3.21}
$$

and

$$I_2 \leqslant [1 + V(h)]\int_{t_1}^{\infty} dv^*(x) \to 0, \tag{3.22}$$

since $v^*(\infty) < \infty$. The result (3.17) thus follows from (3.20)–(3.22). For $t < 0$, (3.16) gives

$$U(t + h) - U(t) \leqslant [1 + V(h)]\int_{-t-h}^{\infty} dv^*(x) \to 0 \qquad \text{as } t \to -\infty, \tag{3.23}$$

which is the result (3.18).

THEOREM 3.3.   *Let $\{X_n\}$ be a renewal process, where the possible values of X_n are nd ($n = \ldots, -1, 0, 1, \ldots$) and $0 < \mu = E(X_n) \leqslant \infty$. Then if*

$$u_n = \sum_{k=1}^{\infty} \Pr\{S_k = nd\}, \tag{3.24}$$

$$\lim_{n \to \infty} u_n = \frac{d}{\mu}, \tag{3.25}$$

and

$$\lim_{n \to -\infty} u_n = 0. \tag{3.26}$$

Proof: For the renewal process $\{Z_k\}$, let

$$v_n = \sum_{k=1}^{\infty} \Pr\{Z_k = nd\} \qquad (n \geqslant 1). \tag{3.27}$$

Also, let

$$w_n = \sum_{k=1}^{\infty} \Pr\{S_1 \leqslant 0, S_2 \leqslant 0, \ldots, S_{k-1} \leqslant 0, S_k = -nd\} \qquad (n = 0, 1, \ldots). \tag{3.28}$$

Then, taking $t = nd - d$, and $h = d$ in Theorem 3.1, we obtain the following discrete versions (3.8) and (3.9):

$$u_n = v_n + \sum_{m=0}^{\infty} w_m v_{n+m} \qquad (n > 0),$$

$$u_n = w_{-n} + \sum_{m=1-n}^{\infty} w_m v_{n+m} \qquad (n < 0). \tag{3.29}$$

Using the fact that

$$v_n \to \frac{d}{E(Z_1)} \qquad \text{as } n \to \infty, \tag{3.30}$$

we obtain from (3.29),

$$\lim_{n\to\infty} u_n = \frac{d}{E(Z_1)}\left(1 + \sum_0^{\infty} w_m\right) = \frac{dE(N_1)}{E(Z_1)} = \frac{d}{\mu}, \tag{3.31}$$

and

$$u_n \leqslant \sum_{-n}^{\infty} w_m \to 0 \qquad \text{as } n \to -\infty, \tag{3.32}$$

as required.

For more recent proofs of the renewal theorem, see Feller and Orey (1961) and Feller (1961).

4. THE DISTRIBUTION OF THE MAXIMUM

4.1. The Sequence $\{M_n\}$

Let

$$M_0 = 0, \qquad M_n = \max(0, S_1, S_2, \ldots, S_n) \qquad (n \geqslant 1); \tag{4.1}$$

clearly, $\{M_n\}$ is a sequence of dependent random variables, which assume nonnegative values. Let

$$G_n(x) = \Pr\{M_n \leqslant x\} \qquad (n \geqslant 0, x \geqslant 0) \tag{4.2}$$

be the distribution function of M_n. In particular, we have

$$G_n(0) = \Pr\{M_n \leqslant 0\}$$

$$= \Pr\{S_1 \leqslant 0, S_2 \leqslant 0, \ldots, S_n \leqslant 0\} = v_n^*; \tag{4.3}$$

the generating function of the v_n^* has been obtained in Section 2. The more general result (Theorem 4.1) giving the double transform of $G_n(x)$ was obtained by Spitzer (1956) using combinatorial methods. Further, we have

$$M_\infty = \lim_{n\to\infty} M_n = \sup_{k\geqslant 0} S_k. \tag{4.4}$$

Theorem 4.2 investigates the condition under which this supremum is finite; if this is the case, the transform of M_∞ can be obtained from Theorem 4.1 by the usual arguments (Theorem 4.3). In Theorem 4.4 we have the most remarkable result that the renewal theorem holds for the sequence $\{M_n\}$. All these results are due to Spitzer [(1956), (1960 b)]; the proofs here use the random variables T_n $(n \geqslant 1)$, where

$$T_n = \min \{k \, (0 \leqslant k \leqslant n) \, | \, S_k = M_n\}$$

$$= \text{the first index } k \text{ at which max } (0, S_1, S_2, \ldots, S_n) \qquad (4.5)$$

$$\text{is attained } (0 \leqslant k \leqslant n).$$

THEOREM 4.1.   *We have*

$$\sum_0^\infty t^n \int_{0-}^\infty e^{-\theta x} \, dG_n(x) = \exp \left[\sum_1^\infty \frac{t^n}{n} \Pr \{S_n \leqslant 0\} + \sum_1^\infty \frac{t^n}{n} \int_{0+}^\infty e^{-\theta x} \, dF_n(x) \right]$$

$$(4.6)$$

$$(|t| < 1, Re(\theta) > 0).$$

Proof: We have

$\Pr \{M_n \leqslant x, T_n = k\}$

$\quad = \Pr \{S_r < S_k \leqslant x \, (r = 0, 1, \ldots, k - 1), S_r \leqslant S_k \, (r = k + 1, k + 2, \ldots, n)\}$

$\quad = \Pr \{S_k - S_r > 0 \, (r = 1, 2, \ldots, k - 1), 0 < S_k \leqslant x,$

$$S_r - S_k \leqslant 0 \, (r = k + 1, k + 2, \ldots, n)\} \qquad (4.7)$$

$\quad = \Pr \{S_1 > 0, S_2 > 0, \ldots, S_{k-1} > 0, 0 < S_k \leqslant x\}.$

$$\Pr \{S_1 \leqslant 0, S_2 \leqslant 0, \ldots, S_{n-k} \leqslant 0\}$$

$\quad = u_k(x)v_{n-k}^* \, (1 \leqslant k \leqslant n, n \geqslant 1);$

also, from (4.3),

$$\Pr \{M_n \leqslant x, T_n = 0\} = v_n^*. \qquad (4.8)$$

Therefore,

$$\Pr \{M_n \leqslant x\} = v_n^* + \sum_{k=1}^n u_k(x)v_{n-k}^* \qquad (n \geqslant 1), \qquad (4.9)$$

while

$$\Pr \{M_0 \leqslant x\} = \begin{cases} 0 & \text{for } x < 0 \\ 1 & \text{for } x \geqslant 0. \end{cases} \qquad (4.10)$$

From (4.9) and (4.10) we obtain

$$\sum_{0}^{\infty} t^n \int_{0-}^{\infty} e^{-\theta x}\, dG_n(x) = 1 + \sum_{1}^{\infty} t^n \left\{ v_n^* + \int_{0+}^{\infty} e^{-\theta x} \sum_{k=1}^{n} du_k(x) v_{n-k}^* \right\}$$

$$= V^*(t) + \sum_{k=1}^{\infty} \int_{0+}^{\infty} e^{-\theta x}\, du_k(x) \sum_{n=k}^{\infty} v_{n-k}^* t^n \qquad (4.11)$$

$$= V^*(t)\left\{ 1 + \sum_{k=1}^{\infty} t^k \int_{0+}^{\infty} e^{-\theta x}\, du_k(x) \right\}.$$

Now, we have

$$u_n(x) = \Pr \{S_1 > 0, S_2 > 0, \ldots, S_{n-1} > 0, 0 < S_n \leqslant x\}$$

$$= \Pr \{S_r < S_n \leqslant x\,(r = 0, 1, \ldots, n-1)\}$$

$$= \Pr \{n \text{ is a ladder index, and } S_n \leqslant x\} \qquad (4.12)$$

$$= \sum_{r=1}^{n} \Pr \{n \text{ is the } r\text{th ladder index, and } S_n \leqslant x\}$$

$$= \sum_{r=1}^{n} f_n^{(r)}(x) \qquad (n \geqslant 1, x > 0),$$

so that

$$1 + \sum_{1}^{\infty} t^n \int_{0+}^{\infty} e^{-\theta x}\, du_n(x)$$

$$= 1 + \sum_{r=1}^{\infty} \sum_{n=r}^{\infty} t^n \int_{0+}^{\infty} e^{-\theta x}\, df_n^{(r)}(x)$$

$$= 1 + \sum_{r=1}^{\infty} [f(\theta, t)]^r \qquad \text{from (2.8)} \qquad (4.13)$$

$$= [1 - f(\theta, t)]^{-1}$$

$$= \exp\left[\sum_{1}^{\infty} \frac{t^n}{n} \int_{0+}^{\infty} e^{-\theta x}\, dF_n(x) \right] \qquad (|t| < 1, Re(\theta) > 0).$$

The required result then follows from (1.30), (4.13), and (4.11).

LEMMA 4.1. *If* $\Pr \{X_n = 0\} < 1$, *then for all* x,

$$\Pr \{S_n > x \text{ i.o.}\} = 0 \qquad \text{or} \quad 1. \qquad (4.14)$$

[Lévy (1939.]

THEOREM 4.2.   (a) *If* $B < \infty$, *and* $\Pr\{X_n = 0\} < 1$, *then with probability one*

$$\sup_{k \geqslant 0} S_k < \infty, \qquad \limsup_{n \to \infty} S_n = -\infty. \tag{4.15}$$

(b) *If* $B = \infty$, *then with probability one*

$$\sup_{k \geqslant 0} S_k = \limsup_{n \to \infty} S_n = +\infty. \tag{4.16}$$

Proof : From Lemma 4.1, we have, in particular, that

$$\Pr\{S_n > 0 \text{ i.o.}\} = 0 \text{ or } 1. \tag{4.17}$$

The reasoning used in the proof of Theorem 1.6 then shows that

(i) if $B < \infty$, then $\Pr\{S_n > 0 \text{ i.o.}\} = 0$.

(ii) if $B = \infty$, then $\Pr\{S_n > 0 \text{ i.o.}\} = 1$.
$$\tag{4.18}$$

The results (a) and (b) follow easily from (i) and (ii).

THEOREM 4.3.   *If* $B < \infty$, *then the distribution function* $G(x)$ *of the limiting random variable* $M_\infty = \lim\limits_{n \to \infty} M_n$ *has the Laplace-Stieltjes transform*

$$\int_{0-}^{\infty} e^{-\theta x} \, dG(x) = \exp\left[-\sum_{1}^{\infty} \frac{1}{n} \int_{0}^{\infty} (1 - e^{-\theta x}) \, dF_n(x) \right] \qquad (Re(\theta) > 0). \tag{4.19}$$

Proof :   If $B < \infty$, then from Theorem 4.2 we find that $M_\infty = \sup\limits_{k \geqslant 0} S_k < \infty$ with probability one; therefore,

$$\lim_{n \to \infty} G_n(x) = G(x), \tag{4.20}$$

where

$$\int_{0-}^{\infty} e^{-\theta x} \, dG(x) = \lim_{t \to 1-0} (1 - t) \sum_{0}^{\infty} t^n \int_{0-}^{\infty} e^{-\theta x} \, dG_n(x)$$

$$= \lim_{t \to 1-0} \exp\left[-\sum_{1}^{\infty} \frac{t^n}{n}[1 - \Pr\{S_n \leqslant 0\}] + \sum_{1}^{\infty} \frac{t^n}{n} \int_{0+}^{\infty} e^{-\theta x} \, dF_n(x) \right]$$

$$= \exp\left[-\sum_{1}^{\infty} \frac{1}{n} \Pr\{S_n > 0\} + \sum_{1}^{\infty} \frac{1}{n} \int_{0+}^{\infty} e^{-\theta x} \, dF_n(x) \right], \tag{4.21}$$

which is the result (4.19).

THEOREM 4.4.   *If* $\{X_n\}$ *is a continuous renewal process with* $E|X_n| < \infty$, *and* $\mu = E(X_n) > 0$, *then*

$$\lim_{n \to \infty} \sum_{0}^{\infty} [G_n(x + h) - G_n(x)] = \frac{h}{\mu}. \tag{4.22}$$

Proof : From (4.9) we have

$$G_n(x) = v_n^* + \sum_{k=1}^{n} u_k(x)v_{n-k}^* \qquad (n \geqslant 1),$$

so that

$$\sum_{0}^{\infty} G_n(x) = \sum_{0}^{\infty} v_n^* + \sum_{n=1}^{\infty} \sum_{k=1}^{n} u_k(x)v_{n-k}^*$$

$$= \sum_{0}^{\infty} v_n^* + \sum_{k=1}^{\infty} u_k(x) \sum_{n=k}^{\infty} v_{n-k}^*. \tag{4.23}$$

To justify the interchange of the order of summation in (4.23), we note that if $\mu > 0$ (which implies that $B = \infty$, $A < \infty$), then Z_1 is a proper random variable and $u(x) = \sum_{1}^{\infty} u_n(x)$ is the renewal function of the process $\{Z_k\}$ (Theorem 2.3), and, moreover, $\sum_{0}^{\infty} v_n^* = e^A < \infty$; therefore,

$$\left| \sum_{k=1}^{\infty} u_k(x) \sum_{n=k}^{\infty} v_{n-k}^* \right| \leqslant e^A \sum_{1}^{\infty} u_k(x) < \infty. \tag{4.24}$$

From (4.23) we thus obtain

$$\sum_{0}^{\infty} G_n(x) = e^A[1 + u(x)] \tag{4.25}$$

and

$$\sum_{0}^{\infty} [G_n(x + h) - G_n(x)] = e^A[u(x + h) - u(x)] \tag{4.26}$$

$$\to e^A \frac{h}{E(Z_1)} = \frac{h}{\mu} \qquad \text{as } x \to \infty.$$

We have thus proved (4.22).

4.2. The Markov Chain $\{W_n\}$

Let $\{W_n\}$ be a sequence of random variables which are independent of the X_n and which satisfy the recurrence relations

$$W_{n+1} = \begin{cases} W_n + X_{n+1} & \text{if } W_n + X_{n+1} > 0 \\ 0 & \text{if } W_n + X_{n+1} \leqslant 0 \end{cases} \tag{4.27}$$

with probability one. For any real number a, if we denote $a^+ = \max(0, a)$, then (4.27) can be written as

$$W_{n+1} = (W_n + X_{n+1})^+. \tag{4.28}$$

The relations (4.27) imply that $\{W_n\}$ is a Markov chain; its properties follow easily from the results derived in Section 4.1. Solving for $W_1, W_2, \ldots$ successively from (4.27), we find that

$$W_n = \max \{S_n - S_r \, (r = 1, 2, \ldots, n), W_0 + S_n\} \qquad (n \geqslant 1). \quad (4.29)$$

Now, since $S_n - S_r = X_{r+1} + X_{r+2} + \cdots + X_n$, $S_n - S_r$ has the same distribution as S_{n-r}, and therefore (4.29) gives the result

$$W_n \sim \max (0, S_1, S_2, \ldots, S_{n-1}, W_0 + S_n), \quad (4.30)$$

where, for two random variables X, Y we write $X \sim Y$ if they have the same distribution. Thus

$$W_n \sim \max (M_{n-1}, W_0 + S_n). \quad (4.31)$$

From Theorem 4.2 it follows at once that if $B = \infty$, then $W_n \to \infty$ with probability one, while if $B < \infty$, then $W_n \to W$ where $W \sim M_\infty$. From (4.28) we see that $M = M_\infty$ satisfies the equation

$$M \sim (M + X_{n+1})^+; \quad (4.32)$$

in Theorem 4.5 we show that $M = M_\infty$ is the unique solution of (4.32) with $\Pr \{M < \infty\} = 1$, in the sense that if there is a second solution N with this property, then $M \sim N$. Let us note here that if we choose $W_0 \sim M_\infty$, then from (4.32),

$$
\begin{aligned}
W_1 &= (W_0 + X_1)^+ \sim (M_\infty + X_1)^+ \sim M_\infty \\
W_2 &= (W_1 + X_2)^+ \sim (M_\infty + X_2)^+ \sim M_\infty \\
&\cdot \quad \cdot \quad \cdot \quad \cdot \quad \cdot \quad \cdot \quad \cdot \quad \cdot \quad \cdot \quad \cdot \quad \cdot \\
W_n &\sim M_\infty \qquad (n \geqslant 1);
\end{aligned}
\qquad (4.33)
$$

the relations (4.33) establish a stationary property of the random variable M_∞.

THEOREM 4.5. *If* $\Pr \{X_n = 0\} = 1$, *then every nonnegative random variable* M *is a solution of* (4.32). *If* $B < \infty$ *and* $\Pr \{X_n = 0\} < 1$, *then* (4.32) *has the unique solution* $M = M_\infty = \sup_{k \geqslant 0} S_k$, *while if* $B = \infty$, *then* (4.32) *has no solution.*

Proof: If $B < \infty$ and $\Pr \{X_n = 0\} < 1$, then we have seen that $M = M_\infty$ is a solution of (4.32). If possible, let there be a second solution N with $\Pr \{N < \infty\} = 1$ and assume that N is independent of the X_n. Then choosing $W_0 \sim N$ we obtain from (4.33) $W_n \sim N$. However, (4.31) gives

$$W_n \sim \max (0, S_1, S_2, \ldots, S_{n-1}, N + S_n), \quad (4.34)$$

so that $\lim_{n \to \infty} W_n \sim M_\infty$. This gives $N \sim M_\infty$, which implies the uniqueness of the solution of (4.32).

If $B = \infty$, and (4.32) has a solution N with $\Pr\{N < \infty\} = 1$, then the above argument shows that $W_n \sim N$. But

$$\max(0, S_1, S_2, \ldots, S_{n-1}, N + S_n)$$
$$\geqslant \max(0, S_1, S_2, \ldots, S_n) = M_n \to \infty, \tag{4.35}$$

so that $W_n \to \infty$ with probability one. This contradicts the hypothesis that $N < \infty$ with probability one, and therefore (4.32) has no solution in this case.

The above theorem is due to Spitzer (1957). Earlier, Lindley (1952) had considered a special form of (4.32), namely, the integral equation

$$G(x) = -\int_0^\infty G(y)\, dF(x - y) \qquad (x \geqslant 0), \tag{4.36}$$

with the condition that the solution $G(x)$ is to be a nondecreasing, right continuous function such that $\lim_{x \to \infty} G(x) = 1$. We shall call such a solution a proper (or regular) solution. Lindley proved that if $E|X_n| < \infty$, then (4.36) has a unique proper solution, or no such solution according as $E(X_n) < 0$ or $E(X_n) \geqslant 0$; this result is easily seen to be equivalent to Theorem 4.5. If we relax the condition that $G(x)$ should be bounded as $x \to \infty$, then $G(x)$ may be called an improper solution. Spitzer [(1957), (1960 a), (1960 b)] established the existence of an improper solution in the case $E(X_n) = 0$, $\mathrm{Var}(X_n) = \sigma^2 < \infty$ [see Complement 9].

5. COMPLEMENTS AND PROBLEMS

Section 1

1. Show that

$$1 + \sum_1^\infty t^n \Pr\{S_1 \leqslant 0, S_2 \leqslant 0, \ldots, S_{n-1} \leqslant 0, S_n = 0\}$$

$$= \exp\left[\sum_1^\infty \frac{t^n}{n} \Pr\{S_n = 0\}\right] \qquad (|t| < 1). \tag{5.1}$$

Hence deduce that if $\Pr\{X_n = 0\} < 1$, then the series $\sum_1^\infty \frac{1}{n} \Pr\{S_n = 0\}$ converges [Spitzer (1960 b)].

Section 2

2. If $E(X_n) = 0$, and $0 < \mathrm{Var}(X_n) = \sigma^2$, then show that $E(Z_1) = \sigma c/\sqrt{2}$, where

$$0 < c = \exp\left[\sum_1^\infty \frac{1}{n}\left(\frac{1}{2} - \Pr\{S_n > 0\}\right)\right] < \infty \tag{5.2}$$

[Spitzer (1960 b)].

Section 3

3. By symmetry it follows from Theorem 3.2 that if $E|X_n| < \infty$ and $\mu = E(X_n) < 0$, then for $h > 0$

$$U(t + h) - U(t) \to \begin{cases} 0 & \text{as } t \to \infty \\ -\dfrac{h}{\mu} & \text{as } t \to -\infty, \end{cases} \tag{5.3}$$

for processes satisfying the condition (3.5).

4. If the X_n do not have a mean, but the condition (3.5) is satisfied, then

$$U(t + h) - U(t) \to 0 \qquad \text{as } t \to \pm\infty \tag{5.4}$$

[Feller and Orey (1961)].

Section 4

5. Show that

$$E(M_n) = \sum_1^n \frac{1}{r} \int_0^\infty x \, dF_r(x) \tag{5.5}$$

[Kac (1954)].

6. Show that the joint characteristic function of

$$M_n = \max(0, S_1, S_2, \ldots, S_n) \text{ and } V_n = -\min(0, S_1, S_2, \ldots, S_n)$$

is given by

$$\sum_0^\infty t^n E[\exp(i\alpha M_n + i\beta V_n)] = \exp\left[\sum_1^\infty \frac{t^n}{n} \int_{0+}^\infty e^{i\alpha x} \, dF_n(x) + \sum_1^\infty \frac{t^n}{n} \int_{-\infty}^{0+} e^{-i\beta x} \, dF_n(x)\right]$$

$$(|t| < 1, \, Im(\alpha) \geqslant 0, \, Im(\beta) \geqslant 0) \tag{5.6}$$

[Spitzer (1956)].

7. Show that if $B < \infty$, the distribution function $G(x)$ of M_∞ can be expressed as

$$G(x) = G(0)[1 + u(x)], \, G(0) = e^{-B}. \tag{5.7}$$

8. *Another Renewal Theorem.* If $\{X_n\}$ is a continuous renewal process with $E|X_n| < \infty$ and $\mu = E(X_n) \geqslant 0$, then show that

$$\lim_{n \to \infty} \sum_{n=1}^\infty \Pr\{x < S_n \leqslant x + h, M_{n-1} < S_n\}$$

$$= \begin{cases} \dfrac{h}{\mu} e^{-A} & (\text{if } \mu > 0) \\[2mm] \dfrac{\sqrt{2h}}{c\sigma} & \text{if } \mu = 0, \sigma^2 < \infty, \end{cases} \tag{5.8}$$

where σ^2 and c are defined in Complement 2 [Spitzer (1960 b)]. If the X_n are positive random variables, (5.8) reduces to Blackwell's renewal theorem.

9. *Zero-Avoiding Transitions.* Let

$$^0G_n(x) = \Pr\{W_1 > 0, W_2 > 0, \ldots, W_{n-1} > 0, W_n \leqslant x\} \qquad (n \geqslant 1, x \geqslant 0).$$
(5.9)

If $\mu \leqslant 0$, show that

$$\sum_{n=1}^{\infty} {}^0G_n(x) = 1 + u(x) < \infty.$$
(5.10)

If $\mu = 0$, $\sigma^2 < \infty$, show that

$$H(x) = c \sum_1^{\infty} {}^0G_n(x),$$
(5.11)

where c is given by (5.2), is an improper solution of the equation (4.36). Further, show that

$$H(x + h) - H(x) \to \frac{h\sqrt{2}}{\sigma} \qquad \text{as } x \to \infty$$
(5.12)

[Spitzer (1960 b)].

10. Let

$$M^+(\theta, t) = \exp\left[\sum_1^{\infty} \frac{t^n}{n} \int_{0+}^{\infty} e^{\theta x} \, dF_n(x)\right] \quad (|t| < [\phi(\theta_0)]^{-1}, Re(\theta) \leqslant \theta_0),$$
(5.13)

$$M^-(\theta, t) = \exp\left[-\sum_1^{\infty} \frac{t^n}{n} \int_{-\infty}^{0+} e^{\theta x} \, dF_n(x)\right] \quad (|t| < [\phi(\theta_0)]^{-1}, Re(\theta) \geqslant \theta_0),$$
(5.14)

where θ_0 is defined in Chapter 2, Section 8. Show that $M^+(\theta, t)$ and $M^-(\theta, t)$ are analytic in the regions in which they are defined, and

$$\frac{1}{1 - t\phi(\theta)} = \frac{M^+(\theta, t)}{M^-(\theta, t)} \qquad \text{if } Re(\theta) = 0,$$
(5.15)

where $\phi(\theta) = E(e^{\theta X_n})$ [Kemperman (1961)]. The result (5.15) is a Wiener-Hopf decomposition.

11. Show that

$$\sum_0^{\infty} t^n \int_{0-}^{\infty} e^{\theta x} \, d_x \Pr\{W_n \leqslant x \mid W_0 = u\}$$

$$= M^+(0, t)\left\{e^{\theta u} + \int_0^u e^{-\theta y} \, d_y V(y, t) + \int_u^{\infty} d_y V(y, t)\right\},$$
(5.16)

where

$$V(y, t) = \sum_{1}^{\infty} t^n v_n^*(y) \tag{5.17}$$

[Kemperman (1961)]. When $u = 0$, this reduces to (4.6).

12. *A First Passage Problem.* Let us consider the first passage time $N = \min \{n \mid S_n \leqslant -b\}$. From Chapter 2, Theorem 8.7, we have

$$E(t^N e^{\theta S_N}) = 1 - [1 - t\phi(\theta)]F(t, \theta). \tag{5.18}$$

Show that

$$E(t^N e^{\theta S_N}) = M^-(\theta, t) \int_b^\infty e^{-\theta y} \, d_y V(y, t) \tag{5.19}$$

and

$$F(t, \theta) = 1 + \sum_{1}^{\infty} t^n \int_{-b}^{\infty} e^{\theta x} \, d_x \Pr \{N > n, S_n \leqslant x\} \tag{5.20}$$

$$= M^+(\theta, t)\left\{1 + \int_0^b e^{-\theta y} \, d_y V(y, t)\right\}.$$

In view of (5.18), it is necessary to prove only one of the two identities (5.19)–(5.20) [Kemperman (1961)].

13. For the random variable N defined in Complement 12, show that

$$\Pr \{N < \infty\} = \begin{cases} 1 - e^{-A}[1 + V(b, 1)] & \text{if } A < \infty \\ 1 & \text{if } A = \infty \end{cases} \tag{5.21}$$

[cf. Chapter 2, Theorem 8.8].

Further Topics in Fluctuation Theory

14. Let P_n be the number of $S_k > 0$ $(k = 1, 2, \ldots, n)$. Show that

$$\Pr \{P_n = k\} = \Pr \{T_n = k\} = u_k v_{n-k}^* \qquad (0 \leqslant k \leqslant n), \tag{5.22}$$

where T_n is defined by (4.5) [Sparre Andersen (1953 a)]. For an elementary proof, see Feller (1959).

15. Show that if $B = \infty$, then $P_n \to \infty$ with probability one, while if $B < \infty$, then $P_n \to P < \infty$ with probability one, where

$$E(t^P) = \exp\left[-\sum_{1}^{\infty} \frac{1 - t^n}{n} \Pr \{S_n > 0\}\right] \qquad (|t| < 1) \tag{5.23}$$

[Spitzer (1956)].

16. *Symmetric Random Variables.* If the distribution of X_n is symmetric, and $\Pr\{X_n = 0\} = 0$, then

$$U(t) = V^*(t) = (1 - t)^{-\frac{1}{2}}, \tag{5.24}$$

so that

$$u_k = v_k^* = \binom{-\frac{1}{2}}{k}(-1)^k. \tag{5.25}$$

Therefore,

$$\Pr\{P_n = k\} = \binom{-\frac{1}{2}}{k}\binom{-\frac{1}{2}}{n-k}(-1)^n. \tag{5.26}$$

17. *The Arc Sine Law.* From (5.26) show that

$$\lim_{n\to\infty} \Pr\left\{\frac{P_n}{n} \leqslant x\right\} = \frac{2}{\pi} \arc \sin x^{\frac{1}{2}} \tag{5.27}$$

(the arc sine law) [see Feller (1957)].

18. *The Generalized Arc Sine Law.* This is described by a family of distribution functions $F_\alpha(x)$ depending on a parameter α ($0 \leqslant \alpha \leqslant 1$) defined as follows:

$$F_0(x) = 0 \text{ if } x < 0, \quad = 1 \text{ if } x \geqslant 0,$$

$$F_1(x) = 0 \text{ if } x < 1, \quad = 1 \text{ if } x \geqslant 1, \tag{5.28}$$

$$F_\alpha(x) = \frac{\sin \pi\alpha}{\pi} \int_0^x u^{\alpha-1}(1 - u)^{-\alpha}\, du \quad (0 < \alpha < 1).$$

In particular,

$$F_{\frac{1}{2}}(x) = \frac{1}{\pi} \int_0^x \frac{du}{[u(1 - u)]^{\frac{1}{2}}} = \frac{2}{\pi} \arc \sin x^{\frac{1}{2}}. \tag{5.29}$$

For $0 < \alpha < 1$ we have

$$\int_0^1 x^r\, dF_\alpha(x) = \alpha(\alpha + 1)\ldots(\alpha + r - 1)/r! \quad (r \geqslant 1). \tag{5.30}$$

19. If $a_n = \Pr\{S_n > 0\} \to \alpha$, show that

$$\lim_{n\to\infty} \Pr\left\{\frac{P_n}{n} \leqslant x\right\} = F_\alpha(x) \tag{5.31}$$

[Sparre Andersen (1954)]. More generally, Spitzer (1956) has shown that (5.31) holds if

$$\frac{a_1 + a_2 + \cdots + a_n}{n} \to \alpha. \tag{5.32}$$

6. REFERENCES

Andersen, E. Sparre. ON SUMS OF SYMMETRICALLY DEPENDENT RANDOM VARIABLES. *Skand. Aktuar.,* **36** (1953a), pp. 123–138.

———. ON THE FLUCTUATIONS OF SUMS OF RANDOM VARIABLES I. *Math. Scand.,* **1** (1953b), pp. 263–285.

———. ON THE FLUCTUATIONS OF SUMS OF RANDOM VARIABLES II. *Math. Scand.,* **2** (1954), pp. 195–223.

Baxter, Glen. AN OPERATOR IDENTITY. *Pacific J. Math.,* **8** (1958), pp. 649–663.

Blackwell, D. EXTENSION OF A RENEWAL THEOREM. *Pacific J. Math.,* **3** (1953), pp. 315–320.

Chung, K. L., and Wolfowitz, J. ON A LIMIT THEOREM IN RENEWAL THEORY. *Ann. of Math.,* **55** (1952), pp. 1–6.

———, and Pollard, H. AN EXTENSION OF RENEWAL THEORY. *Proc. Amer. Math. Soc.,* **3** (1952), pp. 303–309.

Feller, W. AN INTRODUCTION TO PROBABILITY THEORY AND ITS APPLICATIONS. 2nd ed. New York: Wiley, 1957.

———. ON COMBINATORIAL METHODS IN FLUCTUATION THEORY. (The Harald Cramér Volume, pp. 75–91.) New York: Wiley, 1959.

———. A SIMPLE PROOF FOR RENEWAL THEOREMS. *Comm. on Pure and App. Math.,* **14** (1961), pp. 285–293.

———, and Orey, S. A RENEWAL THEOREM. *J. Math. and Mech.,* **10** (1961), pp. 619–624.

Kac, M. TOEPLITZ MATRICES, TRANSLATION KERNELS AND A RELATED PROBLEM IN PROBABILITY THEORY. *Duke Math. J.,* **21** (1954), pp. 501–509.

Kemperman, J. H. B. THE FIRST PASSAGE PROBLEM FOR A STATIONARY MARKOV CHAIN. Chicago: University of Chicago Press, 1961.

Lévy, P. THÉORIE DE L'ADDITION DES VARIABLES ALÉATOIRES. Paris: Gauthier Villars, 1939.

Lindley, D. V. THEORY OF QUEUES WITH A SINGLE SERVER. *Proc. Cam. Phil. Soc.,* **48** (1952), pp. 277–289.

Spitzer, F. A COMBINATORIAL LEMMA AND ITS APPLICATIONS TO PROBABILITY THEORY. *Trans. Amer. Math. Soc.,* **82** (1956), pp. 323–339.

———. THE WIENER-HOPF EQUATION WHOSE KERNEL IS A PROBABILITY DENSITY. *Duke Math. J.,* **24** (1957), pp. 327–344.

———. THE WIENER-HOPF EQUATION WHOSE KERNEL IS A PROBABILITY DENSITY II. *Duke Math. J.,* **27** (1960a), pp. 363–372.

———. A TAUBERIAN THEOREM AND ITS PROBABILITY INTERPRETATION. *Trans. Amer. Math. Soc.,* **94** (1960b), pp. 150–160.

Index

229